THE LACTOSE OPERON

Edited By

JONATHAN R. BECKWITH
Harvard Medical School

and

DAVID ZIPSER
Cold Spring Harbor Laboratory

Cold Spring Harbor Laboratory
1970

Preface

Much of the development of molecular biology has depended on the study of certain key biological systems. The lactose operon of *E. coli* is clearly one of these systems. In the late summer of 1968, Jim Watson suggested to us that it would be useful to have a conference devoted entirely to work on the *lac* operon. It also seemed reasonable to publish the results presented at this meeting together with an extensive review of past work that would be of value and interest to a wide range of biologists and students not now familiar with the *lac* system. Thus evolved the format for this volume. The first ten chapters bring the general reader up to date, familiarizing him with the history, techniques, language and results of *lac* operon studies. Following these chapters, a series of current papers presented at the conference in September 1969 at Cold Spring Harbor give new developments in molecular biology obtained with the *lac* system.

It is hoped that this format will make it possible for the general biological reader and student to obtain easily sufficient background information about the lactose operon, as well as an understanding of the significance of new results first presented in this volume.

Jon Beckwith

David Zipser

Table of Contents

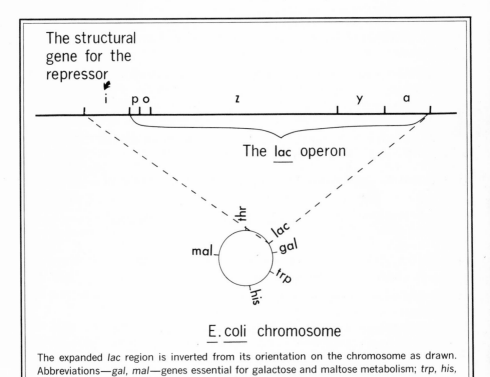

The structural gene for the repressor

i   p o   z   y   a

The *lac* operon

thr
mal   lac
gal
trp
his

E. coli chromosome

The expanded *lac* region is inverted from its orientation on the chromosome as drawn. Abbreviations—*gal, mal*—genes essential for galactose and maltose metabolism; *trp, his, thr*—genes essential for the biosynthesis of tryptophan, histidine and threonine.

The Lactose Operon

The sugar lactose (glucose-4-β-D-galactoside) can be used by the bacterium *Escherichia coli* as its sole source of carbon. The bacterium makes two proteins which are essential specifically for the metabolism of lactose. These are (1) a galactoside permease which is found in the bacterial membrane and directs the transport and accumulation of lactose within the cell and (2) β-galactosidase, an enzyme inside the cell which catalyzes the hydrolysis of lactose into its two component monosaccharides, glucose and galactose. When *E. coli* is grown on most carbon sources, other than lactose, these two proteins are present in very low amounts of the order of 10 or so molecules per cell. However, in the presence of lactose or of other sugars resembling lactose, the rate of synthesis of these proteins is increased by as much as 1000-fold. The "induction" by lactose and certain other galactosides of the synthesis of the two proteins is accompanied by an increase in the amounts of a third protein, thiogalactoside transacetylase. This enzyme is not essential for lactose metabolism and no role has yet been found for it.

The genes which determine the ability of *E. coli* to make and to regulate the synthesis of these proteins are clustered in a small region of the *E. coli* chromosome. The structures of the three proteins are determined by the z gene (β-galactosidase), the y gene (permease) and the a gene (thiogalactoside transacetylase). The transcription of these three genes is initiated at a single site, the *lac* (lactose) promoter (*p*). A group of genes thus transcribed into a single polygenic messenger RNA species is termed an operon. In the absence of an inducer of the *lac* operon, the transcription of the genes is prevented by the presence of the *lac* repressor protein. The repressor most probably acts to stop transcription by binding to the operator (*o*) DNA which lies between the promoter and the structural genes. The inducer allows transcription of the operon by binding to the repressor and causing its release from the operator.

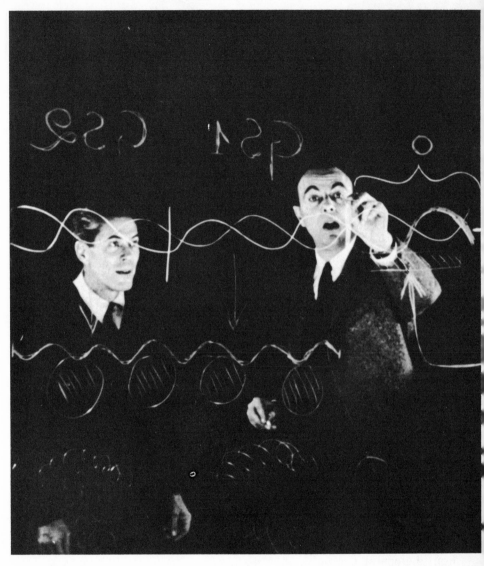

Jacques Monod and Francois Jacob, 1966.

[Photograph courtesy of *Paris-Match*.]

Chapter I

Introduction

FRANÇOIS JACOB and JACQUES MONOD

Institut Pasteur, Paris

When we were kindly invited by the organizers of this conference to prepare an introduction, we, of course, accepted gratefully and started wondering what we should say. The first possibility was to discuss the history of the development of the *lac* operon. This we decided we should not like to do. It is for philosophers, not for scientists, to analyze the vagaries of scientific progress and ponder over the mysteries of inductive logic.

The next possibility was to talk about the future, but we decided that we would not like to do that either. Experience has shown that one is almost invariably beaten at that kind of game. However, having eliminated these two subjects, we discovered that there was nothing left for us to say, except, of course, praise the organizers for their initiative and for their organization.

Since, however, this would make the introduction a little bit too short, the only solution is to say something after all of the history of the system and also indulge in a little vaticination.

As far as history goes, it may be of some interest to simply list what we believe to have been the main turning points in the exploration of the *lac* system. The first, of course, was the choice of the system itself. As always luck was combined there with a systematic approach. It had been known for a long time that there are coliform organisms which do not ferment lactose and yet throw out colonies of lactose fermenters identical to ordinary *E. coli*. On the other hand it had been shown, also many years before, that the fermentation of lactose by *E. coli* was "adaptive." Thus the possibility existed that the lactose-positive phenotype resulted from the interaction of some specific genetic structure and an environment containing galactosides. This was shown indeed to be the case in 1946 (Monod and Audureau), using a strain of *E. coli* "mutabile" isolated from

1

the digestive track of André Lwoff. Hence the designation ML, which stands for "Mutabile Lwoffi" and not for "Monsieur Lwoff," as some tend to believe.

Yet in the late 40's several similar systems showing both genetic and inductive control were being studied in our lab, and the decisive reason for pushing the study of the *lac* system rather than that of another, such as the maltose system, was the possibility of synthesizing galactoside analogs which could serve to dissociate enzyme activity from enzyme induction. This proved successful (Monod et al., 1951) and it is clear that, without the tools provided by the thiogalactosides, it would have been exceedingly difficult to analyze the system.

Almost at once, however, the effects of these artificial inducers revealed a situation which seemed extremely mysterious. Many of the *lac*⁻ mutants proved themselves able to synthesize perfectly normal amounts of galactosidase when induced with IPTG, although they hardly responded or responded not at all to lactose. This riddle haunted us for quite some time and gave rise to a lot of wild speculation of which no written trace exists, luckily. The riddle, of course, was cleared up by the discovery of the inducible permease found as a matter of fact by accident when we were looking for something else (actually for the site of action of the inducer) (Rickenberg et al., 1956). That was a timely discovery because in the adjacent lab experiments were going on which revealed the mechanism of chromosome transfer from male to female cell (Wollman and Jacob, 1955). One could now map the mutants of the *lac* system and show among other things that the *i* mutation had a pleiotropic effect on both *z* and *y*. Clearly the crux of the problem rested in interpreting this mutation.

The scene was set for the so-called PyJaMa experiment which revealed the dominance of the inducible over the constitutive genotype (Pardee et al., 1958). However, merozygotes are a nuisance to work with and stable diploids were badly needed. Without the, again very timely, discovery of the *lac* episome (Jacob and Adelberg, 1959) much of the subsequent work would have been impossible.

Merozygotes have virtues of their own however. It was the PyJaMa experiment which led to a rapprochement of great consequence—namely, the striking formal analogy between this result and the phenomenon of zygotic induction which had been observed a few years before (Jacob and Wollman, 1954). The suggestion was that these two apparently entirely different systems, namely lambda and *lac* which had been studied for several years next door to one another, might share a common logic of regulation. Systematic comparisons of the two systems proved invaluable. The oᶜ mutation, for instance, was discovered because the assumed symmetry between the two systems predicted their existence (Jacob et al., 1960). Similarly i^s mutants could be interpreted by analogy with the super-repressed lambda mutants (Willson et al., 1964).

The rest is more recent history and need not be recalled here. We would, however, note one point. Up to 1961 we repeatedly and obstinately tried to attack the problem of the mode of action of the inducer on the assumption that it had to undergo some covalent alteration. Only as a result of work on enzyme regulation did we at last understand that this assumption was superfluous and almost certainly incorrect (Monod et al., 1963).

It seems to us this conference should have shown that the *lac* system is as yet far from having lost all its charms and mysteries. The isolation of the repressor (Gilbert and Müller-Hill, 1966) and the direct in-vitro study of its interaction with operator (Bourgeois and Monod, 1970) is a fascinating object for studying the nature of elementary regulatory interactions. And while the complete logic of other systems may turn out to be a great deal more complicated, involving a cascade of negative and positive interactions, it is likely that the *lac* system will remain a good model of almost the simplest possible regulatory loop. On the other hand, the difficulties and complexities which reveal themselves in the analysis of more complex systems, such as lambda, might incline one to feel somewhat pessimistic of the prospects of analyzing down to the ultimate level the programming of the development of a metazoan embryo. Except for Cassandra herself, prophets of doom have almost always turned out to be wrong, especially where scientific developments are concerned, and our remarks are not meant to discourage the great enthusiasm with which many molecular biologists are abandoning K12 for BALB C or some other mammal, such as a nematode. But it is worth pointing out that there is always "room at the bottom," as Feynman said. A great deal remains to be learned from bacteria concerning the regulation and machinery of gene expression. The best testimony to the validity of this remark is this conference itself, with the host of new subjects, approaches and methodologies which are being discovered.

REFERENCES

BOURGEOIS, S. and J. MONOD. 1970. Control processes in multicellular organisms, p. 3. *In* G. E. W. Wolstenholme and J. Knight [ed.] A Ciba Foundation Symposium.

GILBERT, W. and B. MÜLLER-HILL. 1966. Isolation of the *lac* repressor. Proc. Nat. Acad. Sci. *56:* 1891.

JACOB, F. and E. A. ADELBERG. 1959. Transfert de caractères génétique par incorporation au facteur sexuel d'*Escherichia coli*. Compt. Rend. Acad. Sci. *249:* 189.

JACOB, F., D. PERRIN, C. SANCHEZ, and J. MONOD. 1960. L'opéron: groupe de gènes à expression coordonnée par un opérateur. Compt. Rend. Acad. Sci. *250:* 1727.

JACOB, F. and E. WOLLMAN. 1954. Induction spontanée du développement du bacteriophage λ au cours de la recombinaison génétique chez *Escherichia coli* K12. Compt. Rend. Acad. Sci. *239:* 317.

MONOD, J. and A. AUDUREAU. 1946. Mutation et adaptation enzymatique chez *Escherichia coli*-mutable. Ann. Inst. Pasteur *72:* 868.

MONOD, J., J. P. CHANGEUX, and F. JACOB. 1963. Allosteric proteins and cellular control systems. J. Mol. Biol. *6:* 306.

MONOD, J., G. COHEN-BAZIRE, and M. COHN. 1951. Sur la biosynthèse de la β-galactosidase (lactase chez *Escherichia coli* la spécificité de l'induction). Biochim. Biophys. Acta *7:* 585.

PARDEE, A. B., F. JACOB, and J. MONOD. 1958. Sur l'expression et le rôle des allèles inductible et constitutif dans la synthèse de la β-galactosidase chez des zygotes d'*Escherichia coli*. Compt. Rend. Acad. Sci. *246:* 3125.

RICKENBERG, H. V., G. N. COHEN, G. BUTTIN, and J. MONOD. 1956. La galactoside-perméase d'*Escherichia coli*. Ann. Inst. Pasteur *91:* 829.

WILLSON, C., D. PERRIN, M. COHN, F. JACOB, and J. MONOD. 1964. Non-inducible mutants of the regulator gene in the lactose system of *Escherichia coli*. J. Mol. Biol. *8:* 582.

WOLLMAN, E. and F. JACOB. 1955. Sur le mécanisme du transfert de materiel génétique au cours de la recombinaison chez *Escherichia coli* K12. Compt. Rend. Acad. Sci. *240:* 2449.

Chapter II

Lac: The Genetic System

JONATHAN R. BECKWITH

Department of Bacteriology and Immunology
Harvard Medical School
Boston, Massachusetts

INTRODUCTION

This chapter will deal with the methods and tools used for genetic analysis of the *lac** operon. The specific problems which arise in the genetic analysis of this system are, in many cases, similar to those encountered in other genetic regulatory units. Therefore, the solutions to these problems can provide a methodology applicable to at least certain of these other systems. The generality of the techniques and approach will be evaluated in this article. A more direct application of these techniques derives from the existence of strains in which the *lac* genes are fused to other bacterial operons, such as the *trp* operon and *pur*E operon (Beckwith, Signer, and Epstein, 1966; Jacob, Ullmann, and Monod, 1965). Since, in such strains, the *lac* genes are now part of the other operon, nearly all the methodology used for analysis of *lac* can be used for that operon. For example, from the *lac-trp* fusion strains, mutations in the *trp*R regulatory gene can be easily selected using techniques normally employed in *lac* genetics (Reznikoff, unpublished results).

HISTORICAL

Most of the major concepts of operon structure, expression and regulation have come out of the work on the *lac* operon of *E. coli*. That *lac* has generated so many of these ideas is due to several factors: (1) The happy coincidence of Monod and Jacob working in the same institute, thus affording a collaboration between two creative minds in the fields of bacterial physiology and regulation and bacterial genetics. The interplay

*See legend to Table 1 and Figure 1 for abbreviations.

5

of these fields has been of obvious importance to the rapid progress in understanding the mechanisms of genetic control. (2) The intuition of Monod, Jacob, and co-workers in formulating substantially correct models on the basis of their genetic and physiological studies. These models have had the attractive features of providing strong predictions and of being rather easily testable (see Jacob, 1966 and Monod, 1966—Nobel prize speeches for some details and historical background). (3) Certain convenient aspects of the chemistry, physiology and genetics of lactose metabolism in *E. coli.* These factors make it a particularly profitable system to analyze. For instance, a large number of easily prepared β-galactosides have permitted (a) a simple enzyme assay, (b) induction with gratuitous inducers and (c) use of chromogenic non-inducing substrates such as XG to distinguish constitutive from inducible strains (see section on galactosides). Other systems, such as the arabinose operon, (Englesberg, Sheppard, Squires, and Meronk, 1969) are more difficult to analyze since the enzyme substrates are unsubstituted monosaccharides, and no hydrolytic enzymes occur in the pathway. Other convenient aspects of the *lac* system will be mentioned later in the article.

The discovery of bacterial conjugation by Lederberg and Tatum (1946a,b) and the refinement of this technique by Wollman, Jacob, and Hayes (1956) permitted an early genetic analysis of the genes determining lactose metabolism. Lederberg and his co-workers were the first to isolate and map crudely a series of *lac⁻* mutations by the F⁺ mating system then available (Lederberg, Lederberg, Zinder, and Lively, 1951; Lederberg, 1952). Most of these mutations mapped in a single locus, defining the region now known as the *lac* locus. The subsequent isolation of Hfr donor strains which in mating experiments donate chromosomal markers in an oriented fashion to the female, allowed a finer analysis of this region. Since the model for operon structure is based on the organization and linkage of these genes, recombination studies determining the nature of this organization were critical. Furthermore, the knowledge of the steps involved in bacterial conjugation allowed the famous "PaJaMa" (Pardee, Jacob, and Monod, 1959) experiments and zygotic induction experiments (Jacob and Wollman, 1956), in which the properties of temporary merozygotes formed during conjugation led to the concept of the repressor.

A critical aspect of the analysis of operons and their regulation is the study of the interaction in the same cell of different alleles of regulatory genes and controlling elements. Since *E. coli* is a haploid organism, such analysis initially was impossible. Even with the discovery of sex in bacteria, the only means available for examining such diploids using the conjugation system was study of temporary merozygotes. However, at about the same time as the "PaJaMa" experiment was being done, a new and very impor-

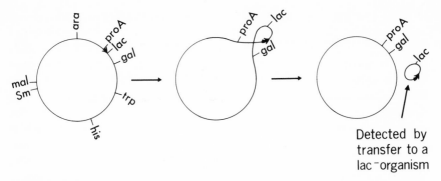

Detected by
transfer to a
lac⁻organism

FIGURE 1. The origin of an F'*lac* episome. The arrow represents the origin and direction of transfer of the bacterial chromosome by this Hfr. Abbreviations used here, in subsequent figures and in the text are as follows: *proA, proC, trp, his*—requirements for proline (two different loci), tryptophan, histidine; *ara, lac, gal, mal, mel*—inability to ferment arabinose, lactose, galactose, maltose, melibiose; Sm, *tonB*, ch1D—sensitivity to streptomycin, bacteriophage T1, chlorate; *attλ, att80*—sites of insertion of temperate phages λ and φ80; *i, p, o, z, y, a*; repressor gene, operator, promoter, structural genes for β-galactosidase, permease and thiogalactoside transacetylase.

tant tool for the analysis of *lac* operon control became available, the F'*lac* episome. From experiments of Adelberg and Burns (1960), it was suggested that sex factors upon recombining out of the bacterial chromosome might occasionally carry adjacent chromosomal regions. Since, fortunately, an Hfr was available transferring *lac* as a terminal marker closely linked to the sex factor, Jacob and Adelberg (1959) found it relatively easy to isolate an F' episome which carried *lac* and no other known bacterial markers (Fig. 1). As such episomes can be maintained in a cell independent of the bacterial chromosome, it was now possible to construct relatively stable merozygotes for accurate complementation studies.

φ80*LAC* AND λ*LAC*

The specialized transducing phages λ and φ80 have played an important role in studies on certain *E. coli* operons. However, the number of loci which could be transduced by such phages has been limited to those which are located close to the sites of insertion of the phage DNA in the bacterial chromosome (Signer, 1966). In 1964, while working in the laboratory of Jacob at the Pasteur Institute, I isolated, by chance, a strain in which the *lac* genes had been transposed from their normal position on the chromosome to a position close to the attachment site for φ80 (*att80*) (Fig. 2A). Ethan Signer, working in the same lab, suggested that we try to get

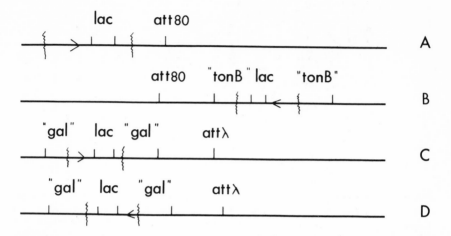

FIGURE 2. Transposition of the *lac* region close to phage attachment sites. Since the *lac* genes are inserted in the chromosome along with the sex factor, the strains are Hfr's with their origins of transfer indicated by the arrows.

a φ80*lac* from the strain. We did (Beckwith and Signer, 1966). This isolation and the subsequent isolation of a different φ80*lac* and of λ*lac* transducing phages have opened up several new approaches to the analysis of the *lac* region. Many of these will be described in detail in this chapter.

As a result of this piece of luck, we subsequently developed a technique for selecting for such happy transpositions; i.e., transpositions of genes to sites close either to *att*80 or *att*λ. In the case of *att*80, this was done by selecting for insertion of an F'*lac* episome into the nearby locus (*tonB*) determining sensitivity to bacteriophage T1 (Fig. 2B, Beckwith and Signer, 1966; Beckwith et al., 1966). This insertion renders the locus inactive and makes the bacteria resistant to T1. In the case of *att*λ, this was done by selecting for insertion of the F'*lac* into the nearby *gal* operon (Beckwith, unpublished results, see Fig. 2C,D), using the technique for selection of *gal* mutants described by Soffer (1962).

GALACTOSIDES USED IN *LAC* ANALYSIS

A wide variety of naturally occurring and chemically prepared galactosides have been used in the analysis of *lac* operon regulation (Table 1). The sugars melibiose (Prestidge and Pardee, 1965; Beckwith, 1963), 6-O-α-D-galactopyranosyl-D-glucose, and raffinose (Schaefler, 1967), α-D-galactopyranosyl-(1-6)-O-α-D-glucopyranosyl-(1-2)-β-D-fructofuranoside, both of which are α-galactosides, can be utilized as carbon sources by *E. coli* (at 42°C for melibiose) only if the *lac* permease, the *y* gene product,

Table 1

	Substrate of β-galactosidase	Inducer	Chromogenic	Usefulness
phenyl-β-D-galactoside (PG)	+	–	–	selection for constitutives
orthonitrophenyl-β-D-galactoside (ONPG)	+	?	yellow	β-galactosidase assay
5-bromo-4-chloro-3-indolyl-β-D-galactoside (XG)	+	–	blue	distinguishing lac-inducible from lac constitutive bacteria
melibiose	–	+	–	assaying for y gene function
raffinose	–	–	–	selection for higher level lac expression or for constitutives
isopropyl-β-D-thiogalactoside (IPTG)	–	+	–	one of the most effective gratuitous inducers
orthonitrophenyl-β-D-thiogalactoside (TONPG)	–	?	–	selecting for lac⁻ mutations, particularly y⁻
methyl-β-D-thiogalactoside (TMG)	–	+	–	inducer; radioactive derivative used in permease assay
2-nitrophenyl-β-D-fucoside (ONPF)	–	–	–	inhibitor of induction
lactobionic acid	weak	–	–	for selecting constitutives or higher level β-galactosidase producers

See Jacob and Monod (1961b) for description of many of these. Others are referred to in the text. Other references: XG—Horwitz, Chua, Curby, Tomson, DaRooge, Fisher, Mauricio, and Klundt, (1964); ONPF—Jayaraman, Müller-Hill, and Rickenberg (1966); lactobionic acid—Langridge, (1969).

9

is functioning. Furthermore, while melibiose is an inducer of the *lac* region, raffinose is not, and, therefore, requires constitutive *lac* expression for its metabolism. Since these α-galactosides are not hydrolyzed by β-galactosidase, but by another enzyme or enzymes, they provide a means of assaying and selecting for *y* gene expression independent of *z* gene expression. One aspect of raffinose metabolism which is both a drawback and an advantage, is that even with constitutive levels of *lac* permease, *E. coli* K12 grows so slowly on this carbon source that sizeable colonies are not formed on raffinose minimal agar for 10 to 14 days. On the one hand, this makes the use of raffinose rather frustrating for bacterial geneticists used to having answers in one or two days; yet, it also makes it possible to select for higher level permease producers from strains (such as those carrying promoter mutants) which make very low levels (Arditti, Scaife, and Beckwith, 1968).

One of the delights of working in the genetics of lactose metabolism is the spectrum of colors that we deal with. For *lac* indicator plates, we can use EMB agar where *lac*[+] colonies have a *green* sheen, or MacConkey agar where *lac*[+] colonies are deep *red* or lactose tetrazolium agar where *lac*[−] colonies are deep *red* (Ohlsson, Strigini, and Beckwith, 1968). The latter plates are useful for distinguishing leaky *lac* mutants from wild-type. Then there is the *yellow* color of nitrophenol measured in the β-galactosidase assay (Pardee et al., 1959). For distinguishing constitutive from inducible strains, the non-diffusing *blue* color produced by the hydrolysis of 5-bromo-3-chloro-2-indolyl-β-D-galactoside (Davies and Jacob, 1968) provides a sensitive test. This compound also is useful for observing different levels of *lac* operon expression among colonies on solid media containing the dye.

The fact that a product of the metabolism of the various galactosides is galactose itself gives rise to a valuable set of selective techniques. Certain mutations which block galactose metabolism confer sensitivity to galactose on the strains carrying them (Soffer, 1962). Those cells which are *lac*[+] and carry such mutations will, therefore, also be sensitive to lactose and other metabolizable galactosides. It then becomes possible to select for *lac*[−] bacteria in such strains by selecting mutants resistant to lactose (Malamy, 1966).

A particularly useful application of the galactose-sensitive selection is in the mapping of the *i* gene and the operator. A difficult problem arises in recombination studies with mutations which affect regulatory genes or controlling elements in *lac*, and, for that matter, in most systems. The phenotype of an *i*[−] or *o*[c] is still *lac*[+]. One has to devise physiological conditions or strains in which the *lac*-constitutive character can be selected against. One technique for doing this is to construct *lac*-constitutive strains which are sensitive to galactose, and use the non-inducing β-galactosidase substrate, phenyl-β-D-galactoside, in the media to kill all constitutive derivatives (Davies and Jacob, 1968). Another is to use the compound orthonitrophenyl-thiogalactoside, which is not an inducer, but when transported into the cells by the *lac* permease, is lethal (Müller-Hill, Crapo, and Gilbert, 1968).

DIPLOID ANALYSIS

Both F'*lac* episomes and the *lac* transducing phages, λ*lac* and ϕ80*lac*, can be used for diploid analysis of the *lac* region. Mutations in the *lac* region have been isolated which exhibit every conceivable type of behavior in complementation studies: recessive constitutivity (i^-) (Jacob and Monod, 1961a); dominant constitutivity (i^{-d}) (Müller-Hill et al., 1968); *cis*-dominant constitutivity (o^c) (Jacob and Monod, 1961a); dominant pleiotropic *lac*$^-$ (i^s) (Willson, Perrin, Cohn, Jacob, and Monod, 1964); *cis*-dominant pleiotropic *lac*$^-$ (polar mutants and p^-) (Jacob and Monod, 1961a; Scaife and Beckwith, 1966). Thus, it is obviously important for any system that all mutations with apparent regulatory properties be thoroughly characterized in complementation studies, before conclusions can be made about the structure affected.

In order to distinguish between, for instance, an i^{-d} and an o^c mutation, a *cis*-trans test must be carried out (Fig. 3). It can be seen from the results of such a test, that the i^{-d} mutation results in constitutivity for the gene

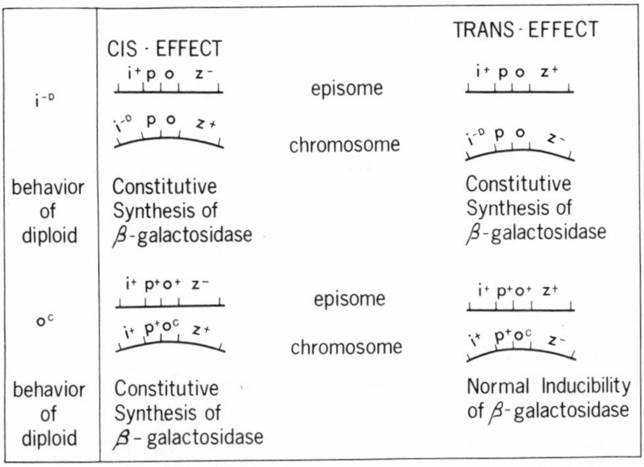

FIGURE 3. The use of *cis*-trans tests to distinguish i^{-D} constitutives from o^c constitutives. See chapter by Gilbert and Müller-Hill for explanation of i^{-D} mutations.

located "in trans" on the episome as well as for the z gene linked to it "in cis". In contrast, the o^c mutation only results in constitutivity for the z gene linked to it "in cis".

It is now possible to isolate F′ episomes carrying any *E. coli* gene. The accumulation of a large array of Hfr's with origins around the chromosome, the ability to select for Hfr's with their origins in predetermined places on the chromosome (Beckwith et al., 1966) and the recently devised simple technique of Low (1968) for isolating F′ factors allow the collection of a series of F′ factors which together cover nearly the entire chromosome. It also now appears likely that transducing phages similar to λ*lac* and φ80*lac* can be isolated for almost any other gene. Gottesman and Beckwith (1969) have described a technique for the isolation of φ80*ara* transducing phages which should be applicable in general to genes on the *E. coli* chromosome.

MAPPING OF THE *LAC* REGION
3-FACTOR CROSSES

A standard method for ordering markers in a small region is by reciprocal 3-factor crosses (Fig. 4, e.g., Gross and Englesberg, 1959). A good deal of the earlier mapping of the *lac* region which led to the order *i-o-z-y* was done in this way. In general, 3-factor crosses have proved fairly reliable. However, marker effects and high negative interference (Jacob and Wollman, 1961), particularly in the case of closely linked mutations, can result in serious mismapping. The problems can be seen, for instance, in the

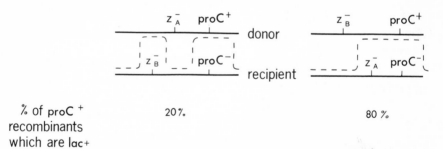

% of proC⁺ recombinants which are lac+   20%.   80 %

FIGURE 4. A reciprocal 3-factor cross. *Reciprocal* 3-factor crosses are essential for conclusive mapping data. Ideally, this is done by Hfr crosses, selecting a marker distal to the *lac* region (e.g. *proC*⁺ in the case of HfrH) and scoring among recombinants for that marker the frequency of *lac*⁺ recombinants. If high negative interference does not make the data inconclusive, substantial differences in frequency should be observed between the two crosses. This is due to the requirement for a quadruple crossover in one case and not the other. This figure depicts a typical result.

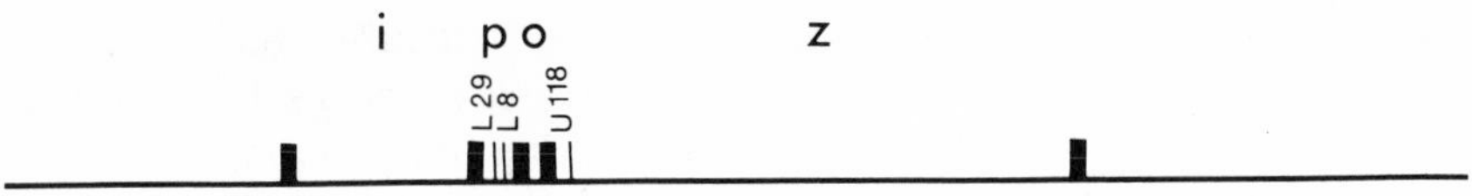

marker in		% of proC $^+$
donor	recipient	recombinants which are lac $^+$
L 8	L 29	0.007
L 29	L 8	0.005
L 8	U 118	0.05
U 118	L 8	0.10
L 29	U 118	0.09
U 118	L 29	0.15

FIGURE 5. Results of reciprocal 3-factor crosses in the lac region. Crosses were carried out as in Fig. 4 (Miller et al., 1968b).

case of recombination between certain promoter mutants and a closely linked z^- mutation (Fig. 5). The high negative interference is so great in these crosses that it is impossible to determine the order of the 3 markers L8, L29 and U118. I feel that a two-fold difference in frequencies observed in reciprocal 3-factor crosses is not enough to give confidence of the order. Such confidence is particularly important in ordering markers in the promoter-operator region and in the adjoining regions of the z and i genes. In these crucial regions which determine the initiation of transcription and translation and their control, any mapping data which is to lead either to new ideas about control mechanisms or to further experiments must be convincing.

DELETION MAPPING

A much more unambiguous method for mapping closely linked muta-tions is by recombination with deletions with ends in the region (Benzer, 1959). Here, rather than comparing two recombination frequencies, a plus or minus answer is expected; the deletion either does or does not recom-bine with a particular mutant. For most genes or operons, the existence of a set of deletions useful for mapping depends on the chance finding of such deletions among mutants isolated spontaneously or with various mutagens. Some of these deletions may be completely internal to the gene or operon (e.g., Malamy, 1966). However, the most convenient way to carry out deletion mapping is to have a large collection of deletions which have one end outside the region under study. These would be a set of deletions beginning with one which removes only a marker or a few markers at one end of the gene cluster, and succeeding ones which cut farther and farther into the operon. Although other deletions can be used for mapping, because of the simplicity of the analysis with these particular deletions, I shall call these "mapping deletions." A collection of such deletions forms what could be called a mapping kit. An example of ordering with mapping deletions in the *lac* operon is shown in Fig. 6. The unambiguous ordering results should be compared with those in Fig. 5 derived from 3-factor crosses.

There are several ways for specifically selecting mapping deletions with one end in the *lac* region. In one case, strains are used in which the *lac* region has been altered by mutation so that none of the structural genes are expressed. From such strains it is possible to select deletions which restore *y* and *a* gene activities by fusing the operon to a nearby functioning gene or operon. Depending on the selection used, these deletions may end either in the *z* gene or somewhere in the controlling element region. One of the convenient aspects of galactoside metabolism in *E. coli* K12 is that it is possible using melibiose to select for the functioning of the *lac y* gene without a requirement for *z* gene activity. Strains which carry either i^s mutations or strong *z* gene polar mutations, and are therefore, phenotypically y^-, are *mel$^-$*. Among *mel$^+$* revertants selected from strains

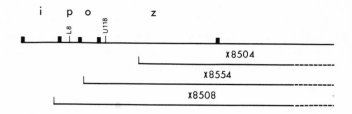

frequency of recombinants			
	Χ8504	Χ8554	Χ8508
L8	+	0.087	0
U118	+	0	0

FIGURE 6. Deletion mapping of *lac* region. Crosses and deletions are described in Ippen et al., 1968b .

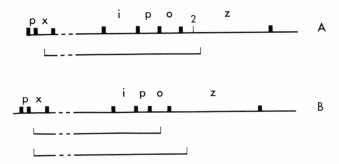

FIGURE 7. Deletions obtained as *mel*⁺ revertants of a polar mutant (A) or i^s mutation (B). "x" represents a nearby unspecified gene with its own promoter, *p*. The marker, 2, is a strong *lac* polar mutant.

carrying these mutations, a certain proportion have restored permease activity as the result of fusion of *lac* to some other gene or operon (Fig. 7; Beckwith, 1964; Jacob, Ullmann, and Monod, 1964; Schwartz and Beckwith, 1969). In the case of the *lac* polar mutation, the deletion must cover at least the polar mutant site (Fig. 7A); with the i^s mutation, the deletion must result in insensitivity to *lac* repressor, since the selections are done in i^s/i^s diploid strains (Fig. 7B). Diploids are used in order to eliminate the very high background of i^s to i^- mutations.

This selection technique is obviously limited in its applications. First, even in *lac*, requirements of the selection may well eliminate certain types of deletions with ends in the controlling element region. With regard to operons other than *lac*, a similar selective technique is necessary; i.e., the ability to select for the expression of a gene distal to the first gene of the operon. Although, for most systems, the structure of the operons and the particular enzymatic steps involved do not allow such selections, they are possible in the histidine operon (selection for growth on histidinol, St. Pierre, 1968) and possibly for tryptophan (selection for growth on anthranilic acid, Margolin and Bauerle, 1966).

A technique for selecting mapping deletions with more general applications derives from the ability to transpose *lac* and other genes to the *att*80 site and to the *gal* locus. Closely linked to the *att*80 site is the *tonB* locus, which has been used extensively as a "deletion selecting" locus (Fig. 8). The gene or genes of the *tonB* locus determine the sensitivity of *E. coli* to the bacteriophages T1 and ϕ80 and to colicins V and B (Gratia, 1964; Wang and Newton, 1969a,b). Mutants resistant to the combination of ϕ80*vir* and colicins V and B, which occur only in this locus, are frequently the result of deletions of at least part of the locus. Many of these deletions extend into nearby unrelated genes. This property of T1ʳ mutations was

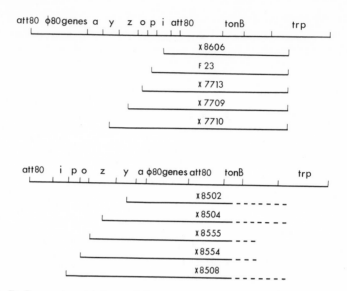

FIGURE 8. *TonB* mapping deletions of the *lac* region. The X-8500 series of deletions are described in Ippen et al., 1968 and Miller et al., 1968b. The others are referred to in the text.

first recognized as a means of selecting mapping deletions by Yanofsky, who used *tonB-trp⁻* deletions to map point mutations in the *trpA* gene (Yanofsky, Carlton, Guest, Helinski, and Henning, 1964). Subsequently, Franklin, Dove, and Yanofsky (1965) showed that in strains lysogenic for bacteriophage φ80, many T1ʳ mutations are deletions extending varying distances into the prophage map. Thus, when *lac* is incorporated in a φ80*lac* prophage, it is clear that many T1ʳ mutations should be deletions which extend in the same way into the *lac* region (Fig. 8).

Strains lysogenic for φ80*lac* have been constructed with *lac* either in its usual orientation relative to other genes on the chromosome (φ80*lac*$_I$) or in inverted orientation (φ80d*lac*$_{II}$) (Fig. 8). As a result, it is possible to isolate mapping deletions extending into either end of the *lac* region (Beckwith et al., 1966; Ippen, Miller, Scaife, and Beckwith, 1968; Miller, Ippen, Scaife, and Beckwith, 1968b). Since, in order to detect *tonB-lac* deletions, the φ80*lac* lysogens must be haploid for the *lac* region, the particular strains used carry a complete deletion of the normally located *lac* region. When *tonB* mutations are selected from φ80d*lac*$_I$ and φ80d*lac*$_{II}$ lysogens, the percentage of those with ends in the *lac* operon are 4% and 1.5% respectively (Miller, Reznikoff, Silverstone, Ippen, Signer, and Beckwith, in preparation).

Several different techniques have been used for isolating *tonB-lac* deletions. (1) In strains lysogenic for φ80d*lac⁺*$_I$ or φ80d*lac⁺*$_{II}$, *tonB* mutants are selected on *lac* indicator plates. *Lac⁻* deletions are then screened by recombination tests to detect those in which the deletion does not remove the entire operon. Most of these are deletions which end in one of the structural genes, *z* or *y* (Beckwith et al., 1966; Miller et al., in preparation). (2) If, instead of using a ϕ80d*lac*$_I$ carrying a wild-type *lac⁺* region, a *lac* promoter mutation is recombined into the prophage, a new type of selection is possible. These strains on *lac* indicator plates score *lac⁻*. A deletion which causes fusion of the *lac* controlling element region to the *trp* operon will restore a *lac⁺* phenotype, if the *trp* operon is being expressed at a high rate (Reznikoff, Miller, Scaife, and Beckwith, 1969; Mitchell and Beckwith, unpublished results). Thus, in such a strain, carrying a *lac* promoter mutation in the prophage and a derepressed allele (*trp*R⁻) of the *trp* regulatory gene, *ton*B deletions have been selected with one end in the *lac* controlling element region. These deletions occur at about 0.01% of the T1^r mutations (Mitchell, Reznikoff, and Beckwith, unpublished results). Finally, if in ϕ80d*lac⁺*$_I$ lysogens, *ton*B mutations are selected on solid media containing the indicator dye XG (see Table 1), deletions ending in the *i* gene are easily detected as deep blue colonies (Miller, Beckwith, and Müller-Hill, 1968). As a result of the use of these several techniques, it has been possible to isolate *ton*B-*lac* deletions with ends in virtually every element of the *lac* region (Fig. 8). This provides a complete kit of mapping deletions. These deletions have been used to conclusively establish the order *i-p-o-z-y-a* (Miller et al., 1968b).

A second analogous system for isolating mapping deletions exists in strains where *lac* is transposed to the *gal* region. Shapiro and Adhya (1969) have found that in strains lysogenic for certain λ derivatives, a selection can be devised to give mapping deletions of the *gal* operon. Further, Adhya, Cleary, and Campbell (1968) have shown that selection for chlorate resistance gives the same sort of deletions due to the existence of the ch1D locus between *gal* and *att*λ. Preliminary studies with strains in which *lac* is transposed to the *gal* region have yielded similar mapping deletions for *lac* (Fig. 9).

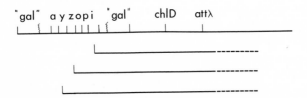

FIGURE 9. Deletions of *lac* transposed to the *gal* region. Using a selection involving a heat-inducible λ lysogen (Shapiro and Adhya, 1969), we have selected deletions cutting into the *i* gene and possibly into *z* (Shapiro et al., 1969; Ippen, Shapiro, and Beckwith, in preparation).

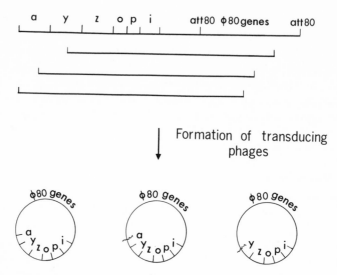

Figure 10. Origin of φ80*lac* transducing phages carrying *lac* deletions.

Finally, another class of mapping deletions can be obtained by isolating transducing phages which include only a portion of the *lac* region (Fig. 10). This type of transducing phage has been used extensively in the mapping of the *gal* operon with λdg phages. However, the types of deletions of *lac* which can be obtained in this way are limited (Beckwith et al., 1966). The isolation of a terminal deletion of the *lac* operon by this technique has provided the information that the enzyme thiogalactoside transacetylase is not essential for lactose metabolism (Fox, Beckwith, Signer, and Epstein, 1966).

Since the techniques used for obtaining these transpositions of the *lac* region can be extended to other bacterial genes, most of these methods of deletion selection should be applicable to other operons. In many cases, this type of system could greatly simplify mapping problems.

One qualification of deletion mapping should be considered. Mapping deletions remove all genetic homology to one side of the mutant sites not included in the deletions. It is quite possible that mutations which lie close to the region covered by the deletion will be unable to recombine with that deletion because of the limited homology. So far no example of this has been found; in all deletion strains where by physiological tests we can demonstrate the existence of an element of the *lac* region, recombinants for the nearest marker can also be obtained. Although this problem is unlikely to generate errors in mapping order, it should be remembered if the deletions are to be used for other purposes.

A very useful method for increasing the sensitivity of the recombination techniques where low levels of recombination are expected is to measure frequencies in strains diploid for the *lac* region. If such strains, carrying two different *lac* mutations, are grown up to high density in liquid media, recombinants accumulate and the frequency of recombinants will be higher than in a transduction or HfrxF$^-$ cross (Ippen et al., 1968; Miller et al., 1968). This technique has been used in mapping point mutants versus deletions.

OTHER USES OF *TRP-LAC* FUSION STRAINS

The properties of those deletions from ϕ80d*lac*$_I$ lysogens which fuse different elements of the *lac* region to the *trp* operon provide further evidence for the structure of this region. *Ton*B deletions which fuse the *i* gene to the *trp* operon (Fig. 8, X8606) have no effect on the expression of the *lac* operon except to render it constitutive. The *lac* operon is not put under *trp*R control, and introduction of an *i*$^+$ gene on an F′ episome restores the normal inducible character (Miller et al., 1968a). Comparable deletions which end in the *p* region either abolish or drastically lower *lac* operon activity in *trp*R$^+$ derivatives, while the *trp*R$^-$ mutation causes an increase in *lac* expression (Fig. 8-F23). A deletion which extends into the operator region and recombines with no *o* or *p* mutations has no effect on the structure of β-galactosidase made under tryptophan control (Fig. 8-X7713; Reznikoff and Beckwith, 1969; Bhorjee, Fowler, and Zabin, 1964). Deletions ending in the *z* gene result in *trp*R control of the *y* and *a* genes (Fig. 8-X7709). Finally, fusion deletions which end in the *y* gene exhibit control of transacetylase activity by the *trp*R gene (Miller et al., in preparation; Fig. 8-X7710).

In addition to providing a mapping system, the existence of *trp-lac* fusions has opened up new approaches to other problems concerning *lac* operon expression and control. Some of these experiments are covered in other chapters in this volume. Other potential uses of these deletions include (1) the possibility that genes, such as the *i* gene, which normally function at a very low rate, can be fused to the *trp* operon in such a way that their product (in this case, the repressor) is made in much higher quantities per cell. (2) We have isolated a number of strains in which the *lac* controlling element region is fused to the *trp*A gene (Fig. 8-F23). It is probable that these strains are producing a protein which is partly tryptophan synthetase A protein and partly a translation of the promoter-operator region. The isolation of such proteins and their sequencing should allow base sequence determination of the promoter and operator (Reznikoff, Mitchell, and Beckwith, unpublished results).

Again, all of these approaches could be applicable to other *E. coli* operons and genes.

ESTIMATING DISTANCES IN THE *LAC* OPERON

It is, of course, of great interest to know something about the size of such regions as the operator and promoter. Ultimately, conclusive information will come from a combination of genetic, biochemical and physical studies. In the meantime, we might ask whether the genetic mapping which has been done in this region leads to any estimates of these distances.

There exists in the literature enough data to make it clear that any estimates of true distances based on recombination frequencies could be off by as much as an order of magnitude. This conclusion comes particularly out of the work of Yanofsky and co-workers (Yanofsky et al., 1964; Drapeau, Brammar, and Yanofsky, 1968) on the *trp*A gene and its product, the tryptophan synthetase A protein, where it is possible to relate true distances to recombination frequencies. The variation in the relationship between recombination frequencies and true distances is probably due, in part, to the sorts of effects seen by Herman (1968) and Zipser (1967). Herman showed that the induction of *lac* expression can have an effect on the frequency of recombination. We have also seen marker effects on map distance (Miller et al., 1968b). Zipser found that recombination frequencies between two very close mutations in the *z* gene were much lower than expected on the basis of other map distances in the *z* gene.

Westmoreland, Szybalski, and Ris (1969) have described a technique for estimating certain distances of the λ genome by electron microscopic observation of certain λDNA heteroduplexes. These heteroduplexes include a deletion of material on one strand, resulting in the formation of a loop on the other representing the length of the deletion. Through such heteroduplex analysis using one of the *lac* transducing phages and various deletions of the controlling element region, it should be possible to obtain, at least, a maximum estimate for the size of these elements.

THE PURIFICATION OF *LAC* DNA

One other use of the tools generally employed in the genetic analysis of the *lac* operon are that they provide a means of purifying *lac* DNA. The ability to make pure DNA preparations of an operon provides a means of answering basic questions about operon expression and regulation. A pure *lac* DNA preparation could be used as a substrate for transcription-translation and repression studies in vitro. The DNA would also serve as a means of detecting by DNA-RNA hybridization specifically *lac* mRNA made either in vivo or in vitro.

The size of the *lac* region (including the *i* gene) can be calculated to be approximately 4.3×10^6 daltons on the basis of the estimated molecular weights of the protein products (see chapters in this volume by Zabin and Fowler; Kennedy; Gilbert and Müller-Hill) and assuming that the *p-o* region is much smaller (Miller et al., 1968b; Shapiro, MacHattie, Eron, Ihler, Ippen, Beckwith, Arditti, Reznikoff, and MacGillivray, 1969) than the average gene. This means that the bacterial chromosome is 0.15% *lac* (Cairns, 1963). Since the size of F'*lac* DNA has been estimated to be between 7.4 and 16×10^7 (Freifelder, 1968; Matsubara, 1968), *lac* would comprise approximately 3.7% of the episomal DNA. The isolation of F'*lac* DNA would thus represent a partial purification of the *lac* genes. The first step in the isolation of F'*lac* DNA is the transfer of the episome into different bacterial species such as *Proteus vulgaris* (Falkow, Wohlhieter, Citarella, and Baron, 1964) or *Serratia marcescens* (Falkow, Marmur, Carey, Spilman, and Baron, 1961), which have DNA with G-C contents quite different from *E. coli*. The F'*lac* DNA can then be separated from the particular chromosomal DNA by density gradient centrifugation.

The DNA of a λ*lac* or a ϕ80*lac* is even more highly enriched for the *lac* genes, being composed of approximately 14% *lac* (Yamagishi, Yoshizako, and Sato, 1966). Moreover, the DNA is more easily isolated than with F'*lac*, simply by inducing the phage of lysogenic strains and isolating the DNA from the phage particles in the lysates.*

It must be remembered that F'*lac* DNA, in addition to carrying the *lac* genes and sex-factor DNA, almost certainly carries some other bacterial genes which were originally located close to the *lac* genes on the chromosome. The same is probably true for the *lac* transducing phages. It is a reasonable possibility that in most studies using these DNA preparations for hybridization with mRNA, species in addition to *lac* mRNA are being detected. This is an important caution relevant to the use of such DNA preparations for any system.

It is clear then that a significant problem in using these partially purified *lac* DNA preparations for studying the *lac* operon is the presence of other genes in the DNA. This complication has recently been overcome by the isolation of *lac* DNA which is free of any other genetic material (Shapiro et al., 1969). This isolation was made possible by the existence of different types of λ*lac* and ϕ80*lac* transducing phages. The separation of DNA

---

*At this writing, the DNA preparation most frequently used as a source of *lac* DNA is a hybrid λh80d*lac* phage carrying the CI857 marker which was derived from a cross between λ and ϕ80d*lac*. The temperature-inducible character of the phage, conferred by the CI mutation, facilitates the making of high-titer phage lysates.

strands from two of these phages and subsequent annealing of appropriate pairs of strands resulted in structures in which the only duplex region was *lac* DNA. The removal of single-stranded DNA regions by a specific endonuclease left pure *lac* DNA.

CONCLUDING REMARKS

The progress in the understanding of how genes work in bacteria has been heavily dependent on the advances in bacterial genetics. The increasing sophistication of the methodology in this field has now made possible almost any conceivable manipulation of genes in *E. coli*. Although many of these manipulations have at first seemed gratuitous (i.e., the isolation of ϕ80*lac* and subsequently λ*lac*, who needs a second phage?), they all ultimately turn out to be useful.

There are still problems remaining in the *lac* operon which will require precise genetic analysis. The portion of the *lac* region around the controlling sites includes the following interesting elements: a messenger RNA stop signal at the end of the *i* gene; the promoter site which may be relatively complex (see Miller, this volume); the operator, and the translation initiation signals at the beginning of *z*. A careful mapping of mutants in these regions in conjunction with base sequence analysis will tell us what sequences are important for the interaction of proteins with DNA.

ACKNOWLEDGMENTS

This work was supported by a career development award and a grant from the National Institutes of Health (GM9027) and grants from the National Science Foundation (GB8247), American Cancer Society and the Jane Coffin Childs Memorial Fund for Medical Research.

APPENDIX

The following are references for published maps of the regions indicated:
i and *o:* Davies and Jacob, 1968; Ippen et al., 1968; Miller et al., 1968a,b.
z: Jacob and Monod, 1961a,b; Jacob and Wollman, 1961; Newton, Beckwith, Zipser, and Brenner, 1965; Malamy, 1966; Cook and Lederberg, 1962; Schwartz and Beckwith, 1969; Ullmann, Jacob, and Monod, 1968; Michels and Zipser, 1969.
y: Jacob and Monod, 1961a,b; Jacob and Wollman, 1961; Malamy, 1966; Beckwith and Signer, 1966.

REFERENCES

ADELBERG, E. A. and S. N. BURNS. 1960. Genetic variation in the sex factor of *Escherichia coli*. J. Bacteriol. *79:* 321.

ADHYA, S., P. CLEARY, and A. CAMPBELL. 1968. A deletion analysis of prophage λ and adjacent genetic region. Proc. Nat. Acad. Sci. *61:* 956.

ARDITTI, R. R., J. G. SCAIFE, and J. R. BECKWITH. 1968. The nature of mutants in the *lac* promoter region. J. Mol. Biol. *38:* 421.

BECKWITH, J. R. 1963. Restoration of operon activity by suppressors. Biochim. Biophys. Acta *76:* 162.

————. 1964. A deletion analysis of the *lac* operator region in *Escherichia coli.* J. Mol. Biol. *8:* 427.

BECKWITH, J. R. and E. R. SIGNER. 1966. Transposition of the *lac* region of *E. coli.* I. Inversion of the *lac* operon and transduction of *lac* by φ80. J. Mol. Biol. *19:* 254.

BECKWITH, J. R., E. SIGNER, and W. EPSTEIN. 1966. Transposition of the *lac* region. Cold Spring Harbor Symp. Quant. Biol. *23:* 393.

BENZER, S. 1959. On the topology of the genetic fine structure. Proc. Nat. Acad. Sci. *45:* 1607.

BHORJEE, J. S., A. V. FOWLER, and I. ZABIN. 1969. Biochemical evidence that the operator locus is distinct from the *z* gene in the *lac* operon of *Escherichia coli.* J. Mol. Biol. *43:* 219.

CAIRNS, J. 1963. The chromosome of *Escherichia coli.* Cold Spring Harbor Symp. Quant. Biol. *28:* 43.

COOK, A. and J. LEDERBERG. 1962. Recombination studies of lactose nonfermenting mutants of *Escherichia coli* K12. Genetics *47:* 1335.

DAVIES, J. and F. JACOB. 1968. Genetic mapping of the regulator and operator genes of the *lac* operon. J. Mol. Biol. *36:* 413.

DRAPEAU, G. R., W. J. BRAMMAR, and C. YANOFSKY. 1968. Amino acid replacements of the glutamic acid residue of position 48 in the tryptophan synthetase A protein of *Escherichia coli.* J. Mol. Biol. *35:* 357.

ENGLESBERG, E., D. SHEPPARD, C. SQUIRES, and F. MERONK, Jr. 1969. An analysis of "revertants" of a deletion mutant in the C gene of the L-arabinose gene complex in *Escherichia coli* B/r: isolation of initiation constitutive mutants (I^c). J. Mol. Biol. *43:* 281.

FALKOW, S., J. MARMUR, W. F. CAREY, W. M. SPILMAN, and L. S. BARON. 1961. Episomic transfer between *Salmonella typhosa* and *Serratia marcescens.* Genetics *46:* 703.

FALKOW, S., J. A. WOHLHIETER, R. V. CITARELLA, and L. S. BARON. 1964. Transfer of episomic elements to *Proteus.* I. Transfer of F-linked chromosomal determinants. J. Bacteriol. *87:* 209.

FOX, C. F., J. R. BECKWITH, W. EPSTEIN, and E. R. SIGNER. 1966. Transposition of the *lac* region of *Escherichia coli.* II. On the role of thiogalactoside transacetylase in lactose metabolism. J. Mol. Biol. *19:* 576.

FRANKLIN, N. C., W. F. DOVE, and C. YANOFSKY. 1965. The linear insertion of a prophage into the chromosome of *E. coli* shown by deletion mapping. Biochem. Biophys. Res. Commun. *18:* 910.

FREIFELDER, D. 1968. Studies on *Escherichia coli* sex factors. IV. Molecular weights of the DNA of several F' elements. J. Mol. Biol. *35:* 95.

GOTTESMAN, S. and J. R. BECKWITH. 1969. Directed transposition of the arabinose operon: a technique for the isolation of specialized transducing bacteriophages for any *Escherichia coli* gene. J. Mol. Biol. *44:* 117.

GRATIA, J. P. 1964. Résistance à la colicine chez *E. coli.* Ann. Inst. Pasteur *107:* 132.

GROSS, J. and ENGLESBERG. 1959. Determination of the order of mutational sites governing L-arabinose utilization in *Escherichia coli* B/r by transduction with phage P1 bt. Virology *9:* 314.

HERMAN, R. K. 1968. Effect of gene induction on frequency of intragenic recombination of chromosome and F-merogenote in *Escherichia coli* K12. Genetics *58:* 55.

HORWITZ, J. P., J. CHUA, R. J. CURBY, A. J. TOMSON, M. A. DaROOGE, B. E. FISHER, J. MAURICIO, and I. KLUNDT. 1964. Substrates for cytochemical demonstration of enzyme activity. I. Some substituted 3-indolyl-β-D-glycopyranosides. J. Med. Chem. *7:* 574.

IPPEN, K., J. H. MILLER, J. SCAIFE, and J. BECKWITH. 1968. New controlling element in the *lac* operon of *E. coli.* Nature *217:* 825.

JACOB, F. 1966. Genetics of the bacterial cell. Science *152:* 1470.

JACOB, F. and E. A. ADELBERG. 1959. Transfer of genetic characters by incorporation into the sex factor of *Escherichia coli.* C. R. Acad. Sci. *249:* 189.

JACOB, F. and J. MONOD. 1961a. On the regulation of gene activity. Cold Spring Harbor Symp. Quant. Biol. *26:* 193.

———. 1961b. Genetic regulatory mechanisms in the synthesis of proteins. J. Mol. Biol. *3:* 318.

JACOB, F., A. ULLMANN, and J. MONOD. 1964. Le promoteur, élément génétique necéssaire à l'expression d'un opéron. C. R. Acad. Sci. *258:* 3125.

———. 1965. Délétions fusionnant l'opéron lactose et un opéron purine chez *Escherichia coli.* J. Mol. Biol. *13:* 704.

JACOB, F. and E. L. WOLLMAN. 1956. Sur les processus de conjugaison chez *Escherichia coli.* I. l'induction par conjugaison ou induction zygotique. Ann. Inst. Pasteur *91:* 486.

———. 1961. Sexuality and the genetics of bacteria. pp. 228–232, 273. Academic Press, London.

JAYARAMAN, K., B. MÜLLER-HILL, and H. V. RICKENBERG. 1966. Inhibition of the synthesis of β-galactosidase in *Escherichia coli* by 2-nitrophenyl-β-D-fucoside. J. Mol. Biol. *18:* 339.

LANGRIDGE, J. 1969. Mutations conferring quantitative and qualitative increases in β-galactosidase activity in *Escherichia coli.* Molec. Gen. Genetics *105:* 74.

LEDERBERG, E. M. 1952. Allelic relationships and reverse mutation in *Escherichia coli.* Genetics *37:* 469.

LEDERBERG, J., E. M. LEDERBERG, N. D. ZINDER, and E. R. Lively. 1951. Recombination analysis of bacterial heredity. Cold Spring Harbor Symp. Quant. Biol. *16:* 413.

LEDERBERG, J. and E. L. TATUM. 1946a. Novel genotypes in mixed cultures of biochemical mutants of bacteria. Cold Spring Harbor Symp. Quant. Biol. *11:* 113.

————. 1946b. Gene recombination in *E. coli.* Nature *158:* 558.

Low, B. 1968. Formation of merodiploids in mating with a class of rec⁻ recipient strains of *Escherichia coli* K12. Proc. Nat. Acad. Sci. *60:* 160.

MALAMY, M. 1966. Frameshift mutations in the lactose operon of *E. coli.* Cold Spring Harbor Symp. Quant. Biol. *31:* 189.

MARGOLIN, P. and R. H. BAUERLE. 1966. Determinants for regulation and initiation of expression of tryptophan genes. Cold Spring Harbor Symp. Quant. Biol. *31:* 311.

MATSUBARA, K. 1968. Properties of sex factor and related episomes isolated from purified *Escherichia coli* zygote cells. J. Mol. Biol. *38:* 89.

MICHELS, C. A. and D. ZIPSER. 1969. Mapping of polypeptide reinitiation sites within the β-galactosidase structural gene. J. Mol. Biol. *41:* 341.

MILLER, J. H., J. R. BECKWITH, and B. MÜLLER-HILL. 1968a. Direction of transcription of a regulatory gene in *E. coli.* Nature *220:* 1287.

MILLER, J. H., K. IPPEN, J. G. SCAIFE, and J. R. BECKWITH. 1968b. The promoter-operator region of the *lac* operon of *Escherichia coli.* J. Mol. Biol. *38:* 413.

MONOD, J. 1966. From enzymatic adaptation to allosteric transitions. Science *154:* 475.

MÜLLER-HILL, B., L. CRAPO, and W. GILBERT. 1968. Mutants that make more *lac* repressor. Proc. Nat. Acad. Sci. *59:* 1259.

NEWTON, W. A., J. R. BECKWITH, D. ZIPSER, and S. BRENNER. 1965. Nonsense mutants and polarity in the *lac* operon of *Escherichia coli.* J. Mol. Biol. *14:* 290.

OHLSSON, B. M., P. F. STRIGINI, and J. R. BECKWITH. 1968. Alleleic amber and ochre suppressors. J. Mol. Biol. *36:* 209.

PARDEE, A. B., F. JACOB, and J. MONOD. 1959. The genetic control and cytoplasmic expression of inducibility in the synthesis of β-galactosidase of *E. coli.* J. Mol. Biol. *1:* 165.

PRESTIDGE, L. S. and A. B. PARDEE. 1965. A second permease for methyl-β-D thiogalactoside in *Escherichia coli.* Biochim. Biophys. Acta *100:* 591.

REZNIKOFF, W. S. and J. R. BECKWITH. 1969. Genetic evidence that the operator locus is distinct from the z gene in the *lac* operon of *Escherichia coli.* J. Mol. Biol. *43:* 215.

REZNIKOFF, W. S., J. H. MILLER, J. G. SCAIFE, and J. R. BECKWITH. 1969. A mechanism for repressor action. J. Mol. Biol. *43:* 201.

ST. PIERRE, M. L. 1968. Mutations creating a new initiation point for expression of the histidine operon in *Salmonella typhimurium.* J. Mol. Biol. *35:* 71.

SCAIFE, J. and J. R. BECKWITH. 1966. Mutational alteration of the maximal level of *lac* operon expression. Cold Spring Harbor Symp. Quant. Biol. *31:* 403.

SCHAEFLER, S. 1967. Isolation of constitutive β-galactoside permease mutants in *Escherichia coli* by selection for raffinose fermentation. Bact. Proc. 54.

SCHWARTZ, D. O. and J. R. BECKWITH. 1969. Mutagens which cause deletions in *Escherichia coli.* Genetics *61:* 371.

SHAPIRO, J. A. and S. L. ADHYA. 1969. The galactose operon of *E. coli* K12. II. A deletion analysis of operon structure and polarity. Genetics *62:* 249.

SHAPIRO, J., L. MACHATTIE, L. ERON, G. IHLER, K. IPPEN, J. BECKWITH, R. ARDITTI,

W. REZNIKOFF, and R. MACGILLIVRAY. 1969. The isolation of pure *lac* operon DNA. Nature *224:* 768.

SIGNER, E. R. 1966. Interaction of prophages at the att80 site with the chromosome of *Escherichia coli.* J. Mol. Biol. *15:* 243.

SOFFER, R. L. 1962. Enzymatic expression of genetic units of function concerned with galactose metabolism in *Escherichia coli.* J. Bacteriol. *82:* 471.

ULLMANN, A., F. JACOB, and J. MONOD. 1968. On the subunit structure of wild-type versus complemented β-galactosidase of *Escherichia coli.* J. Mol. Biol. *32:* 1.

WANG, C. C. and A. NEWTON. 1969a. Iron transport in *Escherichia coli:* Relationship between chromium sensitivity and high iron requirement in mutants in *Escherichia coli.* J. Bacteriol. *98:* 1135.

———. 1969b. Iron transport in *Escherichia coli:* Roles of energy dependent uptake and 2,3-dihydroxy benzoylserine. J. Bacteriol. *98:* 1142.

WESTMORELAND, B. C., W. SZYBALSKI, and H. RIS. 1969. Mapping of deletions and substitutions in heteroduplex DNA molecules of bacteriophage lambda by electron microscopy. Science *163:* 1343.

WILLSON, C., D. PERRIN, M. COHN, F. JACOB, and J. MONOD. 1964. Non-inducible mutants of the regulator gene in the lactose system of *Escherichia coli.* J. Mol. Biol. *8:* 582.

WOLLMAN, E. L., F. JACOB, and W. HAYES. 1956. Conjugation and genetic recombination in *Escherichia coli.* Cold Spring Harbor Symp. Quant. Biol. *21:* 141.

YAMAGISHI, H., F. YOSHIZAKO, and K. SATO. 1966. Characteristics of DNA molecules extracted from bacteriophages ϕ80 and ϕ80pt. Virology *30:* 29.

YANOFSKY, C., B. C. CARLTON, J. R. GUEST, D. R. HELINSKI, and U. HENNING. 1964. On the colinearity of gene structure and protein structure. Proc. Nat. Acad. Sci. *51:* 266.

ZIPSER, D. 1967. Orientation of nonsense codons on the genetic map of the *lac* operon. Science *157:* 1176.

β-galactosidase and Thiogalactoside Transacetylase

IRVING ZABIN and AUDRÉE V. FOWLER

Department of Biological Chemistry
School of Medicine
Molecular Biology Institute
University of California, Los Angeles

A complete description of the *lac* operon in *Escherichia coli*, its expression and its regulation, must include detailed knowledge of the protein products of its structural genes. These proteins are three: β-galactosidase, whose function is to catalyze the hydrolysis of lactose; the galactoside permease (or "M" protein), which is involved in transport and accumulation of lactose within the cell; and thiogalactoside transacetylase, whose function is still under investigation. It is the purpose of this chapter to summarize information on the chemistry of β-galactosidase and thiogalactoside transacetylase, and to relate such information where possible to the genetic elements of the *lac* operon. Much of the earlier work on β-galactosidase has been reviewed by Cohn (1957) and by Wallenfels and Malhotra (1961). The "M" protein is discussed in detail by Kennedy elsewhere in this volume.

β-GALACTOSIDASE

Isolation. β-galactosidase has been obtained in pure state from ML and K-12 strains of *E. coli* by fairly conventional methods of protein purification employing ammonium sulfate precipitations and DEAE cellulose or DEAE-Sephadex column procedures (Hu, Wolfe, and Reithel, 1959; Karlsson, Koorajian, Zabin, Sjostrand, and Miller, 1964; Craven, Steers, and Anfinsen, 1965). No differences have been observed between the proteins from the two sources, and it is assumed they are identical. Crystallization of the enzyme was first achieved by Wallenfels and Zarnitz (1957) by addition of ammonium sulfate to solutions of the protein in the presence of sodium chloride.

Composition. The crystalline protein was found to contain 16.1% nitrogen, 0.93% sulfur, and to contain no sugar or phosphate (Wallenfels, Zarnitz, Laule, Bender, and Keser, 1959). The amino acid composition determined in several laboratories by automatic amino acid analysis is shown in Table 1. On the basis of a minimum mol wt of 135,000, the protein contains approximately 1170 residues. The rather high content of aromatic amino acids accounts for the extinction coefficient of 1.91 (Wallenfels et al., 1959) or 2.09 cm² per mg protein (Craven et al., 1965).

Molecular weight. Earlier estimates of the mol wt of the native protein are now known to have been high. From more recent determinations values have been reported of 518,000 based on an $S_{w,20}$ of 16.1 and a diffusion constant of 3.13×10^{-7} cm²sec⁻¹ (Sund and Weber, 1963), and 540,000 by sedimentation equilibrium methods (Craven et al., 1965). The validity of these values is supported by approximations from electron micrographs (Karlsson et al., 1964) and by studies of subunit sizes presented below. For this review the mol wt of 540,000 is taken as correct.

Table 1. Amino acid composition of β-galactosidase

	Residues per 135,000 mol wt		
	(1)	(2)	(3)
Tryptophan	35	—	32
Lysine	29	26	27
Histidine	36	41	36
Arginine	74	77	73
Aspartic Acid	123	120	122
Threonine	65	62	70
Seri	67	64	69
Glutamic Acid	142	130	145
Proline	67	59	71
Glycine	85	82	84
Alanine	93	88	94
Half-Cystine	19	23	17
Valine	75	72	75
Methionine	24	27	21
Isoleucine	48	49	44
Leucine	110	111	112
Tyrosine	36	28	34
Phenylalanine	45	42	45
Total	1,173	—	1,171

(1) Craven et al., 1965.
(2) Wallenfels, K., C. Streffer, and C. Gölker, 1965.
(3) This laboratory.

Higher polymers of $β$-galactosidase which are present in minor amounts have been studied by Appel, Alpers, and Tompkins (1965) who noted at least seven enzymatically-active electrophoretic forms in extracts, with S values in sucrose of as high as 34 S. Marchesi, Steers, and Shifrin (1969) have found that the renaturation from urea of such multiple forms, also termed isoenzymes, results in the formation of the 16 S molecule. This finding indicates that the higher polymers are composed of the same subunits as the major form of $β$-galactosidase.

SUBUNIT STRUCTURE

The question of how many polypeptide chains are present in $β$-galactosidase, their size, and whether they are identical or different has been difficult to answer. From studies of the last half-dozen years particularly, it is quite certain that the protein is a tetramer. Because of sometimes contradictory evidence, the more difficult problem has been to determine the nature of the monomeric structure. However, after consideration of all evidence, it now seems clear that the monomer is a single long polypeptide chain. Such evidence, primarily from the chemical point of view, is reviewed next. Conclusions regarding the structure of $β$-galactosidase drawn from complementation experiments are presented elsewhere in this volume by Ullmann and Perrin.

Tetrameric structure. Equilibrium dialysis studies with the inhibitor phenyl-$β$-D-thiogalactoside gave results indicating approximately five binding sites per mole of enzyme (Cohn, 1957). At the time these experiments were performed, the mol wt of $β$-galactosidase was estimated to be about 700,000 or 750,000. The actual calculated value obtained was one binding site for a protein mol wt of 133,000, or four sites for a protein of 532,000, in remarkable agreement with the mol wt of the native protein obtained later by the physical methods mentioned above. If the reasonable assumption is made that the number of binding sites is a measure of the number of monomers in a polymeric protein, "protomers" in the terminology of Monod, Wyman, and Changeux (1965), $β$-galactosidase by this criterion is a tetramer.

The same conclusion was reached by Zipser (1963) through the use of an elegant hybridization technique which depends on the fact that $β$-galactosidase can be dissociated in urea and reassociated by careful removal of urea to give enzymically-active protein. When a small amount of radioactive $β$-galactosidase was mixed with a large excess of $β$-galactosidase containing heavy isotopes, the mixture next dissociated with urea and then reassociated, hybrid molecules (radioactive and heavy) were obtained. These were separated on rubidium chloride gradients and the density of the hybrid was compared to the original molecules. The shift in density of the radioactive hybrid was one-quarter of the difference between the densities of the parent enzymes. These results meant not only that subunits obtained in urea were one-quarter the size of the native protein but in addition, from the shape of the hybrid peak in the gradient, that each of the subunits was identical.

Quite different experiments also support in a less direct manner the tetrameric structure. Perrin (1963) isolated and characterized a number of proteins immunologically related to β-galactosidase but enzymatically inactive. Certain pairs of these cross-reacting materials complement to give active enzyme, and the complemented enzyme sediments in sucrose identically to the native protein, and more rapidly than either of the individual components. Further, the approximate sizes of the latter materials in several cases were one-quarter and one-half of the complemented product. A detailed study of a cross-reacting material from another mutant by Steers and Shifrin (1967) showed that the enzymatically inactive but complementing protein had a mol wt of 247,000. Clearly, this substance must be a dimer.

Direct evidence for the tetrameric nature of β-galactosidase was obtained by electron microscopy of crystalline β-galactosidase using negative staining techniques (Karlsson et al., 1964). As mentioned above, the mol wt calculated from the observed dimensions of the molecule suggest a mol wt of slightly more than 500,000, and of importance here, a division of the molecule into four equal parts was clearly evident.

Strong evidence adding further support to the tetrameric structure comes from physical studies with the dissociating solvents urea and guanidine. Reduced and acetamidated β-galactosidase completely dissociates into a subunit in 5 M guanidine with an $S_{w,20}$ of 3.65 and a diffusion constant of 2.5×10^{-7} cm^{2}sec^{-1}. The mol wt from these values is 147,000 (Wallenfels, Sund, and Weber, 1963). Chemically unmodified β-galactosidase in 6 M guanidine was found to yield a single subunit also, and the mol wt by the Archibald method was 135,000 (Ullmann, Goldberg, Perrin, and Monod, 1968b). Wallenfels et al. (1963) and Shifrin and Steers (1967) obtained similar mol wt of 118,000 in 6 or in 8 M urea.

All of the results mentioned here, the study of binding sites, hybridization, immunologically related protein, electron micrographs, and dissociation in urea or guanidine lead to the conclusion that β-galactosidase is a tetrameric protein. What, then, is the nature of each fourth of the molecule? The next question to consider is whether the minimum chemical mol wt is the same as that of the monomeric mol wt.

Minimum molecular weight. Per tetrameric molecule, β-galactosidase contains approximately 112 residues of lysine and 300 residues of arginine, or a maximum of 412 peptide bonds susceptible to cleavage by trypsin. If the minimum chemical mol wt is one-fourth the mol wt of the complete protein, no more than about 100 different peptides can result; if it is one-eighth, no more than about 50 can result, and so on. Steers, Craven, Anfinsen, and Bethune (1965) prepared peptide maps after treatment of β-galactosidase with trypsin and were able to distinguish approximately 86 ninhydrin positive components. This is in excellent agreement with a minimum chemical mol wt of one-fourth the molecule, particularly when the difficulty of separation of such a large number of peptides is taken into account. It is also true that cleavage does not occur at every lysine or arginine residue. In studies of the sequence of amino acids in β-galactosidase now underway in this laboratory, approximately 60 tryptic peptides have been obtained so far in pure form; 10 of these have more than one basic amino acid due in most cases to lysylprolyl or arginylprolyl groups. An early estimate of the number of tryptic peptides based on very preliminary results was too low (Zabin, 1963a).

Per tetrameric molecule, β-galactosidase contains approximately 96 methionine residues. The number of peptides obtained by cleavage with cyanogen bromide (BrCN) has been used to determine the minimum chemical mol wt in a similar manner. In experiments by Steers et al. (1965), the number of peptides resulting from BrCN treatment were estimated to be 20 to 25 by polyacrylamide electrophoresis after gel filtration of the peptide mixture. These results were confirmed by Katze, Sridhara, and Zabin (1966) who estimated 23 peptides by amino-terminal analysis of the BrCN peptide mixture with the Sanger reagent.

It is clear, then, that by estimation of the number of peptides after treatment with trypsin and with BrCN, the minimum chemical mol wt of β-galactosidase is the same as that of the monomeric mol wt. These experiments do not allow any clear-cut decision regarding the number of polypeptide chains in β-galactosidase, however. They suggest, in conjunction with those of the preceding section, that there are four chains, one per monomer. They do not rule out two or more different chains, AB, or ABC, etc. per monomer, but since each quarter of the molecule is identical to the next, two monomers cannot be AAB and the remaining two ABB. Also, these experiments do not rule out the possibility that two or more polypeptide chains held together by covalent but non-peptide bonds exist in each monomer.

Number of polypeptide chains. The determination of end groups has added strong support for the conclusion that β-galactosidase contains four polypeptide chains, each the mol wt of the monomer. The presence of approximately two-thirds of a mole of threonine per 135,000 g at the amino terminal position was observed by Cohn (cited by Monod, 1959) and confirmed by many workers (Wallenfels and Arens, 1960; Steers et al., 1965; Brown, Koorajian, Katze, and Zabin, 1966). Preliminary treatment of the protein with dilute acid, which would be expected to hydrolyze N-formyl groups, or with 70% formic acid, dilute trimethylamine, or sodium dodecyl sulfate prior to analysis revealed no additional amino acid. No N-acetyl groups could be detected. These experiments were carried out using the dinitrofluorobenzene procedure; when amino-terminal analysis was performed by the Stark and Smyth carbamylation method, the yield of threonine was 1 mole per 135,000 g of protein (Brown et al., 1966). By cleavage of dinitrophenyl-β-galactosidase with BrCN, DNP-threonyl-homoserine was isolated readily, indicating the amino-terminal sequence to be threonylmethionine (Katze et al., 1966).

Important evidence concerning the structure of β-galactosidase has been obtained from carboxyl-terminal analyses. Treatment with carboxypeptidase B allowed the release of quantities of lysine close to 1 mole per 135,000 g of protein, while carboxypeptidase A released at most traces of amino acids. Hydrazinolysis also showed that lysine is the only carboxyl-terminal amino acid (Koorajian and Zabin, 1965; Brown, Koorajian, Katze, and Zabin, 1966; Korenman, Craven, and Anfinsen, 1966). These experiments were carried out with protein denatured by heating in sodium dodecyl sulfate or with protein modified by carboxymethylation. Under each of these circumstances no amino acid other than lysine could be shown to be carboxyl-terminal.

It is obvious that the results so far summarized are entirely consistent with the view already expressed, that β-galactosidase is composed of four identical polypeptide chains each of mol wt 135,000. There have been, however, several reasons to question this conclusion. The first is simply that most polypeptide chains whether in proteins containing one or more than one polypeptide chain are half or less than half this size. The average mol wt of *E. coli* proteins by amino-terminal analysis of broken cell mixtures has been estimated, in fact, to be about 50,000 (Waller, 1963). This is not a serious objection, of course, and some proteins are now known to contain relatively long polypeptide chains. The DNA polymerase of *E. coli* is a single polypeptide chain of mol wt 109,000 (Jovin, Englund, and Bertsch, 1969). A second objection was that complementation experiments could be interpreted to indicate the presence of different polypeptide chains within the monomeric structure. It is now clear (Ullmann and Perrin, this vol.) that complemented enzyme is different from native enzyme.

A third and serious reason to question this conclusion is that studies from several laboratories have shown that in dissociating solvents other than urea and guanidine, polypeptide chains smaller than 135,000 can be demonstrated. When β-galactosidase was oxidized by performic acid or was dissolved in 30% formic acid and 70% acetic acid, measurements of particle sizes in the ultracentrifuge of 43,000 or 46,000 were obtained

(Wallenfels et al., 1963). Carboxymethylated protein in 70% formic acid yielded material with an average mol wt of approximately 50,000 (Steers et al., 1965). These results are puzzling. If the monomer is composed of smaller distinct polypeptide chains, it is difficult to see why guanidine, a powerful dissociating agent, should not have revealed their existence. If such smaller chains are held together by disulfide bridges, these would be broken by oxidation or by reduction prior to carboxymethylation, although they would remain stable in formic and in formic-acetic acid solutions. Furthermore, *β*-galactosidase has been reported to contain no disulfide bonds (Craven et al., 1965) and the presence of a sufficient number of these bonds to account for these results should easily have been detectable. Also measurement of subunit size in guanidine was carried out in the presence of 0.1 M mercaptoethanol, (Ullmann et al., 1968b) a concentration easily capable of reducing disulfide to mercaptan. Therefore, the results cannot be explained by the presence of disulfide bridges.

If the postulated smaller chains are held together by simple ester or amide bonds which could split under acid conditions, *α*-amino groups should remain available for analysis, and after hydrolysis carboxyl-terminal amino acids would similarly be available. Yet no additional amino-terminal (Steers et al., 1965; Brown et al., 1966) nor carboxyl-terminal (Brown et al., 1966) amino acids could be demonstrated after acid treatment.

It is far more reasonable to assume that particularly labile peptide bonds can be hydrolyzed with these acids. In studies on the structure of thiogalactoside transacetylase with a very sensitive amino-terminal procedure, considerable random cleavage was observed after exposure of this protein to 70% formic acid (Brown, Koorajian and Zabin, 1967). The possibility of this kind of random cleavage of *β*-galactosidase by 70% formic acid as an alternate explanation for their results was in fact noted by Steers et al. (1965).

Cleavage of peptide bonds must also account for the results of Wallenfels and Gölker (1966). When the product obtained by performic acid oxidation was treated with leucine aminopeptidase, considerable amounts of methionine, alanine, serine, glutamic acid, valine, threonine and aspartic acid were released. This is contrary to the results reported by Givol, Craven, Steers, and Anfinsen (1966) who found no release of amino acids by treatment of either native or carboxymethylated *β*-galactosidase with leucine aminopeptidase. Unpublished results in this laboratory agree with those of Givol et al. Cleavage of peptide bonds must account again for the observation of Wallenfels and Gölker (1966) that more arginine than lysine is hydrolyzed when carboxypeptidase B was added to oxidized *β*-galactosidase, a result not duplicated in other laboratories.

Another possibility which may account for some of the contradictory results mentioned here is suggested by the experiments of Givol et al. (1966), who showed that β-galactosidase retains essentially native enzymic activity, antigenicity, and sedimentation behavior after treatment with trypsin or papain under certain conditions. Such preparations were shown to have many sites of cleavage by polyacrylamide gel electrophoresis in 8 M urea-acetic acid and by leucine aminopeptidase treatment. If then, a particular preparation of enzyme had been subject to limited proteolytic digestion during the course of its isolation from extracts of *E. coli,* subsequent analysis of the presumed unaltered protein could lead to spurious end groups. This kind of possibility may be the explanation for the several reports (Wallenfels and Arens, 1960; Wallenfels and Gölker, 1966) that glutamic acid in a quantity about half that of threonine occupies an amino-terminal position in β-galactosidase, an observation which has not been confirmed. The presence of small amounts of proteolytic contaminants in carboxypeptidase B could have accounted similarly for the appearance of new peptide fragments in polyacrylamide gels after treatment of the protein with this reagent (Korenman et al., 1966).

Until unique polypeptide fragments smaller than 135,000 mol wt can be isolated, or until smaller chains held together covalently by non-peptide bonds can be demonstrated, it is our view that the chemical evidence in favor of a single polypeptide chain is overwhelming. Additional support for this conclusion has been obtained by studies with mutant protein.

CORRELATION TO STRUCTURAL GENE

Colinearity and orientation. The total length of the gene (z) which specifies the structure of β-galactosidase has been estimated by recombination frequencies to be about 0.7 map units, or 3500 nucleotide pairs in the DNA of the bacterium (Jacob and Monod, 1961). The z gene, then, should specify a protein with a unique sequence of some 1170 amino acids, a number identical with that obtained by amino acid analysis of hydrolysates of the pure protein (Craven et al., 1965). One goal has been to relate the linear sequence in the β-galactosidase polypeptide chain to the genetic map. By inference from the effect of nonsense mutations on translation of the *lac* operon, the amino-terminal portion of the polypeptide has been suggested to correspond to the beginning, or operator-proximal portion of the structural gene (Newton, 1966). Direct demonstration that this is so has been achieved by immunological and structural studies of mutant protein (Fowler and Zabin, 1966; Katze et al., 1966; Brown, Brown and Zabin, 1967a).

Extracts of a number of strains with nonsense mutations in the z gene (Newton, Beckwith, Zipser and Brenner, 1965) were shown to form precipitin lines with anti-β-galactosidase in the Ouchterlony assay (Fowler and

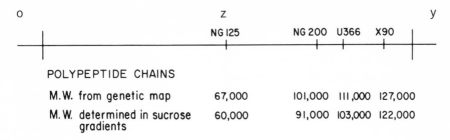

FIGURE 1. Co-linearity of β-galactosidase and its gene.

Zabin, 1966). This observation allowed a test of the genetic prediction that the effective length of a structural gene determines the length of the polypeptide chain product, that is, that the gene and protein are colinear. The experiment was carried out with four different nonsense mutant strains, each with the site of mutation in the z gene determined by Newton et al. (1965) as shown in Fig. 1. Approximate mol wt of the immunologically active component from each strain were obtained by sucrose density gradient centrifugation of crude extracts with the Ouchterlony method used to locate the position of each peak. Clearly, the experimentally determined values (Fig. 1) agree remarkably well with those predicted.

These results also show orientation of the protein to its structural gene. Since polypeptide chains are synthesized in a direction from amino- to carboxyl-terminal (Dintzis, 1961), a chain terminated prematurely by a nonsense mutation must be the amino-terminal segment. If operator-proximal and operator-distal correspond to amino- and carboxyl-terminal ends of the polypeptide, respectively, each chain should be of increasing mol wt in the same relation as the map order. Since this is the case, orientation must be as indicated.

This conclusion has been verified by direct chemical studies as well (Brown et al., 1967a). From an ochre mutant strain (X 90, Fig. 1) in which the site of the mutation is close to the operator-distal end, a protein has been isolated in essentially pure form, using the Ouchterlony assay to monitor purity. The mol wt was found to be 122,000 by sedimentation equilibrium measurement, confirming the value previously obtained from sucrose gradient centrifugation. The material was highly reactive immunologically against anti-β-galactosidase. It contained, like β-galactosidase itself, the amino-terminal sequence threonylmethionine, but unlike β-galactosidase, it contained no carboxyl-terminal lysine. Instead, glycine and serine were released by carboxypeptidase A treatment. Therefore the operator-distal end of the z gene specifies the carboxyl-terminal lysine of β-galactosidase.

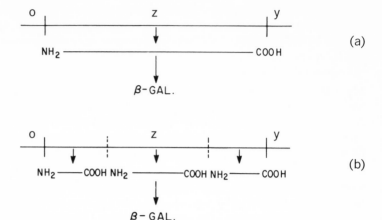

FIGURE 2. Alternatives for β-galactosidase subunit structure.

The isolation of the X 90 polypeptide chain of a mol wt almost that of the minimum mol wt of the native protein adds further support to the conclusion that the monomer of β-galactosidase is a single, long polypeptide chain. However it might be argued that smaller chains, even with a segment absent from one, might still bind together too firmly to dissociate. The placement of the coding site for carboxyl-terminal lysine is important in this regard. If the z gene were composed, for example, of three cistrons, each specifying a single polypeptide chain as in Fig. 2b, the lysine detected as the only carboxyl-terminal residue could be derived from any one of the three chains. The carboxyl-terminal residues of the other chains would be blocked to analysis by the carboxypeptidase or hydrazinolysis procedures. According to Fig. 2a, however, carboxyl-terminal lysine *must* be specified by the operator-distal end of the z gene, as has been shown.

Threonylmethionine was demonstrated to be the amino-terminal sequence of β-galactosidase by dinitrophenylation of the protein followed by BrCN cleavage, isolation, and identification of DNP-threonylhomoserine (Katze et al., 1966). Because this sequence is relatively specific for β-galactosidase, the method could be applied to crude extracts containing the wild-type protein. Attempts were made to prove directly that the operator-proximal segment of the z gene codes for the amino-terminal portion of the polypeptide chain by isolating DNP-threonylhomoserine from crude extracts of various nonsense mutants after the same chemical treatment. The experiment was successful for mutant strain X 90, but for two other nonsense mutants, one of which maps near the center, and another which maps close to the operator-proximal end of the z gene, this sequence could not be demonstrated to be present. The explanation for this negative result is not known, but it may be that the incomplete chains formed by the two strains are produced in lower quantities or are degraded more rapidly.

Some quite different experiments indicate that the operator-proximal segment of the z gene is the coding site for amino-terminal threonine. Lacroute and Stent (1968) determined the time after addition of radioactive threonine to induced cultures for first appearance of amino-terminal threonine in isolated β-galactosidase. This coincided very closely with the time determined (Kepes and Beguin, 1966) for first appearance of enzyme activity after induction. This result is expected for a single polypeptide chain by the same reasoning discussed above regarding carboxyl-terminal lysine.

The operator locus and the structural gene. The operator locus is adjacent to the z gene in the *lac* operon (Beckwith, this vol.), and might, in addition to serving as the site for repressor binding, contain information eventually translated into the structure of β-galactosidase. A careful examination of the β-galactosidase isolated from an operator constitutive mutant strain (o_{67}^c) showed no differences from the wild type (Steers, Craven, and Anfinsen, 1965). However, further examination of the genetic characteristics of this strain revealed that it did not contain a deletion in the operator locus as thought at first, but instead is most probably an i^-o^c double mutant (Beckwith, unpubl.). If the operator locus were indeed part of the structural gene, the β-galactosidase produced by o_{67}^c might contain an amino acid substitution near its amino-terminal end which would affect its properties in no way.

A strain especially suitable for resolving this question was isolated by Reznikoff and Beckwith (1969) in which a deletion extends from near the beginning of the B gene of the *trp* operon to the end of the *lac* operator, removing most or all of the latter. In this strain (X 7713) very low levels of β-galactosidase are formed, but in an R^-trp derivative, β-galactosidase is produced at levels of about 5–10% of wild type. Since the enzyme is expected to be the same as wild type, these results argue strongly that the operator locus is distinct from the z gene.

Support for this conclusion was obtained by direct examination of the protein itself (Bhorjee, Fowler, and Zabin, 1969). It was found to be identical to the native protein in a number of parameters such as sedimentation, heat inactivation, Michaelis and inhibition constants, and in reaction with antibody. The most critical test of identity, however, is the amino-acid sequence at the amino-terminal end of β-galactosidase. Given that orientation is such that operator-proximal specifies amino-terminal, if the operator locus were part of the z gene, the β-galactosidase formed should have at its amino-terminus not the normal threonylmethionine but instead the sequence specified by that part of the *trp* B gene remaining, which is known to be different. When the protein of X 7713 R⁻*trp* was examined, it was in fact found to have the normal sequence.

The conclusion that the operator is distinct from the z gene is therefore most likely, but it can be questioned on the grounds that the operator might be translated into a polypeptide normally cleaved at the peptide bond immediately preceding the threonylmethionine portion of the chain. If this were so, a highly specific mechanism must be invoked in which such hydrolysis occurs no matter what the composition of the cleaved fragment might be. This seems highly unlikely. Finally, the mutant strain was isolated not on the basis of a functioning β-galactosidase but as a *lac⁻* strain. The probability that just the right kind of deletion was obtained by chance which could allow the formation of normal enzyme seems quite low. It seems safe therefore to conclude that the operator locus does not specify any part of the structure of β-galactosidase.

IMMUNOLOGICAL CHARACTERISTICS

β-galactosidase is an excellent immunogen, and antibodies prepared against this protein have been exceedingly useful in studying the mechanism of synthesis of induced enzymes (Cohn, 1957). The production of cross-reacting material (CRM) by certain mutant strains of *E. coli* unable to produce enzymically active β-galactosidase has been utilized to obtain crucial evidence in support of the operon model for the regulation of protein synthesis (Jacob, Perrin, Sanchez, and Monod, 1960). The complementing proteins already mentioned in the studies of Perrin (1963) have been isolated with an assay procedure involving their cross-reacting ability and their competition with β-galactosidase for the antiserum. It is obvious that the greater the resemblance of a CRM to the native protein, the greater its extent of reaction with antibody. The mutant proteins studied by Perrin are almost certainly proteins of strains carrying missense mutations, with single amino acid substitutions. Such proteins, as already noted, have mol wt consistent with single amino acid substitutions, the strains are not suppressible, nor do they ordinarily exhibit polarity.

Many mutant proteins derived from strains carrying mutations in the z gene do not compete with the native protein for antibody, although the presence in crude extracts of some of them has been demonstrated by complementation. It has been found, however, that some proteins which do not react with antibody by the usual tests can be detected by more sensitive immunological techniques. The Ouchterlony method of double diffusion in agar has been used to detect nonsense mutant protein as discussed above and is a simple, sensitive assay which can be used in a quantitative manner. If the antibody preparation is found to form precipitin lines against non-β-galactosidase protein, it can be purified readily by absorption with appropriate extracts (Fowler and Zabin, 1968).

With this method and with the micro-complement fixation procedure, reactions of a number of mutant β-galactosidase proteins with anti-β-galactosidase were examined. Prematurely-terminated chains from nonsense mutants could be grouped into two general classes, those of mol wt about 50 to 70,000, and those of mol wt about 90 to 122,000. Within each class, the polypeptide chains appear identical on Ouchterlony plates, but the chains of one class are different from those of the next as indicated by fusion with spurring of precipitin lines. Since the reaction with antibody is destroyed by treatment of mutant protein with heat or sodium dodecyl sulfate, the antigen-antibody reaction must be dependent on a specific three-dimensional conformation. The existence of the two classes suggests that each has a conformation somewhat different from the other but also similar to that of the native complete protein. Interestingly, polypeptide chains of certain deletion mutants can be grouped into one or the other of the two classes of nonsense mutant proteins exactly as predicted from knowledge of the position of the deletion (Fowler and Zabin, 1968). Hu (1969) has also reported that cross-reacting material can be detected in extracts of some deletion mutants.

THIOGALACTOSIDE TRANSACETYLASE

Isolation. Thiogalactoside transacetylase catalyzes the transfer of the acetyl group from acetyl coenzyme A to the 6-OH of a thiogalactoside acceptor such as isopropyl-β-D-thiogalactoside (IPTG). The first demonstration of the presence of this enzyme in crude extracts depended on paper chromatographic separation of acetyl-^{14}C-IPTG from ^{14}C-IPTG (Zabin, Képes and Monod, 1959). For routine use during purification, an alkaline hydroxamate assay was developed to measure the enzyme. Acetyl phosphate, phosphotransacetylase, and catalytic amounts of coenzyme A served as the source of acetyl coenzyme A and after decomposition of excess donor, acetyl-IPTG was estimated colorimetrically (Zabin, Képes, and Monod, 1962; Zabin, 1963b). More sensitive analytical procedures were developed by Alpers, Appel and Tompkins (1965), by Fox and Kennedy (1967), and by Leive and Kollin (1967). The latter two depend on the separation of ^{14}C-acetyl-IPTG from ^{14}C-acetyl coenzyme A by ion exchange resins.

The protein has been obtained in pure state by ammonium sulfate fractionation and DEAE-cellulose and carboxymethyl cellulose chromatog-

Table 2. Amino acid composition of Thiogalactoside Transacetylase*

	Residues per 32,000 mol wt
Tryptophan	3
Lysine	14
Histidine	11
Arginine	14
Aspartic Acid	34
Threonine	15
Serine	14
Glutamic Acid	21
Proline	15
Glycine	22
Alanine	13
Half-cystine	3
Valine	26
Methionine	8
Isoleucine	20
Leucine	14
Tyrosine	11
Phenylalanine	10
Total	268

*Zabin, 1963b.

raphy. It formed crystals readily from ammonium sulfate solutions (Zabin, 1963b).

Composition. The amino acid composition of the crystalline material is shown in Table 2. The protein contains approximately 270 amino acid residues per minimum molecular weight of 32,000. Sugar and phosphate are absent from the molecule (Zabin, 1963b).

Molecular weight. By sedimentation equilibrium the molecular weight was found to be 65,300 ± 4,400. The sedimentation constant was 5.0 S (Goldwasser, 1963).

Like β-galactosidase, thiogalactoside transacetylase has been reported to form higher polymers. These higher forms dissociate to the normal molecule in the presence of IPTG (Appel et al., 1965).

SUBUNIT STRUCTURE

Dimeric structure. In 6 M guanidine containing 0.5% mercaptoethanol, the protein showed a single peak in the ultracentrifuge. The mol wt by the method of sedimentation equilibrium was found to be 29,700 ± 2,000. Since this value is close to one-half the mol wt of the native protein, this result indicates that thiogalactoside transacetylase is a dimer composed of subunits of identical size (Brown, Brown, and Zabin, 1967b).

Minimum molecular weight. The protein contains approximately 28 moles of lysine and 28 moles of arginine per 65,300 g. After treatment of the reduced, carboxymethylated material with trypsin, 28 to 30 ninhydrin-positive spots could be seen following electrophoresis and chromatography on paper. Almost half of these peptides contained arginine. Some insoluble material remaining after digestion was found to contain only small quantities of the two basic amino acids. These results therefore support the conclusion that the transacetylase is a dimer of two identical polypeptide chains.

The same conclusion was reached from studies with BrCN. The native enzyme contains 16 methionine residues per molecule, and following cleavage of carboxymethylated protein 8 bands were observed by electrophoresis in polyacrylamide gels containing 8 M urea. The number of peptides resulting from cleavage was also estimated by analysis of amino terminal amino acids using a sensitive procedure employing radioactive fluorodinitrobenzene. This method also yielded 8 peptides. It was noted that correction was necessary for considerable random splitting in 70% formic acid, the solvent ordinarily used for BrCN cleavage, and it has been pointed out above that such random cleavage might account for some of the contradictory data obtained in the study of the structure of *β*-galactosidase.

When a sample of reduced, carboxymethylated protein was treated first with BrCN and next with trypsin, 35 ninhydrin-positive spots were seen on paper. Since for a dimer of two identical chains 38 peptides are expected, this result further supports the conclusion already drawn (Brown, Brown, and Zabin, 1967b).

Amino-terminal analyses. From the data just described, thiogalactoside transacetylase should contain two moles of a single amino acid per mole of enzyme. This was not found to be the case. By both the Sanger method and the Stark and Smyth carbamylation procedure, approximately 0.5 mole of aspartic acid (or asparagine) and 0.4 mole of methionine were found. The same result was obtained after treatment of the protein under conditions expected to cleave N-formyl groups (Brown, Koorajian, and Zabin, 1967). These results have been interpreted to indicate not that two different polypeptide chains are present in the protein, but that heterogeneity exists at the amino-terminus of otherwise identical chains. Such heterogeneity may occur by proteolytic action; this might be after the protein has been synthesized, or might be before completion of synthesis at a step related to removal of N-formyl groups from the chain. Whatever the explanation in this case, non-stoichiometry at the amino-terminus of proteins is commonly observed.

Carboxyl-terminal analyses. In contrast to the results of the preceeding section, analyses of the carboxyl-terminal amino acid yielded clear-cut results. By treatment of denatured protein with carboxypeptidase A, valine was released in quantities approaching 2 moles per mole of protein, and serine was hydrolyzed at a lower rate indicating a COOH-terminal sequence of Ser Val-COOH (Brown, Koorajian, and Zabin, 1967). These results add support to the conclusion that thiogalactoside transacetylase is a dimer of two identical polypeptide chains, with the proviso that some heterogeneity exists at the amino-terminus.

RELATIVE RATES OF SYNTHESIS

Measurement of β-galactosidase enzyme activity and thiogalactoside transacetylase enzyme activity after addition of one or another *lac* inducer to exponentially growing cells demonstrated coordinate expression of the two activities; more effective inducers elicited the formation of high levels of both enzymes, while poor inducers allowed the appearance of only low levels of both enzymes (Jacob and Monod, 1961). If it is assumed that assay of enzyme activity is a direct measure of enzyme protein uncomplicated by degradation or by the presence of activators or inhibitors for either enzyme, such results mean that the relative rates of synthesis of the two proteins are in a constant ratio. It would, of course, be of interest from the point of view of the mechanism of protein synthesis and its control to determine the numerical value of this ratio. At the time of presentation of the operon model for the control of protein synthesis, no prediction could be made regarding this value. However, when it became clear that single mRNAs are very likely transcribed from the whole bacterial operon and that translation is ordinarily initiated from only one site at or near the 5' end of the mRNA, the simplest prediction is that protein molecules within a bacterial operon are synthesized at identical rates. Molecule in this sense refers to that sequence specified by the cistron, i.e., the minimum mol wt of the protein.

Early comparisons of the enzyme activity of highly purified preparations of β-galactosidase to the activity in crude extracts suggested that a fully induced or a constitutive ML strain of *E. coli* produces the enzyme in a quantity of about 5 or 6% of the total protein under normal conditions of growth at 37°C (Cohn, 1957). When thiogalactoside transacetylase was purified to homogeneity (Zabin, 1963b), a similar calculation indicated that this enzyme was present in the same cell extract to the extent of about 0.15% (Nishi and Zabin, 1963). Tests with anti-thiogalactoside transacetylase showed that the only serological reactant in crude extracts was enzymically active protein (Berg and Zabin, 1964).

These results indicated that the ratio of β-galactosidase to thiogalactoside transacetylase was unexpectedly high, more than 30:1 by weight. Since the minimum mol wt are 135,000 and 32,000, respectively, the number of molecules (as monomers) are in a ratio of about 7:1. Such calculations are approximate; it is known that at least for ML strains, the relative quantity of the two enzymes may vary by a factor of about two under different conditions of growth (Nishi and Zabin, 1963). It is also true that specific activities of enzymes in crude extracts often vary from culture to culture; different preparations of pure enzymes as well are sometimes found to have differing specific activities. Though such values are usually within ten or twenty per cent, specific activities for pure β-galactosidase almost twice as high as those generally found have been reported recently (Ullmann, Jacob, and Monod, 1968a).

It would be of interest to determine this ratio by methods which do not depend on enzyme activities. Nevertheless, the available evidence indicates that proteins specified by the structural genes of the *lac* operon are not synthesized at equimolar rates; for ML strains the ratio is normally in the range of 5 to 7, and for K-12 strains perhaps 3.5 to 5 (Brown, Brown, and Zabin, 1967b). It should be noted that equimolar synthesis occurs for the enzymes of the tryptophan operon (Morse, Baker, and Yanofsky, 1968) and of the galactose operon (Wilson and Hogness, 1969).

CONCLUDING REMARKS

The contribution of protein chemistry has been to allow the clarification of some of the genetic aspects of the *lac* operon and to support the operon model of Jacob and Monod. The presence of a single kind of polypeptide chain in β-galactosidase indicates that the *z* gene is a single cistron. The same is true for the *a* gene specifying the structure of thiogalactoside transacetylase. Examination of the protein produced by *z* gene mutant strains by chemical and immunochemical procedures has led to the conclusion that the protein is oriented to its gene in a manner exactly as predicted. By such methods it has also been possible to distinguish the controlling elements in the *lac* genome from the first structural gene.

A goal of protein structural work is to define completely the structure of the molecule under consideration. While a delineation of the three-dimensional structure of β-galactosidase can hardly be attempted at the present time, it does seem possible to determine the primary sequence in this polypeptide chain. This shall be a difficult and time-consuming study, but the availability of a large number of mutant strains can aid immensely in the solution of this problem. Conversely, when the primary structure of β-galactosidase is known, it can be expected to provide a very useful basis for the further study of gene-protein relationships.

Finally, questions of evolutionary interest can now be posed. The *z* gene is unusually long; did it evolve through gene duplication? What structural relationships, if any, exist between β-galactosidase and thiogalactoside transacetylase, and between these, the "M" protein, and the *lac* repressor protein? Further chemical study of the *lac* operon appears to offer a continuing and unique opportunity to obtain insight into fundamental biological questions.

ACKNOWLEDGMENT

Supported in part by a Grant, AI-04181 from the National Institutes of Health.

REFERENCES

ALPERS, D. H., S. H. APPEL, and G. M. TOMKINS. 1965. A spectrophotometric assay for thiogalactoside transacetylase. J. Biol. Chem. *240:* 10.

APPEL, S. H., D. H. ALPERS, and G. M. TOMKINS. 1965. Multiple molecular forms of β-galactosidase. J. Mol. Biol. *11:* 12.

BERG, A. and I. ZABIN. 1964. Immunological studies on β-galactosidase and thiogalactoside transacetylase: Proteins of the lactose system in *Escherichia coli.* J. Mol. Biol. *10:* 289.

BHORJEE, J. S., A. V. FOWLER, and I. ZABIN. 1969. Biochemical evidence that the operator locus is distinct from the z gene in the *lac* operon of *Escherichia coli.* J. Mol. Biol. *43:* 219.

BROWN, J. L., D. M. BROWN, and I. ZABIN. 1967a. β-Galactosidase: Orientation and the carboxyl-terminal coding site in the gene. Proc. Nat. Acad. Sci. *58:* 1139.

———, ———, ———. 1967b. Thiogalactoside transacetylase: Physical and chemical studies of subunit structure. J. Biol. Chem. *242:* 4254.

BROWN, J. L., S. KOORAJIAN, J. KATZE, and I. ZABIN. 1966. β-Galactosidase: Amino- and carboxyl-terminal studies. J. Biol. Chem. *241:* 2826.

BROWN, J. L., S. KOORAJIAN, and I. ZABIN. 1967. Thiogalactoside transacetylase: Amino- and carboxyl-terminal studies. J. Biol. Chem. *242:* 4259.

CRAVEN, G. R., E. STEERS, Jr., and C. B. ANFINSEN. 1965. Purification, composition, and molecular weight of the β-galactosidase of *Escherichia coli* K_{12}. J. Biol. Chem. *240:* 2468.

COHN, M. 1957. Contributions of studies on the β-galactosidase of *Escherichia coli* to our understanding of enzyme synthesis. Bact. Rev. *21:* 140.

DINTZIS, H. M. 1961. Assembly of the peptide chains of hemoglobin. Proc. Nat. Acad. Sci. *47:* 247.

FOWLER, A. V. and I. ZABIN. 1966. Co-linearity of β-galactosidase with its gene by immunological detection of incomplete polypeptide chains. Science *154:* 1027.

———, ———. 1968. β-Galactosidase: Immunological studies of nonsense, missense and deletion mutants. J. Mol. Biol. *33:* 35.

FOX, C. F. and E. P. KENNEDY. 1967. A micro radiochemical assay for thiogalactoside transacetylase. Anal. Biochem. *18:* 286.

GIVOL, D., G. R. CRAVEN, E. STEERS, Jr., and C. B. ANFINSEN. 1966. Effect of limited digestion by proteolytic enzymes on *Escherichia coli* β-galactosidase. Biochim. Biophys. Acta *113:* 120.

GOLDWASSER, E. 1963. Sedimentation constant and molecular weight of thiogalactoside transacetylase. J. Biol. Chem. *238:* 3306.

HU, A. S. L. 1969. Cross-reacting material produced by *lac* deletion mutants of *Escherichia coli* K_{12}. Biochim. Biophys. Acta *174:* 387.

HU, A. S. L., R. G. WOLFE, and F. J. REITHEL. 1959. On the preparation and purification of β-galactosidase from *E. coli* ML 308. Arch. Biochem. Biophys. *81:* 500.

JACOB, F. and J. MONOD. 1961. Genetic regulatory mechanisms in the synthesis of proteins. J. Mol. Biol. *3:* 318.

JACOB, F., D. PERRIN, C. SANCHEZ, and J. MONOD. 1960. L'opéron: Groupe de gènes à expression coordonnée par un opérateur. Compt. Rend. Acad. Sci. *250:* 1727.

JOVIN, T. M., P. J. ENGLUND, and L. L. BERTSCH. 1969. Enzymatic synthesis of deoxyribonucleic acid. XXVI. Physical and chemical studies of a homogeneous deoxyribonucleic acid polymerase. J. Biol. Chem. *244:* 2996.

KARLSSON, U., S. KOORAJIAN, I. ZABIN, F. S. SJÖSTRAND, and A. MILLER. 1964. High resolution electron microscopy on highly purified β-galactosidase from *Escherichia coli*. J. Ultrastructure Res. *10:* 457.

KATZE, J., S. SRIDHARA, and I. ZABIN. 1966. An amino-terminal peptide of β-galactosidase: Its detection in crude extracts of wild type and nonsense mutants of *Escherichia coli*. J. Biol. Chem. *241:* 5341.

KEPES, A. and S. BEGUIN. 1966. Peptide chain initiation and growth in the induced synthesis of β-galactosidase. Biochim. Biophys. Acta *123:* 546.

KOORAJIAN, S. and I. ZABIN. 1965. Carboxypeptidase studies on β-galactosidase: Detection of one C-terminal lysine per monomer. Biochem. Biophys. Res. Commun. *18:* 384.

KORENMAN, S. G., G. R. CRAVEN, and C. B. ANFINSEN. 1966. Determination of the carboxyl-terminal amino acid residue of the β-galactosidase of *Escherichia coli* K_{12}. Biochim. Biophys. Acta *124:* 160.

LACROUTE, F. and G. S. STENT. 1968. Peptide chain growth of β-galactosidase in *Escherichia coli*. J. Mol. Biol. *35:* 165.

LEIVE, L. and V. KOLLIN. 1967. Synthesis, utilization and degradation of lactose operon mRNA in *Escherichia coli*. J. Mol. Biol. *24:* 247.

MARCHESI, S. L., E. STEERS, Jr., and S. SHIFRIN. 1969. Purification and characterization of the multiple forms of β-galactosidase of *Escherichia coli*. Biochim. Biophys. Acta *181:* 20.

MONOD, J. 1959. Biosynthese eines enzyms. Angew. Chem. *71:* 685.

MONOD, J., J. WYMAN, and J. P. CHANGEUX. 1965. On the nature of allosteric transitions: A plausible model. J. Mol. Biol. *12:* 88.

MORSE, D. E., R. F. BAKER, and C. YANOFSKY. 1968. Translation of the tryptophan messenger RNA of *Escherichia coli*. Proc. Nat. Acad. Sci. *60:* 1428.

NEWTON, A. 1966. Effect of nonsense mutations on translation of the lactose operon of *Escherichia coli.* Cold Spring Harbor Symp Quant. Biol. *31:* 181.

NEWTON, W. A., J. R. BECKWITH, D. ZIPSER, and S. BRENNER. 1965. Nonsense mutants and polarity in the *lac* operon of *Escherichia coli.* J. Mol. Biol. *14:* 290.

NISHI, A. and I. ZABIN. 1963. Effect of temperature on the differential rate of synthesis of proteins of the lactose operon in *E. coli.* Biochem. Biophys. Res. Commun. *13:* 320.

PERRIN, D. 1963. Immunological studies with genetically altered β-galactosidases. Ann. N. Y. Acad. Sci. *103:* 1058.

REZNIKOFF, W. S. and J. R. BECKWITH. 1969. Genetic evidence that the operator locus is distinct from the z gene in the *lac* operon of *Escherichia coli.* J. Mol. Biol. *43:* 215.

SHIFRIN, S. and E. STEERS, Jr. 1967. The effect of urea on subunit interactions of β-galactosidase from *Escherichia coli* K_{12}. Biochim. Biophys. Acta *133:* 463.

STEERS, Jr., E., G. R. CRAVEN, and C. B. ANFINSEN. 1965. Comparison of β-galactosidases from normal ($i^-o^+z^+$) and operator constitutive ($i^-o^cz^+$) strains of *E. coli.* Proc. Nat. Acad. Sci. *54:* 1175.

STEERS, Jr., E. and S. SHIFRIN. 1967. Characterization of the β-galactosidase from a lactose-negative, complementing mutant of *Escherichia coli* K_{12}. Biochim. Biophys. Acta *133:* 454.

STEERS, Jr., E., G. R. CRAVEN, C. B. ANFINSEN, and J. L. BETHUNE. 1965. Evidence for nonidentical chains in the β-galactosidase of *Escherichia coli* K_{12}. J. Biol. Chem. *240:* 2478.

SUND, H. and K. WEBER. 1963. Untersuchungen über milchzuckerspaltende enzyme. XIII. Gröbe und gestalt der β-galaktosidase aus *E. coli.* Biochem. Z. *337:* 24.

ULLMANN, A., F. JACOB, and J. MONOD. 1968a. On the subunit structure of wild-type versus complemented β-galactosidase of *Escherichia coli.* J. Mol. Biol. *32:* 1.

ULLMANN, A., M. E. GOLDBERG, D. PERRIN, and J. MONOD. 1968b. On the determination of molecular weight of proteins and protein subunits in the presence of 6 M guanidine hydrochloride. Biochemistry *7:* 261.

WALLENFELS, K. and A. ARENS. 1960. Untersuchungen über milchzuckerspaltende enzyme. XI. Die reaction von 2,4 dinitrofluorbenzol mit β-galaktosidase von *E. coli,* modell versuche mit insulin und ribonuclease. Biochem. Z. *333:* 395.

WALLENFELS, K. and C. GÖLKER. 1966. Untersuchungen über milchzuckerspaltende enzyme. XVIII. Zur frage der endgruppen der β-galaktosidase. Biochem. Z. *346:* 1.

WALLENFELS, K. and O. P. MALHOTRA. 1961. Galactosidases, p. 239. *In* M. L. Wolfrom [ed.] Advances in carbohydrate chemistry. Academic Press, New York.

WALLENFELS, K., C. STREFFER, and C. GÖLKER. 1965. Untersuchungen über milchzuckerspaltende enzyme. XVII. Aminosaureanalysen an β-galactosidase verschiedyner ML-mutanten von *E. coli.* Biochem. Z. *342:* 495.

WALLENFELS, K., H. SUND, and K. WEBER. 1963. Die untereinheiten der β-galaktosidase aus *E. coli.* Biochem. Z. *338:* 714.

WALLENFELS, K. and M. L. ZARNITZ. 1957. Kristallisation der *β*-galaktosidase aus *Escherichia coli.* Angew Chem. *69:* 482.

WALLENFELS, K., M. L. ZARNITZ, G. LAULE, H. BENDER, and M. KESER. 1959. Untersuchen über milchzuckerspaltende enzyme. III. Reingung, kristallization und eigenschaften der *β*-galaktosidase von *Escherichia coli* ML 309. Biochem. Z. *331:* 459.

WALLER, J. P. 1963. The NH_2-terminal residues of the proteins from cell-free extracts of *E. coli.* J. Mol. Biol. *7:* 483.

WILSON, D. W. and D. S. HOGNESS. 1969. The enzymes of the galactose operon in *Escherichia coli.* IV. The frequencies of translation of the términal cistrons in the operon. J. Biol. Chem. *244:* 2143.

ZABIN, I. 1963a. Proteins of the lactose system. Cold Spring Harbor Symp. Quant. Biol. *28:* 431.

————. 1963b. Crystalline thiogalactoside transacetylase. J. Biol. Chem. *238:* 3300.

ZABIN, I., A. KEPES, and J. MONOD. 1959. On the enzymic acetylation of isopropyl *β*-D-thiogalactoside and its association with galactoside-permease. Biochem. Biophys. Res. Comm. *1:* 289.

————, ————, ————. 1962. Thiogalactoside transacetylase. J. Biol. Chem. *237:* 253.

ZIPSER, D. 1963. A study of the urea-produced subunits of *β*-galactosidase. J. Mol. Biol. *7:* 113.

Chapter IV

The Lactose Permease System of *Escherichia coli*

EUGENE P. KENNEDY

Department of Biological Chemistry
Harvard Medical School
Boston, Massachusetts

THE CONCEPT OF PERMEASE:
ITS ORIGIN AND PRESENT STATUS

The discovery of a specific system for the transport and accumulation of β-galactosides in *Escherichia coli* was reported in a preliminary account by Cohen and Rickenberg (1955). This was soon followed by a more complete description (Rickenberg et al., 1956) which made it clear that the transport system is an integral part of the mechanisms by which lactose is utilized in this organism. The 1956 paper also included a formal definition of the concept of permeases, introducing a terminology which was later to prove a source of controversy.

The independent studies of Pardee (1957) led to the finding in *E. coli* of a system for the accumulation of melibiose, an α-galactoside, and it was recognized that this system was identical with that described by Rickenberg et al. (1956). Later work led to the finding of a second transport system for melibiose, distinct from the *lac* system, (Prestidge and Pardee, 1965; Ganesan and Rotman, 1966).

In the original definition of *permease* this term was applied to the entire transport system (Rickenberg et al., 1956). A permease was defined as a system, protein in nature, resembling an enzyme in its properties of steric specificity and kinetics, that functions in the catalytic transfer of a substrate across the osmotic barrier of the cell. The authors explicitly stated that this definition did not make any assumptions about the mode of action of the permease, but did involve two essential hypotheses: first, that permease-catalyzed transport involves the transitory formation of a

49

specific complex between the permease protein and the substrate, and second, that the permease is a system which is functionally specialized and does not take part in the intracellular metabolism of the substrate.

The postulate that permeases are distinct from systems for metabolism is now, however, open to serious question. The uptake by *E. coli* of some nutrilites such as thiamine (Kawasaki et al., 1969), and a family of sugars which includes glucose, fructose and mannose (Tanaka et al., 1967) is now known to be intimately associated with their phosphorylation. When phosphorylation is prevented, the free nutrilite is not accumulated against a concentration gradient. The initial step of metabolism appears to be an essential part of the transport system for these substances, since it leads to the retention of the phosphorylated derivative within the cell.

In retrospect, the discovery of the lactose transport system in *E. coli* is a landmark in the study of membrane-localized processes. The existence in bacteria of specific transport systems which mediate the passage of hydrophilic molecules across the cell boundary was recognized only belatedly, although in the 1950's the work of Davis and of Doudoroff, reviewed by Cohen and Monod (1957), had focused attention on the *cryptic* character of certain enzyme systems in bacteria. Intact cells of certain strains of bacteria are incapable of metabolizing a given substrate, but cell-free extracts contain the enzymes needed for metabolism. In the intact cell, the substrate apparently does not penetrate to the cryptic enzyme system. The cryptic character, however, is highly selective. A given bacterial strain may grow readily on one sugar, but be incapable of taking up another of closely similar structure. The discovery of a specific, genetically controlled system for the transport of lactose not only solved the puzzle of why certain mutant strains are cryptic toward lactose, but also pointed the way to a general theory of membrane transport in bacteria (Cohen and Monod, 1957).

The introduction of the term permease was vigorously opposed by some workers on the grounds that it would be appropriate only for an enzyme. Indeed, although a membrane-localized protein has now been identified as the product of the permease or *y* gene of the *lac* operon, there is still no evidence for its enzymatic function. Whatever the merits of the controversy about terminology, however, the permease concept focused attention on the essential role of specific proteins in bacterial transport processes, and indeed in membrane transport processes generally. The present intense activity in the study of bacterial transport proteins, reviewed by Pardee (1968), can be traced in large part to this origin.

One difficulty which has arisen with the widespread use of the term permease has been the tendency to assume that each permease is a single protein. Thus, the product of the *y* gene is often called the *lac* permease.

However, the accumulation of β-galactosides against a concentration gradient via the *lac* system requires a continuing supply of metabolic energy and is obviously a complex process dependent upon enzymatic machinery other than the product of the *y* gene. The transport of sulfate into *Salmonella typhimurium* appears to involve the products of four cistrons, one of which is a sulfate-binding protein localized in the periplasmic space rather than the membrane (Dreyfuss and Pardee, 1966). The presence of the sulfate binding protein alone is not sufficient for transport. The PEP-linked* phosphotransferase system which appears to be closely related to the transport system for glucose requires at least four distinct proteins for its function (Roseman, 1969). In view of this evidence for the complexity of bacterial transport systems, it would seem highly desirable to assign purely descriptive names to newly discovered proteins thought to play a role in bacterial transport processes, and to reserve the name permease for the entire transport system of which they may be parts.

DIVERSITY OF SYSTEMS FOR THE TRANSPORT OF GALACTOSE AND GALACTOSIDES IN *E. coli.*

Four transport systems with partially overlapping specificities for galactose and α- and β-galactosides have been distinguished in *E. coli* (Ganesan and Rotman, 1966; Rotman et al., 1968). The first of these to be discovered was the *lac* system, which can be defined as the transport system of which the product of the *y* gene is an integral part. This designation seems much preferable to the suggestion (Prestidge and Pardee, 1965) that it be renamed TMG (see footnote) permease I. The latter name would emphasize a trivial property of the system, its affinity for an unnatural substrate for which it is by no means specific, rather than its role as an integral part of the lactose system in *E. coli.*

A second system, described by Prestidge and Pardee (1965), transports TMG but has little affinity for lactose or ONPG. It has been designated TMG permease II. It can be induced by growth in the presence of galactinol or the α-galactoside melibiose. The genetic regulation of this transport system is coordinated with that of the enzyme α-galactosidase (Burstein, 1968; Buttin, 1968). The induction of the permease and α-galactosidase in K-12 strains is temperature-sensitive and does not take place during growth at 37°C or higher. Normal induction appears to take place at

---

*The following abbreviations and trivial names are used: NEM, N-ethylmaleimide; ONPG, o-nitrophenyl-β-D-galactoside; TDG, β-D-galactosyl-1-thio-β-D-galactoside; IPTG, isopropyl 1-thio-β-D-galactoside; TMG, methyl-1-thio-β-D-galactoside; melibiose, 6-O-α-D-galactosyl-D-glucose; allolactose, 6-O-β-D-galactosyl-D-glucose; glycerol β-galactoside, 1-O-β-D-galactosyl-D-glycerol; TPG, phenyl 1-thio-β-D-galactoside; m-Cl CCP, carbonyl cyanide m-chlorophenylhydrazone.

temperatures of 30°C or lower. The permease and α-galactosidase synthesized during growth below 30°C are not inactivated if the cells are
shifted to 40°C (Buttin, 1968). When derivatives of a K-12 strain were
selected for their ability to grow on melibiose at 40°C, these were found
to be partially constitutive (Buttin, 1968), supporting the suggestion that
it is induction which is temperature-sensitive. In contrast, induction of the
α-galactoside system in *E. coli* B strains is normal at 37°C. The ML strain
of *E. coli* lacks TMG permease II and α-galactosidase whether grown at
low or high temperature (Buttin, 1968).

   A third transport system, described by Rotman (1959), functions effectively in the concentration of D-galactose and methyl-1-β-D-galactopyran-
oside but not methyl-1-thio-β-D-galactopyranoside (TMG) (Ganesan and
Rotman, 1966; Rotman et al., 1968). This permease has been called the
methyl-galactoside or MG permease. There is evidence that it plays an
essential physiological role in the retention of intracellular galactose in
E. coli. (Rotman and Radojkovic, 1964; Wu et al., 1969). D-fucose is an
effective inducer of the MG permease.

   Rotman et al. (1968) have also observed a fourth transport system which
appears in cells after induction by growth in the presence of D-fucose.
D-galactose and L-arabinose appear to be the only sugars of a number
which have been tested which are effectively transported by this system,
which has been termed the galactose permease (Rotman et al., 1968).
It should be kept in mind, however, that the MG permease may be the
system of greatest physiological importance in the induction of the *gal*
system and in growth on galactose (Wu et al., 1969).

GENETIC REGULATION OF THE *lac* PERMEASE

   In their first studies of the *lac* permease, Rickenberg et al. (1956)
recognized that some essential component of the system is controlled by
a gene (the y gene) at a locus distinct from the z gene, the structural gene
for β-galactosidase. This conclusion has been confirmed and extended in
genetic studies too numerous to be considered in detail here. Evidence
to be considered in a later section of this chapter indicates that the y gene
is the structural gene for a membrane-localized protein (M protein) which
specifically binds galactosides and is an essential part of the transport
system in intact cells.

   The discovery that the *lac* permease and β-galactosidase are coordinately
regulated as a functional genetic unit was of central importance in the
development of the theory of the operon (Jacob and Monod, 1961). In
addition, the recognition of the function of the permease clarified several
aspects of the kinetics of induction of β-galactosidase and hence of protein
biosynthesis. Many inducers of the *lac* system are substrates for the
transport system, which by concentrating the inducer, plays an essential

role in its own induction. Anomalies such as the "auto-catalytic" kinetics of induction at low concentrations of inducer and the "all-or-none" nature of the induced state under these conditions could now be resolved (Monod, 1956; Novick and Weiner, 1957; Cohn and Horibata, 1959).

PROPERTIES OF THE *LAC* TRANSPORT SYSTEM: ACCUMULATION OF GALACTOSIDES AGAINST A CONCENTRATION GRADIENT

Two operationally distinct types of experiments have been used to investigate the function of the *lac* transport system. In the first of these, the "up-hill" accumulation of galactosides against a concentration gradient is measured, while in the second, the rate of hydrolysis of ONPG by intact cells, in which transport is the rate-limiting step, is measured. Since the accumulation system is tightly linked to sources of metabolic energy, and since these links are almost certainly enzymatic in nature, accumulation is intrinsically a more complex process than carrier-mediated entry of ONPG into energy-poisoned cells.

Labeled thiogalactosides are most often used to study accumulation, since these gratuitous substrates cannot be hydrolyzed by β-galactosidase. The thiogalactosides, however, may undergo acetylation or phosphorylation by reactions which are apparently secondary to transport. The accumulation of lactose, of ONPG, and other O-galactosides can be studied in z^-y^+ mutants lacking β-galactosidase (Rickenberg et al., 1956; Winkler and Wilson, 1966).

In a typical experiment, the radioactive thiogalactoside is mixed with a suspension of cells of *E. coli* (usually about 5×10^8/ml) and at accurately measured time intervals, samples are pipetted onto a Millipore filter, rapidly filtered and washed with medium lacking the galactoside. In earlier studies, the cells were often chilled on the filter and washed with ice-cold medium. However, it has been shown by Leder and Perry (1967) that washing with cold medium may lead to a rapid loss of accumulated substrates. It is therefore preferable to wash the cells with medium at the same temperature employed during the incubation. The cells, loaded with radioactive substrate, are then counted directly without removing them from the filter.

KINETICS AND SPECIFICITY OF THE ACCUMULATION PROCESS

In their early study of the *lac* permease system, Rickenberg et al. (1956) found that the affinity of the cells for labeled TMG is like that of an enzyme for its substrate. A double reciprocal plot of the levels of TMG accumulated in the cell versus the external TMG concentration showed a linear relationship, as in the familiar Lineweaver-Burk treatment of enzyme saturation. Furthermore, when an unlabeled thiogalactoside was added to the system, competitive inhibition was observed. These facts strongly argue that the binding of a galactoside to a limited number of specific sites (presumed to be protein in nature) is an essential step in uptake and accumulation via the *lac* system.

Rickenberg et al. (1956) described the relation between the level of accumulation of a galactoside at equilibrium and the external concentration by an expression formally similar to the Michaelis-Menten equation:

$$G_{in} = Y \frac{G_{ex}}{G_{ex} + K_t} \qquad (1)$$

In this equation, G_{in} is the internal concentration of galactoside, Y is maximum internal concentration of galactoside which can be achieved when the system is saturated, and K_t is the concentration of external galactoside which leads to half-saturation of the system.

Kepes and Monod (1957) showed that the initial rate of entrance of a labeled galactoside similarly is a function of the external galactoside concentration:

$$V_{in} = V_{in}^{max} \frac{G_{ex}}{G_{ex} + K_t} \qquad (2)$$

In cells with an adequate supply of metabolic energy, the exit of galactosides from the cell exhibits apparent first-order kinetics, being a linear function of internal concentration of galactoside:

$$V_{ex} = G_{in} K_{ex} \qquad (3)$$

The apparent failure of the exit process to exhibit saturation kinetics was consistent with the hypothesis advanced by Rickenberg et al. (1956) that the exit of galactosides from the cell represented non-specific leakage rather than a carrier-mediated process. However, Kepes (1960), Koch (1964) and Winkler and Wilson (1966) have provided three lines of evidence that the exit of galactosides, like their entry, is largely a carrier-mediated process. First, it has been shown that p-chloromercuribenzoate, a sulfhydryl reagent which blocks the carrier-mediated transport of galactosides, greatly reduces the rate of exit of sugar from previously loaded cells (Kepes, 1960). Further, the temperature coefficient of the exit process is high, like that of the entry process (Koch, 1964). This temperature dependence cannot be explained by leakage through cracks or pores. Finally, the initial rates of loss of galactoside from pre-loaded cells was measured by Winkler and Wilson (1966) who found that the apparent K_t for exit depended strikingly on the energy metabolism of the cell. The exit of lactose and of ONPG from cells poisoned with sodium azide plus iodoacetate were found to be saturable processes, with values of K_t for exit closely similar to those for entry. In cells with unimpaired supplies of metabolic energy, K_t for exit was very much higher, so that for all practical purposes exit may be described by eq. (3). Winkler and Wilson (1966) found, in agreement with Kepes (1960), that p-chloromercuribenzoate greatly reduced the rate of exit of sugars from pre-loaded cells and concluded that the simple diffusion component of the exit process could account for only a small fraction of the total exit rate. The implication of these findings for the mechanism of accumulation of sugars via the *lac* system will be discussed in a later section of this paper.

At equilibrium, the rate of exit of sugars from the cell must equal the rate of entry:

$$V_{in} = V_{ex} \qquad (4)$$

Under conditions of saturation:

$$V_{in}^{max} = V_{ex}^{max} = Y \; k_{ex} \qquad (5)$$

The kinetics of uptake of several sugars which are substrates for the *lac* permease system have been determined in terms of the constants defined by equations 1–5, and are summarized in Table 1, which includes data from the review by Kepes and Cohen (1962) and later authors.

Table 1. Specificity and kinetic properties of the *lac* transport system

Substrate	K_t	Max. capacity micromoles/g	Time for half-equil. (Min.)
Lactose	0.07 mM 0.9 mM (a)	550 (4°C) 125 (34°C)	2.4
TMG	0.5 mM	300 (14°C) 52 (34°C)	0.75
TDG	0.02 mM 0.05 mM (b)	40 (26°C)	1.35
Melibiose	0.2 mM (c)		—
TPG	0.25 mM	32 (26°C)	<0.25
ONPG	1.0 mM	9 (34°C)	

Unless otherwise indicated, data are those of Kepes and Cohen (1962). Where the temperature is not specified, it is usually 26 to 28°C. Cells of ML strains were used from most determinations listed, except for the studies with lactose and ONPG cited by Kepes and Cohen (1962) in which the K12 strain W2244 ($i^+z^-y^+$) was employed. (a) Winkler and Wilson (1966) using ML 308–225. (b) Value based on protective effect of TDG in intact cells (Carter et al., 1968). (c) Value based on inhibition of ONPG hydrolysis by intact cells (Carter et al., 1968).

The Table also shows the values for some sugars of $t_{1/2}$, the time required for the internal concentration of sugar to reach half the equilibrium value (Kepes, 1960). These values vary over a surprisingly wide range. The process of accumulation of a galactoside against a concentration gradient is undoubtedly complex. The kinetics of the overall process cannot yield detailed information about the molecular mechanisms of transport. Nevertheless, kinetic analysis may help to identify models which must be rejected. For an extended discussion of the kinetics of the *lac* system, the reader may consult a recent paper by Koch (1967).

EFFECT OF TEMPERATURE ON THE ACCUMULATION PROCESS

As might be expected, the initial rate of entry of galactosides into the cell during the process of accumulation via the *lac* system increases with rising temperature. For most substrates which have been studied (such as TMG, lactose and ONPG), however, the steady-state level of accumulation is affected paradoxically by temperature, with levels of accumulation much higher at 14°C than at 37°C (Kepes and Cohen, 1962). When TDG is the substrate, however, the result is strikingly different, with levels of accumulation at 34°C about the same as at 14°C. This and other differences between the behavior of TDG and that of the other substrates tested may be related to the fact that TDG binds to the membrane protein at a site different from that for the other substrates.

EFFECT OF UNCOUPLING AGENTS ON ACCUMULATION

Inhibitors which uncouple oxidative phosphorylation, such as dinitrophenol, sodium azide and derivatives of carbonyl cyanide phenylhydrazone, effectively prevent the accumulation of galactosides against a concentration gradient via the *lac* system. These uncoupling agents, however, do not prevent the carrier-mediated *entry* of ONPG into cells.

Of the uncouplers tested, the carbonyl cyanide phenylhydrazones (Heytler, 1963) are among the most potent. The effects of inhibitors of this type on respiration and respiration-dependent phosphorylation in *E. coli* have been studied in some detail by Cavari et al. (1967). At concentrations of 1–5 μM, carbonyl cyanide *m*-chlorophenylhydrazone completely blocks oxidative phosphorylation, and under certain conditions inhibits the oxidation of succinate. At similar concentrations, it prevents the accumulation of β-galactosides via the *lac* system. Dinitrophenol (1–5 mM) and sodium azide (5–10 mM) have long been known to be effective inhibitors of galactoside accumulation (Cohen and Rickenberg, 1955), but relatively high concentrations of these metabolic poisons are needed.

Unpublished experiments by Levinthal and Levinthal, quoted by Fields and Luria (1969), indicate that colicins E_1 and K may function by blocking the supply of energy derived from aerobic respiration. Consistent with this interpretation is the finding by Fields and Luria (1969) that colicins E_1 and K inhibit the accumulation of galactosides via the *lac* system but not the carrier-mediated entry of ONPG into cells, in a fashion qualitatively similar to that of sodium azide, and other uncouplers. Fields and Luria (1969) also measured the levels of ATP in cells treated with colicins, and found that they were indeed depressed, but not to levels much below about one-third those of the control cells.

When cells of *E. coli* are allowed to accumulate a radioactive galactoside against a concentration gradient until a steady-state intracellular level has been achieved, and an uncoupling agent such as dinitrophenol (Kepes, 1960) or colicins E_1 and K (Fields and Luria, 1969) is then added, the accumulated galactoside is promptly lost from the cell. This important result reveals that the *retention* of the galactoside at levels higher than the extracellular concentration requires a continuing expenditure of metabolic energy. Metabolic work must be done not only to bring the galactoside into the cell, but also to keep it there against a concentration gradient. The loss of galactoside could be the result either of an increased rate of exit or a decreased rate of entry in the presence of the metabolic poison. The former appears to be the case. The rate of exit of radioactive TMG from pre-loaded cells is greatly increased by uncoupling agents, while the rate of entry is almost unaffected (Koch, 1964). The availability of metabolic energy to the system leads to up-hill accumulation by causing the retention of the galactoside, probably by decreasing the affinity of the carrier for its substrate on the inner surface of the membrane (Winkler and Wilson, 1966).

EFFECTS OF FLUORIDE AND IODOACETATE

Aerobically-grown cells of *E. coli* oxidizing succinate as a carbon source, are not inhibited in the accumulation of galactoside via the *lac* system by 30mM sodium fluoride (Kennedy, unpubl.). The accumulation process thus probably does not depend upon continuing glycolysis, since fluoride readily penetrates intact cells of *E. coli* and at this concentration should be an effective inhibitor of the enolase reaction (Kennedy and Scarborough, 1968).

Iodoacetate (1 mM) has been used in the studies of Winkler and Wilson (1966), in addition to 30 mM azide, to eliminate sources of metabolic energy as completely as possible from cells under study. The rationale of this use of iodoacetate is that it presumably blocks glycolysis at the level of the oxidation of 3-phosphoglyceraldehyde, preventing the glycolytic generation of ATP. Iodoacetate at the concentrations used undoubtedly had such an effect in their experiments. However, iodoacetate is not a

58   Kennedy

highly selective reagent; it attacks sulfhydryl proteins generally. The membrane protein component of the *lac* permease system has a reactive cysteine essential for its function and can be inactivated by iodoacetate as well as by p-chloromercuribenzoate and N-ethylmaleimide (Kennedy, unpubl.). The effects of iodoacetate on the *lac* transport system may therefore be critically dependent upon its concentration and the conditions of the experiment.

ACCUMULATION IN ANAEROBIC CELLS

The accumulation of galactosides in cells grown anaerobically on lactose as principal carbon source was studied by Fields (1968). The cells were treated with chloramphenicol to prevent their adaptation to aerobic conditions during harvesting and testing. The anaerobic cells were found to accumulate TMG, and this accumulation was prevented by colicin E_1, just as in the aerobically-grown cells in the experiments of Fields and Luria (1969).

In a more detailed investigation of the accumulation process in anaerobic cells, Pavlasova and Harold (1969) found that uncoupling agents such as dinitrophenol and m-Cl-CCP abolished accumulation. The levels of intracellular ATP were not depressed by treatment with uncoupling agents under conditions in which the accumulation of TMG was prevented, nor was the turnover of protein affected by the metabolic poisons. The accumulation of amino acids was prevented by the uncoupling agents, but the uptake of α-methyl glucoside and of glycerol, substrates which require phosphorylation for their retention in the cell, was not affected. It was suggested that the utilization of metabolic energy for those transport systems which lead to the accumulation of unaltered substrates against a concentration gradient, i.e., "active" transport systems, was blocked by the uncoupling agents in the anaerobic cells, while the utilization of metabolic energy for other purposes, such as protein synthesis, was unaffected.

ENERGY REQUIREMENT FOR ACCUMULATION

In an attempt to measure the amount of metabolic energy needed for the uptake of one mole of thiogalactoside via the *lac* system, Kepes (1957, 1960) measured the respiration of induced cells of strain ML 30 in the presence and in the absence of added thiogalactoside. To reduce the basal rate of respiration, no carbon source was added to the medium. Under these conditions, in the absence of thiogalactoside the rate of oxygen uptake was found to be 5–10 μmoles of O_2 per g of dry weight per min. Saturation of cells with TMG brought about an increment of 8.9 ± 3 μmoles/g/min. From calculations of the rate of uptake of TMG, which required correction for the rate of entry thought to occur independently of metabolic energy, Kepes concluded that the uptake of 3.8 moles of TMG was accompanied by an increment of 1 g-atom of oxygen. Kepes suggested that in view of the approximate nature of the calculations the TMG/O ratio might reasonably be assumed to be 3, which might reflect the utilization of one energy-rich phosphate bond in the process of transport of one sugar molecule. Kepes evidently assumed that the P/O ratio in *E. coli* is 3.0. The P/O ratio observed in cell-free extracts of *E. coli,* as in cell-free preparations from most other bacteria, usually is not higher than 1.0 (Gel'man et al., 1967).

A serious difficulty in interpreting Kepes' estimate as to the energy requirement for transport of galactosides via the *lac* system arises from his assumption that the increment in oxygen uptake observed upon the addition of a thiogalactoside is the response to the additional work required for transport, which in turn involves the assumption that respiration in *E. coli* is "tightly coupled" and regulated by the rate of breakdown of ATP and other energy-rich compounds, as is the case for higher organisms. However, bacterial respiration appears not to be tightly coupled as judged from experiments with cell-free preparations (Ishikawa and Lehninger, 1962). Furthermore, an examination of the energetics of bacterial growth in *Aerobacter aerogenes* leads to the conclusion that respiration in living cells of this organism is not tightly coupled (Senez, 1962). *A. aerogenes* grows much more slowly on nitrate as sole source of nitrogen than on ammonia, but the rate of aerobic utilization of glucose is not correspondingly reduced.

Kepes (1957) considered the possibility that the increment of oxygen uptake attendant upon the addition of TMG might be caused by traces of metabolizable sugar in the thiogalactoside preparation. In an attempt to obviate this difficulty, he measured the rate of release of $^{14}CO_2$ from endogenous sources in cells grown on labeled fructose, and found that the addition of TMG as a substrate for accumulation increased the rate of $^{14}CO_2$ production by about 75%. However, the possibility must still be considered that the addition of small amounts of unlabeled exogenous sugar may stimulate the rate of production of CO_2 from endogenous sources.

AN EFFECT OF ATP ON THE LACTOSE TRANSPORT SYSTEM

Cells of ML 308 were subjected to mild osmotic shock under carefully defined conditions by Scarborough et al. (1968). The addition of ATP to such shocked cells greatly stimulated the rate of transport of ONPG. The effect was specific for purine nucleoside triphosphates, of which ATP was most active. The activation by ATP showed the kinetics of saturability with half-maximal effects being observed at about 0.9 mM ATP. These observations have since been confirmed by West (1969).

The effects of ATP in stimulating the transport of ONPG were reduced in the presence of potassium ion (Scarborough et al., 1968). However, as the authors pointed out, these effects of ATP and of potassium ion may well be very indirect, since these factors play such a fundamental role in cell physiology. Nevertheless, the possibility must be considered that ATP itself is the form of metabolic energy available to drive the lactose accumulation system. The experiments of Pavlasova and Harold (1969), as well as those of Fields and Luria (1969) which show that uncoupling agents block the accumulation of galactosides via the *lac* system in anaerobic cells make it rather unlikely that ATP itself is the direct energy source. Pavlasova and Harold (1969) in fact showed that accumulation via the *lac* system could be completely blocked under conditions in which no significant change in the levels of ATP could be detected. It is possible, however, that uncoupling agents may also inhibit ATP-driven transport systems. The Na^+, K^+-requiring ATPase of animal tissues, thought to be an essential component of the sodium pump mechanism, is inhibited by oligomycin and similar uncoupling agents (Matsui and Schwartz, 1966). This is true even with the Na^+, K^+-ATPase of erythrocytes, which do not carry out oxidative phosphorylation (Van Groningen and Slater, 1963). The effects of uncoupling agents on accumulation of galactosides in anaerobic cells may, therefore, be interpreted in one of two ways. It may indicate that the system is driven by reversal of the terminal steps of oxidative phosphorylation and only indirectly by ATP, or alternatively may indicate that uncoupling agents block membrane-localized energy transductions generally, whether these are driven by ATP directly, or are steps in oxidative phosphorylation.

Despite extensive efforts to find an ATPase activity in cell-free extracts dependent upon M protein and stimulated by thiogalactoside, no such enzyme system has as yet been found.

EFFECTS OF THE FUNCTION OF THE *lac* TRANSPORT SYSTEM ON METABOLISM OF PHOSPHOLIPIDS

Nikaido (1962) reported that the functioning of the *lac* permease is accompanied by an increased labeling of the phospholipid fraction of the cell. This led to the suggestion that phosphatidic acid may act as a transport carrier for β-galactosides in *E. coli* in a fashion fundamentally similar to the proposed role of this phospholipid in the active transport of sodium (Hokin and Hokin, 1963). More recent investigations of the mechanism of sodium transport, however, have not supported the idea that phosphatidic acid is the carrier in this process.

In a more detailed investigation of the "phospholipid effect" which accompanies the function of the *lac* transport system, Tarlov and Kennedy (1965) confirmed the findings of Nikaido (1962) and further found that the effect is not specific for the labeling of phosphatidic acid. An increment in the labeling of phospholipid from serine-3-^{14}C and from glycerol-1,3-^{14}C can also be detected when a thiogalactoside is added to the medium as a substrate for the *lac* transport system. Thus there is no reason to believe that phosphatidic acid plays a special role in the transport process. It is important to note that the experiments of Nikaido (1964) and of Tarlov and Kennedy (1965) were carried out with resting cells supplemented with a carbon source (succinate) but in the absence of a source of nitrogen. Under these conditions, phospholipid biosynthesis is severely repressed. Tarlov and Kennedy (1965) suggested that the increased labeling of phospholipid as the cells begin to accumulate thiogalactoside is a result of a transient relaxation of the general inhibition of phospholipid biosynthesis in these resting cells.

CHEMICAL FORM OF ACCUMULATED GALACTOSIDES

In attempting to determine whether the uptake of galactosides via the *lac* system is a true "up-hill" process, Cohen and Monod (1957) considered the possibility that the internal galactosides may not be in free solution, but rather may be bound to macromolecular constituents of the cell, presumably proteins. The authors pointed out that this is extremely unlikely since the accumulated galactosides may exceed 5% of the dry weight of the cell. The question has been resolved by an investigation of the physical state of the intracellularly accumulated galactosides. Sistrom (1958) prepared osmotically-sensitive spheroplasts of *E. coli* by treatment with lysozyme in the presence of EDTA. The spheroplasts were prevented from bursting by the addition of hypertonic (0.2 M) phosphate. The cells so treated were sensitive osmometers, and the changes in internal cell volume could be measured as a function of the turbidity of the cell suspension. Sistrom (1958) found that such spheroplasts actively concentrated galactosides, and from the accompanying changes in cell volume concluded that the bulk of the intracellular galactoside must be in free solution. These experiments not only shed light on the osmotic activity of the internal galactoside, but also provide evidence that accumulation via the *lac* system is not dependent upon periplasmic proteins or other factors which are lost when cells are treated with lysozyme in the presence of EDTA.

Kepes (1960) reported that lactose was the sole reducing sugar detectable by paper chromatography when cells of strain W2244, which cannot utilize lactose, were allowed to accumulate this sugar. Winkler and Wilson (1966) confirmed this result in experiments in which cells of the β-galactosidase-less strain ML 308-225 accumulated radioactive lactose. After extraction of the cells with trichloroacetic acid and subsequent paper chromatography of the extract, 98% of the accumulated material was found to be lactose. In a similar experiment with labeled ONPG, 95% of the radioactivity accumulated was found to be unaltered ONPG.

The phosphorylation of α-methyl glucoside, glucose and several other sugars is thought to be intimately related to their transport in *E. coli* and in other microorganisms (Simoni et al., 1967; Roseman, 1969). For this reason it becomes of crucial importance to determine whether phosphorylation is a *necessary* step in the accumulation of sugars via the *lac* system. Since the phosphorylated form of the sugar may be a transient intermediate in the process of accumulation, an experiment was carried out in which cells of the strain ML 308-225, lacking β-galactosidase, were exposed to radioactive lactose for only 30 sec. A small portion of the suspension was sampled to determine the total uptake of radioactive lactose, and the remainder of the suspension was extracted with hot aqueous ethanol. The entire extract was then passed over a column of Dowex-1 formate designed to separate sugars from sugar phosphates essentially as described by Tanaka and Lin (1967). No significant radioactivity was detected in the phosphorylated fraction (Rumley and Kennedy, unpubl.). The sensitivity of the method was such that an amount of phosphorylated sugar equal to 1% of the lactose accumulated after 30 sec could have been detected. In contrast, in a control experiment with radioactive α-methyl glucoside as substrate, the phosphorylated fraction accounted for all of the sugar accumulated after 30 sec.

ROLE OF THIOGALACTOSIDE TRANSACETYLASE

Rickenberg et al. (1956) noted that, when TMG was incubated for prolonged periods with cells of *E. coli* provided with an exogenous carbon source, a derivative of the radioactive sugar was slowly formed as revealed by paper chromatography. Herzenberg (1961) subsequently identified this compound as the 6-O-acetyl derivative. An enzyme (thiogalactoside acetylase) discovered by Zabin et al. (1959) was found to catalyze the acetylation of TMG and other galactosides according to the following equation:

$$\text{Galactoside} + \text{acetyl CoA} \longrightarrow \text{6-O-acetylgalactoside} + \text{CoA}$$

The enzyme was crystallized and studied in detail by Zabin (1963a). Thiogalactoside acetylase is the product of the *a* gene of the *lac* operon (Zabin et al., 1962). It was at first thought that this enzyme might play an essential role in galactoside transport. However, the affinity of the enzyme for thiogalactosides is very much lower than the affinity of the transport system for these substrates, and the affinity of the enzyme for O-galactosides such as lactose is even lower. The enzyme is localized in the soluble supernatant fraction of the cell rather than in the membrane.

Finally, there is no evidence for a rapid turnover of acetyl galactosides during transport. All of these factors argue against involvement in the transport process (Kepes and Cohen, 1962).

By transduction with phage 80 *lac,* Fox et al. (1966) were able to construct mutants of genotype $z^+y^+a^-$. In these mutants, the distal end of the *a* gene was deleted. Any (hypothetical) genes of the *lac* operon distal to the *a* gene would therefore be eliminated. Such mutants, completely lacking acetylase, transport galactosides normally and have a full complement of the *lac* membrane protein (Fox et al., 1966). The acetylase-negative strains also grow normally on lactose, both at high and low concentrations. This is decisive evidence that the acetylase, whatever its function may be, is not a part of the *lac* transport system.

Wilson and Kashket (1969) applied the useful autoradiographic technique of Zwaig and Lin (1966) in a search for mutants of *E. coli* with an altered capacity to accumulate radioactive TMG. In this procedure, clones were allowed to grow on agar plates containing labeled thiogalactoside. Sterile Whatman #1 filter paper was then pressed on the plate. Portions of each clone were retained on the paper in a pattern which replicated the plate. An autoradiograph of the paper was then made. Clones which accumulated radioactive TMG were revealed as dark spots on the X-ray film, while clones which did not accumulate the galactoside were much lighter. Using this method, Wilson and Kashket (1969) found mutant clones which accumulated levels of TMG higher than those found in wild type. These mutants were of two types. The first type accumulated large amounts of TMG-6 phosphate, while the second was acetylase-negative.

A further investigation of the second type revealed that the gradual acetylation of TMG by the wild-type clones resulted in the loss of some radioactive sugar from the cells, since the acetylated derivative is excreted into the medium and cannot be brought back into the cell against a concentration gradient. The acetylase-negative cells, in which this process did not take place, therefore, retained high levels of the radioactive sugar for longer periods of time.

Wilson and Kashket (1969) confirmed the finding of Fox et al. (1966) that acetylase-negative strains show no detectable differences from wild type in respect to their growth on lactose.

The radioautographic procedure developed by Wilson and Kashket should prove useful in screening for acetylase-negative mutants in mapping the *a* gene.

MEDIATED ENTRY OF ONPG INTO INTACT CELLS TREATED WITH ENERGY POISONS

In wild-type strains of *E. coli* the enzyme β-galactosidase is localized within the cell at sites to which substrates added to the medium cannot readily penetrate in the absence of the *lac* permease system (Rickenberg et al., 1956). The rate-limiting step in the overall process of hydrolysis of ONPG by intact cells is the passage of the substrate across the membrane, since disruption of the cell membrane with toluene increases the rate of ONPG hydrolysis by a large factor (Rickenberg et al., 1956). The exact value of this "crypticity factor" depends upon the conditions of the experiment (Koch, 1964), but destruction of the membrane barrier always increases the rate of ONPG hydrolysis by at least a factor of 10 in fully induced wild-type cells.

Herzenberg (1959) studied the kinetics of the hydrolysis of ONPG by z^+y^+ and z^+y^- (cryptic) strains. At low concentrations of ONPG the rate of splitting was much higher in the cells containing the *lac* permease system and the process exhibited saturation kinetics, with half-maximal rates at less than 1 mM ONPG in the medium. In contrast, the rate in the cryptic strain increased linearly with ONPG concentration up to 40 mM ONPG, and thus appeared to be limited only by a non-saturable diffusion-like process. It should be mentioned in this regard that entry of ONPG into the cell by diffusion cannot readily be distinguished kinetically from entry mediated by carriers for which the sugar has low affinity. At concentrations much below K_t the saturation of the carrier will be a pseudo-linear function of concentration. Koch (1964) reported that the transport of ONPG into cryptic (z^+y^-) cells has a very high temperature coefficient, the rates at 28°C being 30 to 70 times higher than at 0°C. These high values appear to eliminate leakage through pores in the intact cells, since diffusion of this kind should not have such a high temperature coefficient. It is probable that under physiological conditions the membrane of *E. coli* is an extremely effective barrier against hydrophilic molecules of the size of ONPG and other galactosides. Such sugars enter the cell either by way of the *lac* permease system, or (less efficiently) by way of other carriers for which the galactosides have only low affinity. Such an interpretation is also supported by the work of Kepes (1960) who found that cells of the y^- strain ML 35 took up radioactive TMG only very slowly, and were unable to accumulate the sugar at levels higher than those in the medium. The presence of other unlabeled β-galactosides did not interfere with the uptake of radioactive TMG. However, when the cells were allowed to take up radioactive TMG, and glucose (20 mM) was then added, the radioactive TMG was expelled from the cells. These results suggest that TMG may slowly enter the y^- cell by means of a carrier for which glucose can compete.

Most workers have interpreted the finding that energy poisons do not greatly reduce the carrier-mediated entry of ONPG as indicating that metabolic energy is not needed for the step in which the galactoside traverses the membrane itself (Koch, 1964; Fox and Kennedy, 1965; Fields and Luria, 1969; Pavlasova and Harold, 1969). The observed reduction of about one-third in the rate of entry of ONPG may be reasonably ascribed to the fact that the effect of energy poisons is to increase the rate of exit of galactosides from the cell. A fraction of the ONPG molecules brought into the poisoned cells via the transport system may escape prior to hydrolysis. On the other hand, Kepes (1960) has suggested a model in which metabolic energy would be required even for the mediated entry of galactosides into the cell and has proposed that the blocking of energy sources by the metabolic poisons is incomplete. According to Kepes, residual supplies of energy may permit the mediated entry of ONPG to continue. Although this possibility cannot be dismissed, several factors appear to make it unlikely. In the first place, it is unlikely that such a wide variety of metabolic poisons, including substances as different as the carbonyl cyanides and colicins, which completely block accumulation, would in each case reduce the energy supply available for the entry reaction by only about one-third. Furthermore, if the rate of entry of ONPG into energy-poisoned cells is dependent upon remaining endogenous reserves of energy, it would be likely that these would be rapidly exhausted. However, the rate of hydrolysis of ONPG by intact cells poisoned by azide continues at a constant rate and does not slow even after 1 hr at 28°C (Koch, 1964).

TDG is an effective inhibitor of ONPG hydrolysis in intact cells containing the *lac* permease system, but does not affect the rate of entry into cryptic cells (Herzenberg, 1959). Since TDG has high affinity for the *lac* permease (Table 1) and very low affinity for β-galactosidase (Rickenberg et al., 1956) it is clear that it interferes with the overall process of hydrolysis of ONPG by blocking transport. The rate of ONPG hydrolysis in intact energy-poisoned cells corrected for the rate found in the presence of saturating concentration (5 mM) of TDG is, therefore, an accurate and convenient measure of the rate of transport mediated by the *lac* permease system. This system has the great advantage that the complications of energy coupling are eliminated, and transport can be followed colorimetrically. There is strong evidence that the rate of ONPG hydrolysis in such cells is a measure of the amount of functional M protein (Carter et al., 1968).

Koch (1964) found that the transport of ONPG via the *lac* system is much more sensitive to the action of formaldehyde than is β-galactosidase. Hence, treatment of cells with formaldehyde can also be used to estimate the rate of entry of ONPG by routes other than the *lac* permease. The action of formaldehyde on the transport system is reversible and probably involves the formation of a complex with an essential and reactive cysteine on the M protein, since formaldehyde protects against irreversible inhibition by N-ethylmaleimide (Carter et al., 1968). Although very useful for routine studies, formaldehyde is less specific than TDG in blocking transport via the *lac* permease and at higher concentration inhibits β-galactosidase even in intact cells.

COUNTERFLOW EXPERIMENTS

Koch (1964) reported that when induced cells of strain ML 30 were loaded with radioactive TMG and then suspended in fresh medium, the addition of unlabeled β-galactosides greatly speeded the exit of the radioactive sugar from the cells. Koch suggested that this may indicate that loaded carriers traverse the membrane more rapidly than unloaded carriers.

On the other hand, as pointed out by Winkler and Wilson (1966), the presence of high concentrations of unlabeled sugars inside the cell does not speed the uptake of radioactive sugar added to the medium, as is evident from experiments reported by Kepes (1960). If the loaded carriers traverse the membrane more rapidly, this effect should be observed in both directions. In a later, more detailed study of the effects of unlabeled sugars on the 'trans' side of the membrane, Robbie and Wilson (1969) found that the rate of influx under certain conditions can be increased by pre-loading cells with a non-radioactive sugar, but the effect is comparatively small. Winkler and Wilson (1966) proposed an alternative explanation for the fact that external galactoside speeds the exit of labeled galactoside from the cell. They suggested that sugar molecules leaving the cell are partly confined by a diffusion barrier in the space external to the cell membrane, and thus have a high probability of being recaptured before diffusion into the medium. The presence of unlabeled galactosides in the medium prevents this recapture by competition for the carrier, thus trapping the labeled sugar in the external space.

When energy-poisoned cells are equilibrated with high levels of unlabeled galactoside, quickly washed, and then incubated with low concentrations of radioactive galactoside, a transient accumulation of radioactive sugar by the cells is observed, attaining intracellular levels of labeled sugar considerably higher than in the medium (Koch, 1964; Winkler and Wilson, 1966). A transient counterflow gradient of this type is not observed in y^- mutants (Winkler and Wilson, 1966). In their kinetic analysis of this type of counterflow phenomenon, Rosenberg and Wilbrandt (1957) concluded that it is a manifestation of a mobile carrier system, and cannot be the result of adsorption at fixed sites.

INHIBITION OF THE *lac* TRANSPORT SYSTEM BY SUBSTRATES OF THE GLUCOSE TRANSPORT SYSTEM

When cells of *E. coli* are grown on succinate or casamino acids as carbon source, transport via the *lac* system is not inhibited by glucose or its non-utilizable analog α-methylglucoside which is transported by the glucose permease. However, if the cells are grown on glucose as carbon source, the activity of the *lac* permease (and of β-galactosidase) is reduced as the result of catabolite repression, and in addition glucose or α-methylglucoside become powerful inhibitors of *lac* transport (Kepes, 1960; Koch, 1964; Winkler and Wilson, 1967; Boniface and Koch, 1967). The inhibitory effects of glucose and its analogs on transport appear not to be a simple consequence of catabolite repression during growth, since the *lac* transport system in cells grown on gluconate, which also gives rise to severe catabolite repression, is not inhibited by glucose or α-methylglucoside (Winkler and Wilson, 1967).

In an examination of the specificity of inhibition in glucose-grown cells, Winkler and Wilson (1967) found that 1-deoxyglucose and 2-deoxyglucose effectively inhibited *lac* transport whereas 6-deoxyglucose did not. These workers concluded that there is a good correlation between the affinity of sugars for the glucose transport and their inhibitory effect on the *lac* permease in glucose grown cells.

Kepes (1960) suggested that the glucose transport system shares a common carrier or *transporteur* with the *lac* system, and the inhibition of the *lac* system by substrates of the glucose system represents competition for this *transporteur*. However, the inhibition of the transport of β-galactosides by α-methylglucoside is noncompetitive (Winkler and Wilson, 1967; Boniface and Koch, 1967). Furthermore, the inhibition is not reciprocal; in glucose-grown cells, TMG does not inhibit the uptake of α-methylglucoside (Winkler and Wilson, 1967). Finally, if glucose-grown cells are pre-loaded with unlabeled α-MG, no transient stimulation of uptake as a result of counter-flow can be detected when radioactive TMG is added to the medium. These results indicate that the *lac* and glucose permeases do not share or compete for the same carrier, and put severe limitations on the hypotheses advanced by Kepes (1960) and Koch (1964).

In glucose-grown cells, α-MG inhibits the mediated transport of ONPG in energy-poisoned cells, as well as the up-hill accumulation of galactosides against a gradient. Clearly, the effect of α-MG is not simply interference with the sources of metabolic energy which are coupled to accumulation via the *lac* transport system.

A possible explanation for the inhibitory effects on the *lac* permease of substrates for the glucose transport system which is consistent with the known facts can be formulated on the hypothesis that the functioning of the PEP-linked phosphotransferase system (known to be required for the uptake of substrates via the glucose permease) leads to the formation of some product which is inhibitory to the *lac* transport system. Although the glucose system is partially constitutive, its activity in glucose-grown cells is about 5 times higher than in cells grown on casein hydrolysate

(Winkler and Wilson, 1967). The rate of production of inhibitor during the transport of substrates of the glucose system would, therefore, be expected to be higher in glucose-grown cells. The noncompetitive character of the inhibition and the lack of reciprocal inhibition would also be consistent with this explanation. Winkler and Wilson (1967) found that maximum inhibition of the *lac* transport system in glucose-grown cells required about 15 sec after the addition of α-methylglucoside, which would also support the inhibitor theory. Boniface and Koch (1967) however, under somewhat different conditions, could find no time lag in the inhibition by α-methylglucoside.

Boniface and Koch (1967) studied the degree of inhibition of *lac* transport by α-MG in cells during the transition from growth on succinate to growth on glucose and vice versa. The results suggested that *lac* permease units incorporated into the membrane in the absence of glucose remained resistant to inhibition by α-MG during subsequent growth on glucose, but permease units synthesized during growth on glucose were sensitive to inhibition. This, in turn, led to the hypothesis that inhibition occurs only when the *lac* permease and glucose permease are synthesized together at sites which permit them to interact. The evidence supporting this suggestion is necessarily quite indirect.

RELATION BETWEEN THE *lac* TRANSPORT SYSTEM AND THE PEP-LINKED PHOSPHOTRANSFERASE SYSTEM

The phosphorylation of many sugars in bacterial systems is catalyzed by a phosphotransferase linked to the utilization of phosphoenolpyruvate:

1. $\text{H Pr} + \text{PEP} \xrightarrow{\text{Enz I}} \text{H Pr-P} + \text{Pyruvate}$

2. $\text{H Pr-P} + \text{Sugar} \xrightarrow{\text{Enz II}} \text{Sugar-P} + \text{H Pr}$

Work on this system has recently been reviewed by Roseman (1969).

Enzyme II, which catalyzes reaction 2 in the above scheme, appears to be a membrane-bound complex which may involve two or more proteins. A requirement for lipid has also been detected (Roseman, 1969). The Enz II complex shows a high degree of sugar specificity. In contrast, Enz I and H Pr function in the phosphorylation of all sugars which are substrates for the phosphotransferase system. In 1967, Tanaka et al., showed that mutants of *E. coli* which are defective in Enz I are pleiotropic and have lost the ability to grow on glucose, fructose, mannitol and sorbitol. These mutants (MM-6 and GN-2) still grow well on galactose or lactose.

Roseman (1969) has proposed that the PEP-linked phosphotransferase system affords a general mechanism for driving sugar transport (including the *lac* transport system) in *E. coli*. The balance of evidence, however, appears to rule out this possibility.

In mutants MM-6 and GN-2, accumulation of β-galactosides via the *lac* system is essentially normal, (Ascensio et al., 1963; Fraenkel et al., 1964). Roseman has attempted to explain this fact in the context of his hypothesis by pointing out that these mutants may be leaky, i.e., may contain 5 to 10% of the activity of Enz I found in wild type. This explanation requires the *ad hoc* assumption that the lactose and galactose transport systems can function at almost full efficiency at levels of Enz I which are completely unable to support the transport of glucose or fructose. Roseman (1969) has also pointed out that a tight mutant lacking any detectable Enz I is unable to grow on a variety of sugars including lactose (Fox and Wilson, 1968), and has interpreted this to mean that the *lac* permease is dependent upon the phosphotransferase system. However, Fox and Wilson (1968) also reported that this mutant (1103), when induced with TMG, contained the same level of *lac* permease and β-galactosidase as wild type. This result, not quoted by Roseman (1969), thus clearly shows that the defect in 1103 which prevents growth on lactose is not in the *lac* transport system.

Strain 1101 (Fox and Wilson, 1968) which lacks H Pr likewise fails to grow on lactose as sole carbon source. Perlman and Pastan (this volume) have considerably clarified the nature of the pleiotropic effects in these mutants. These workers have found that although 1101 and 1103 fail to grow on lactose alone, both will grow on lactose in media supplemented either with cyclic AMP or IPTG. Apparently, the mutants are more sensitive to catabolite repression than the parent strain.

The genetic and biochemical evidence from the analysis of mutants lacking either Enz I or H Pr thus clearly indicates that the *lac* transport system is not dependent upon the PEP-linked phosphotransferase. This conclusion is supported by the recent, more detailed studies of Fox and Epstein. These workers have isolated a number of Enz I-negative mutants, including at least one amber mutant, which have normal *lac* transport. Similarly, a number of H Pr-negative strains, including several deletion mutants, are not affected in the ability to transport galactosides via the *lac* permease (C. F. Fox, pers. commun.).

The phosphorylation of TMG and other β-galactosides under specified conditions can readily be observed both in intact cells of *E. coli* and in cell-free extracts. This phosphorylation appears to be dependent upon the PEP-linked phosphotransferase system. TMG is the sugar most often studied in this regard. It should be recalled that it is not a highly specific substrate for the *lac* transport system. The overlapping specificity of transport systems for galactose, TMG and other β-galactosides has been discussed above. TMG also appears to be a substrate for the PEP-linked system for the phosphorylation of glucose, with a K_m of 10 to 20 mM (Schillinger and Kennedy, unpubl.).

Is the phosphorylation of β-galactosides an essential step in their transport via the *lac* system? When radioactive lactose, a more specific substrate for the *lac* system is used rather than labeled TMG, no phosphorylated lactose can be detected in the initial phases of the accumulation reaction. This result, together with the genetic evidence discussed above, indicates that phosphorylation by the PEP-linked system is not necessary for accumulation by the *lac* permease, but may occur as a side reaction. Wilson and Kashket (1969) isolated mutants from both ML and K-12 strains in which an unusually high proportion of TMG taken up in the cell is recovered in the phosphorylated form. When the time-course of uptake via the *lac* system was compared with that of phosphorylation, it was found that the uptake of the free sugar preceded its phosphorylation (Fig. 1) (Kashket and Wilson, 1969). This result is exactly the reverse of that observed when the uptake of α-MG is studied in experiments of brief duration. In the latter case, only traces of free α-MG can be detected at early time intervals, the bulk of the radioactive sugar being the phosphorylated form, as would be expected if phosphorylation is an essential step in its accumulation by the cell.

Kashket and Wilson (1969) examined cell-free extracts from wild-type cells and from mutants which accumulate high levels of TMG-6-P. Phosphorylation of TMG via the PEP-linked phosphotransferase reactions was higher in extracts from the mutant strains. These workers then isolated a y^- derivative of the hyperphosphorylating strain. Extracts from this y^- derivative retained increased capacity to phosphorylate TMG, which is thus shown not to be dependent upon the *lac* permease. Interestingly, intact cells of this y^- mutant (ML 308-811 C) did not accumulate significant amounts of TMG or its phosphate, a further indication that the phosphorylation of TMG follows its internal accumulation.

In a preliminary communication, Kundig et al. (1966) described experiments in which cells of the K-12 strain W 2244 ($i^+z^-y^+gal^+$) were osmotically shocked after treatment with EDTA in a procedure based on that of Nossal and Heppel (1966). Cells induced for the *lac* system by previous growth on IPTG lost 50% to 85% of their ability to concentrate TMG when subjected to the shock procedure. A parallel loss in the system for the uptake of α-MG was noted. The shock procedure caused the cells to leak 50% to 80% of their content of H Pr into the medium.

In some experiments, a dramatic restoration of the ability of the cells to take up labeled TMG and α-MG was observed when purified H Pr was added to the medium in relatively high concentration. The authors re-

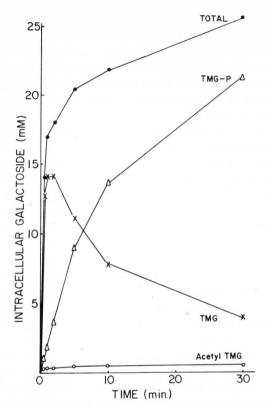

FIGURE 1. Time-course of TMG accumulation, phosphorylation and acetylation by intact cells of strain ML 308–811 ($i^-z^-y^+a^+$). Cells were grown to exponential phase in amino acid medium with 0.5% glucose, centrifuged, washed and re-suspended in minimal medium 63 containing 0.5 mM ^{14}C-TMG. The total radioactive TMG taken up by the cell was determined at the indicated time intervals, as well as the intracellular content of TMG-6-P and acetyl TMG. From Kashket and Wilson (1969) with permission of the authors and publishers.

marked that the results of the shock procedure varied substantially in terms of viability, ability to accumulate glycosides, and the response to H Pr. For example, despite extensive efforts to standardize the procedure, viabilities ranged from 0% to 90%. Of 26 cell preparations, 11 responded to treatment with H Pr.

Cells of strain W 2244 which had not been induced by growth on IPTG did not accumulate TMG before or after shock, nor did treatment with H Pr affect the uptake of TMG. The accumulation of α-MG in the shocked uninduced cells responded to the addition of H Pr as expected. Roseman (1969) has interpreted these results as indicating that the accumulation of galactosides via the *lac* system is dependent upon the phosphotransferase system, and indeed this appears to be the strongest available evidence in support of this view.

In considering the "reconstitution" experiments of Kundig et al. (1966), it may be relevant that labeled TMG was used in these studies since it is a better substrate for phosphorylation than other β-galactosides. Lactose would be preferable from this point of view, since it is relatively more specific for the *lac* permease.

An alternative explanation of the effects of H Pr might be that the treatment of the shocked cells with this protein leads to a high level of phosphorylation of TMG by the pathway studied by Kashket and Wilson (1969). It is possible that the shock treatment also results in the loss of sugar phosphatase(s) which are not added back with the H Pr, thus making retention of TMG-6-P within the cells more efficient. The results of Kashket and Wilson (1969) indicate that ML 308-811 C (z^+y^-) does not accumulate significant amounts of TMG-P even though it contains the enzymatic machinery for phosphorylation. TMG must enter the cell via the *lac* permease in order to be phosphorylated. This would account for the failure of Kundig et al. (1966) to observe effects of H Pr on uninduced cells. Thus TMG might be retained in the "reconstituted" cells by two separate processes, the *lac* system which does not involve phosphorylation, and also by a trapping mechanism, dependent upon phosphorylation. The latter pathway would be that stimulated by H Pr. As was noted above, in those experiments in which Kundig et al. (1966) were able to observe effects of added H Pr, the base line accumulation in the absence of the added protein was never completely abolished, but reduced only by 50% to 80%.

IDENTIFICATION OF THE MEMBRANE PROTEIN COMPONENT OF THE *lac* TRANSPORT SYSTEM

Genetic analysis of the *lac* system provided decisive evidence that the product of the *y* gene must play an essential role in the lactose transport system. Attempts to identify a specific enzyme as the product of this gene have thus far been unsuccessful. Efforts to find a labeled protein in the soluble fraction in the cell which might be the product of the *y* gene, although initially encouraging, have also met with failure (Naono et al., 1965; Kolber and Stein, 1966). In the experiments of Kolber and Stein, cells of *E. coli* induced, or uninduced, were grown in the presence of ^{14}C- or tritium-labeled amino acids, respectively. Upon fractionation of the extracts, these workers claimed to have detected a soluble protein in the induced cells, different from β-galactosidase and acetylase, which was not present in the uninduced cells and was therefore thought to be the expression of the *y* gene. These experiments, however, are subject to criticism on technical grounds (Kennedy, 1969). Stein (1969) has recently suggested that the soluble protein previously observed may be a breakdown product of the M protein, or a product unrelated to the transport system.

In 1965, a membrane-localized protein was discovered to be an essential component of the *lac* transport system (Fox and Kennedy, 1965). These investigators searched for inhibitors of the transport system of the type which function by irreversible attachment to proteins. N-ethylmaleimide (NEM), which has a high but not complete specificity for the sulfhydryl groups of proteins, proved most useful for this purpose. The sensitivity of the *lac* permease system to sulfhydryl poisons has long been known (Cohen and Monod, 1957).

In the experiments of Fox and Kennedy (1965) the rate of hydrolysis of ONPG by intact, energy-poisoned cells was used as an assay for the *lac* transport system to avoid complications which might arise from inactivation of enzymes needed to supply energy for accumulation assays. Conditions were found in which the transport of ONPG was completely blocked by NEM, without affecting β-galactosidase or acetylase. Clearly some component, other than the two known proteins of the *lac* system, is needed for transport and is sensitive to NEM. The addition of TDG to the medium prevented inactivation, and this effect of TDG exhibited saturation kinetics (Fox and Kennedy, 1965; Carter et al., 1968) leading to the conclusion that the NEM-sensitive component has high affinity for TDG, and the binding of TDG prevents inactivation by NEM. These properties made it possible to label the NEM-sensitive component with some specificity. Cells were first incubated with unlabeled NEM in the presence of saturating amounts of TDG, thus reducing the background level of proteins which can react with NEM. After removal of the TDG and cold NEM, the cells were treated with radioactive NEM. An examination of the intracellular distribution of proteins so labeled, using induced or uninduced cells labeled with ^{3}H- or with ^{14}C-NEM, respectively, provided evidence that the NEM-sensitive, TDG-binding protein which is essential for the transport system is localized in the particulate, membrane-containing fraction of the cell. Since the function of the protein in the transport system is not understood, it has been given the non-committal name of *membrane protein* or M protein.

From the known properties of the protein, determined in such experiments with intact cells, it was possible to devise a chemical test for its presence in cell-free fractions of *E. coli* based on its affinity for TDG, and the effect of bound TDG in preventing its reaction with labeled NEM (Fox and Kennedy, 1965; Fox et al., 1967; Carter et al., 1968).

Genetic Control of the M Protein Component of the Lactose Transport System

The classical studies of Rickenberg et al. (1956) made it clear that some essential element of the *lac* transport system is regulated by the *y* gene. When cell-free particulate fractions of wild-type and mutant strains of *E. coli* were examined for M protein, that is, a protein with a specific affinity for TDG, the binding of which prevents its reaction with labeled NEM, such a protein was found only in *y*[+] strains (Fox et al., 1967). The results of a study of some ML strains is shown in Table 2. A number of K-12 strains were also tested with similar results (Fox et al., 1967).

These results made it clear that the M protein is regulated by the *y* gene of the *lac* operon. This regulation, however, may be indirect. To obtain some information as to whether the *y* gene is the structural gene for the

Table 2. Genetic control of the membrane protein component of the *lac* transport system in ML strains of *E. Coli*

Strain	Protein-bound NEM ($\mu\mu$moles/mg protein)		M protein ($\mu\mu$moles/mg protein)
	no TDG	0.01 m TDG	
ML 308	200	86	111 ± 5
($i^-z^+y^+a^+$)	188	87	
Uninduced	204	85	
ML 3	94	99	N.S.
($i^+z^+y^-a^-$)	97	99	
Induced	105	102	
ML 308–225	250	126	119 ± 5
($i^-z^-y^+a^+$)	245	132	
Uninduced	260	129	
ML 35	89	97	N.S.
($i^-z^+y^-a^-$)	90	95	
Uninduced	99	95	
ML 30	235	110	135 ± 3
($i^+z^+y^+a^+$)	239	104	
Induced	246	103	
	246	109	
ML 30	124	123	N.S.
(Uninduced)	124	127	

The particulate membrane-containing fraction was prepared and assayed as described by Fox et al. (1967). The values given for M protein represent the difference (in picomoles per mg protein) in radioactive NEM bound in the presence and in the absence of saturating levels of TDG. The standard error of the difference of the two means is also indicated. Values marked N.S. indicate no significant difference. From Fox et al. (1967) with permission of the authors and publishers.

Table 3. Relation of TDG binding and gene dosage

Strain	TDG bound by membrane fraction (Picomoles/mg protein)	Percent M protein in membrane fraction
ML 308 ($i^-z^+y^+a^+$)	79	3%
A 324-4 ($i^-z^+y^+a^+/F'i^+z^+y^+a^+$)	150	(6%)
Y 90-3 (phage 80 d*lac*/F'*lac*)	330	(12%)

The binding of TDG to the membrane fraction was measured as described in Table 5. The percentage of M protein in the membrane fraction of ML 308 was determined by disc electrophoresis of extracts in buffers containing sodium dodecyl sulfate as described by Jones and Kennedy (1969). The content of M protein in the other strains was estimated on the assumption that binding is directly proportional to the concentration of M protein.

protein, the behavior of temperature-sensitive mutants was examined. Several spontaneous revertants of the y^- mutant CA 8204, a K-12 derivative, were isolated which exhibited the *lac*$^+$ phenotype when grown at 25°C but not at 42°C. The *lac* transport system in such mutants, measured either by ONPG hydrolysis in intact cells, or the accumulation of thiogalactosides, was temperature-sensitive in these mutants (Fox et al., 1967). One mutant (8204-ts 3) was studied in some detail. In cell-free extracts of this strain, M protein, measured by the technique of reaction with labeled NEM, showed a temperature sensitivity for the binding of TDG parallel to the temperature sensitivity of the *lac* transport system in the living cells. To assure that the temperature-sensitive character was indeed a result of a mutation in a gene of the *lac* operon, strain 8204-ts-3 (*HfrH* Sm^s) was mated with strain X-5097 (F$^-$Sm^r pro-*lac*$_{del}$). Eight *pro*$^+$ *sm*^{r} *lac*$^+$ recombinants were examined. In all eight, the transport system showed the same temperature sensitivity as the parent 8204-ts 3 (Fox et al., 1967). These results, taken together with the other genetic evidence, strongly support the conclusion that the *y* gene is the structural gene for the M protein. This conclusion is also borne out by experiments on the direct binding of TDG to be described below. The number of TDG-binding sites in the cell-free particulate fraction of a number of strains has been found to be roughly proportional to gene dosage (Table 3).

CHARACTERIZATION OF THE M PROTEIN

The M protein is firmly bound to the membrane fraction of the cell, and cannot be extracted by repeated washing with aqueous buffers. It can, however, be extracted with buffers containing detergents, whether non-ionic (Triton X-100) or ionic (sodium dodecyl sulfate). Early attempts to purify the protein employed Triton X-100 to extract the protein. Some purification can be achieved by fractionation on columns of DEAE equili- brated with Triton X-100 (Fox and Kennedy, 1965) but efforts to charac- terize the protein were more successful using sodium dodecyl sulfate as detergent (Jones and Kennedy, 1969). In one such experiment, the M protein in particulate fractions was labeled with radioactive NEM under conditions similar to those of Table 2, in which the addition of TDG specifically prevented about 60% of the labeling of the protein. Thus, 60% of the total radioactive protein labeled in the absence of TDG would be

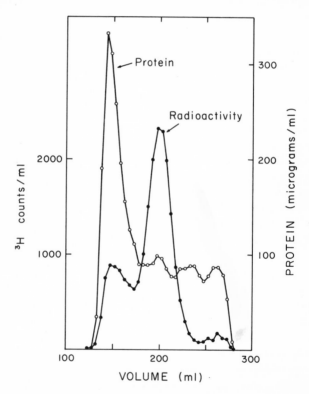

FIGURE 2. Chromatography of labeled M protein on Sephadex G-150 in the presence of sodium dodecyl sulfate. The M protein in cell-free particulate fractions was specifically labeled with tritiated NEM, extracted with buffer containing 1% sodium dodecyl sulfate, and chromato- graphed on a column of Sephadex G-150 (100 by 2.5 cm) previously equilibrated with 1% sodium dodecyl sulfate. Samples of 5 ml each were collected and assayed for total protein and for radioactivity. From Jones and Kennedy (1969) with permission of the authors and publishers.

expected to be a single species—the M protein. The labeled proteins were extracted with buffers containing sodium dodecyl sulfate, and fractionated on a column of Sephadex G-150 previously equilibrated with the detergent (Jones and Kennedy, 1969). The results are shown in Fig. 2. About 60% of the total count was recovered in a single peak at a position in the chromatogram expected for proteins of mol wt of 31,000 separate from the main peak of protein. When the material taken from the radioactive peak was pooled and rechromatographed, its position in the chromatogram was unaltered (Jones and Kennedy, 1969). In control experiments in which the labeling of M protein was prevented by the addition of TDG, the major peak of radioactivity was not present. The peak thus represents M protein.

Extracts of the labeled protein were also analyzed by disc electrophoresis in buffers containing sodium dodecyl sulfate as described by Shapiro et al. (1967). The mol wt of the M protein determined by this method was 29,000 (Jones and Kennedy, 1969), in good agreement with the value obtained by chromatography on Sephadex. Guthrie and Pardee (1969) have recently also found a mol wt of about 30,000 for M protein.

Many proteins are known to dissociate into subunits upon treatment with sodium dodecyl sulfate in the presence of a reducing agent. The mol wt of about 30,000 assigned to the M protein on the basis of its behavior under these conditions during fractionation on Sephadex and disc gel electrophoresis may, therefore, be the mol wt of some subunit of the functional molecule.

AMOUNTS OF M PROTEIN IN *E. Coli*

Analysis by disc electrophoresis of extracts of the membrane fraction of *E. coli* after growth on labeled amino acids indicate that about 0.35% of the total protein of fully induced cells of strain ML 30 is M protein (Jones and Kennedy, 1969). Zabin (1963b) estimates that strain ML 308 when grown with vigorous aeration at 37°C contains acetylase equivalent to about 0.15% of the total protein. Since the mol wt of the subunits of the two proteins is closely similar, it would appear that there are about twice as many subunits of M protein produced as of acetylase. However, it should be emphasized that the estimations of the abundance of the two proteins was carried out with different strains under different experimental conditions. It would be advisable to repeat these experiments under conditions in which acetylase and M protein are measured in the same extracts.

THE INTERACTION OF M PROTEIN WITH SUGARS

The kinetics and specificity of the interaction of M protein with sugars which leads to its protection against NEM has been studied in intact cells and in cell-free preparations by Carter et al. (1968). Radioactive

S-succinyl-cysteine was isolated from partial acid hydrolysates of the protein after reaction with NEM prepared from labeled maleic anhydride, indicating that a reactive cysteine on the M protein is the site of reaction with NEM.

The kinetics of the reactions by which TDG exerts its protective effect have been described in the following simplified formulation:

$$M + TDG \rightleftharpoons M \cdot TDG$$

$$\text{NEM} \Big\downarrow \tag{1}$$

$$\text{M-NEM}$$

$$-d(M)/dt = k\ \alpha(M_{total}) \tag{2}$$

$$\alpha = \frac{(M)}{(M) + (M \cdot TDG)} \tag{3}$$

It is assumed that only the free form of M protein is available for reaction. The M · TDG complex is of the Michaelis-Menten type. Its formation is readily reversible and is very much faster than the rate of reaction of the protein with NEM.

If the molar concentration of NEM is high in relation to the concentration of protein and remains constant through the reaction, the reaction of M protein with NEM should follow pseudo first-order kinetics with k the apparent first order reaction constant (Carter et al., 1968). In the presence of TDG, however, only that fraction α of the total M protein which is free will be available for reaction. This fraction α is a function of the TDG concentration and the dissociation constant K_D of the complex (Eqs. 4, 5).

$$K_D = \frac{(M)\ (TDG)}{(M \cdot TDG)} \tag{4}$$

$$K_D = \frac{\alpha(TDG)}{1 - \alpha} \tag{5}$$

Thus the dissociation constant for the M · TDG complex can be calculated from measurements of the rate of reaction of the protein with NEM at various concentrations of TDG. This procedure led to a value of 5×10^{-5} M based on measurements in intact cells, and 7×10^{-5} M in experiments with cell-free fractions (Carter et al., 1968). These values are in satisfactory agreement with previous measurements for K_t based on the accumulation of TDG by intact cells (Table 1).

When substrates for the lactose transport system were tested for their ability to protect against NEM, they were found to fall into two distinct

Table 4. Classification of substrates for the *lac* permease system based on their effect in protecting M protein against sulfhydryl reagents

I Little or no protective effect	II Protective effect	
Lactose ONPG	High affinity	{ TDG Melibiose
TMG IPTG	Low affinity	{ Phenyl-β-galactoside Glycerol-β-galactoside Allolactose

classes (Table 4). Sugars of class I exhibited little or no protective effect when tested at concentrations of 5 mM, a level considerably above their K_t for transport. Furthermore, when sugars of this class were added to systems containing TDG and NEM, the protective effect of the TDG was not diminished. This finding eliminates the possibility that sugars of class I are bound to the same site as TDG but their binding does not lead to protection of the reactive cysteine.

Of the substrates tested, only TDG and melibiose were found to have a high affinity for the site which leads to protection of the cysteine (site II). Phenyl-β-galactoside, glycerol-β-galactoside and allolactose, however, did have detectable affinity for site II, although too low to be measured accurately.

The simplest working hypothesis to account for these observations is that the M protein has two binding sites for sugars which it transports. This surprising conclusion has recently been confirmed by direct tests of the binding of radioactive TDG to cell-free preparations of M protein described in Table 6.

It is possible that site II serves a regulatory function in the cell. If some metabolite accumulated in the cell during growth on lactose with affinity for site II, transport of lactose at site I would be reduced.

DIFFERENTIAL INACTIVATION OF THE *lac* TRANSPORT SYSTEM IN STARVED CELLS

When cells of *E. coli* are vigorously aerated while starved for a carbon source, the *lac* transport system is inactivated during the course of 2 to 3 hr (Rickenberg et al., 1956). The activity of β-galactosidase in the same cells remains essentially unaltered. This inactivation was studied in greater detail by Koch (1963) who showed that it could largely be prevented by the addition of a utilizable carbon source, such as succinate.

Carter et al. (1968) reported that saturation of the transport system with TDG, a non-utilizable sugar, also protected against inactivation almost as well as succinate, suggesting that it is the auto-oxidation of the essential cysteine residue on the M protein which is responsible for inactivation during aeration. This conclusion was supported by the finding that after brief periods of aeration, activity could almost completely be restored by treatment of the cells with β-mercaptoethanol. If the cells were shaken for an hour or longer however, the inactivation was essentially irreversible.

The effect of succinate in preventing inactivation, together with the evidence that a sulfhydryl is involved in the process, suggests that *E. coli* may possess enzymatic machinery linked to metabolism to keep functional membrane proteins in the reduced state. It is believed that such mecha-

Table 5. Binding of ^{3}H-TDG to M protein in cell-free particulate fraction of *E. Coli*

Experiment 1 A-324-4 induced	Ratio 3H/^{32}P in pellet	Picomoles TDG bound
1. 0.05 mM ^{3}H-TDG	1.416	690
	1.412	
	1.426	
2. 0.05 mM ^{3}H-TDG + 10 mM cold TDG	0.924	(0)
	0.988	
	0.962	
3. 0.05 mM ^{3}H-TDG + 0.01 M Sodium azide	1.408	695
	1.465	
	1.427	
Experiment 2 A-324-4 not induced		
1. 0.05 mM TDG-^{3}H	0.965	0
	0.952	
	0.990	
2. 0.05 mM TDG-^{3}H + 10 mM cold TDG	0.942	
	0.977	
	0.953	

Cells of strain A-324-4 (i$^-$z$^+$y$^+$a$^+$ pro$^-$/F' i$^+$z$^+$y$^+$a$^+$ pro$^+$) were grown on glycerol as carbon source in the presence or in the absence of 0.5 mM IPTG as an inducing agent. The cells were harvested, washed and sonically disrupted. Intact cells were removed by low-speed centrifugation. Portions of the extract were equilibrated with 0.05 mM ^{3}H-TDG in 0.1 M phosphate buffer of pH 7.0 for 30 min. at 28°C. The buffer contained ^{32}P equal in total count to the tritium. In control tubes the radioactive TDG was displaced from specific binding sites by the addition of unlabeled TDG (10 mM). The membrane fragments containing M protein were sedimented at 39,000 × g for 1 hr. at 0°C. The supernatant was carefully removed, and the pellet, containing about 3 mg of protein was taken up without washing in a 5% solution of Triton X-100 for counting in triplicate.

nisms are operative in mammalian erythrocytes, and that they are essential to the maintenance of the structural integrity of the erythrocyte (Scheuch et al., 1961).

DIRECT MEASUREMENT OF THE BINDING OF TDG TO M PROTEIN

A new method has been devised in this laboratory for measuring the binding of TDG to M protein directly, avoiding the use of NEM. It is a limitation of all binding assays, equilibrium dialysis experiments, and the like, that the molar concentration of binding protein must approach that of the ligand, if a significant fraction of the ligand is to be bound. To achieve the highest concentration of M protein, binding is therefore measured in the pellet obtained by high-speed centrifugation of cell-free membrane fractions. This is greatly facilitated by a double-label procedure.

The particulate membrane fraction is equilibrated with 0.05 mM TDG-^{3}H in a phosphate buffer containing ^{32}P equal in total count to the tritium. Control experiments show that the ^{32}P equilibrates with at least 95% of the total vol of the system. After equilibration, the membrane fragments are sedimented by high-speed centrifugation, and after careful removal of the supernatant (but without washing), the pellet is taken up in a solution of Triton X-100 for counting. The adsorption of TDG to the membrane fragments is revealed by an increment of the ratio of tritium to ^{32}P. This increment is abolished if an excess of cold TDG is added, indicating that binding takes place on a limited number of saturable sites. The binding reaction is not affected by azide or other energy poisons (Table 5). Cells grown on succinate which have not been induced for the *lac* system contain no specific binding sites for TDG, as defined by this assay.

A variety of sugars was tested for ability to displace radioactive TDG from the M protein. Results shown in Table 6 reveal that 5 mM melibiose effectively displaces TDG from its binding site. However, the addition of

Table 6. Displacement of TDG from M protein by other sugars

Additions	^{3}H-TDG bound (picomoles)
None	400
5 mM Melibiose	19
5 mM TMG	396
5 mM IPTG	335
5 mM α-Methylglucoside	410
5 mM Galactose	405
5 mM Glucose	410

The conditions of the assay were essentially the same as those shown in Table 5.

5 mM TMG is without detectable effect. Similar results were obtained with glucose, α-methyl glucoside, and galactose. IPTG at a concentration of 5 mM has only a slight effect in displacing TDG.

These observations offer strong confirmatory evidence that melibiose and TDG share a binding site on the M protein for which many other substrates of the *lac* transport system have little affinity.

MODELS FOR THE LACTOSE TRANSPORT SYSTEM

Models currently proposed to account for the function of the *lac* transport system in *E. coli* are of two general kinds. Accumulation of a sugar is explained in the first type of model by postulating a cycle of transformations of the sugar itself. Transporter models proposed by Kepes (1960) and further developed by Koch (1964) are examples of this type, as is the accumulation of phosphorylated sugars by the PEP-linked phosphotransferase mechanism.

In the second type of model, it is not the substrate but the carrier which undergoes a cycle of transformations, such that the affinity of the carrier for its substrate is much less on the internal (cytoplasmic) side of the membrane than on the exterior surface. The models proposed by Fox and Kennedy (1965) and Winkler and Wilson (1966) are of this general kind.

The transporter model introduced by Kepes in 1960 is shown in Fig. 3. Its essential postulate is that the sugar traverses the membrane barrier

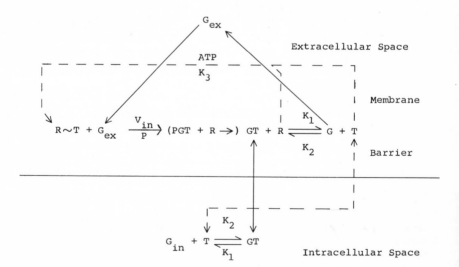

FIGURE 3. Model of the permease system according to Kepes (1960).

only after combination with a substance called the transporter. The chemical nature of the transporter is not specified; however, the sugar-transporter complex is postulated to have physico-chemical characteristics which permit it to traverse the membrane barrier freely. The transporter could thus conceivably be a phospholipid.

The role of the permease protein in the Kepes model is to catalyze a reaction between an activated form of the transporter and the sugar.

$$R \sim T + G_{ex} \xrightarrow{\quad P \quad} G - T + R \tag{1}$$

This reaction is postulated to be virtually irreversible and to be rate-making for the entire process. On the internal face of the membrane, the G-T complex dissociates spontaneously. The equilibrium is postulated to be far in favor of dissociation. The transporter liberated on the interior of the membrane may be reactivated at the expense of the metabolic energy for the start of another cycle.

An essential feature of this scheme is the requirement of metabolic energy for the *entry* of galactosides in the permease catalyzed process. This aspect of the model appears to offer serious difficulty. Most workers are now of the opinion that while *accumulation* requires metabolic energy, permease-mediated entry, as in the transport of ONPG into azide-poisoned cells, is independent of metabolic energy. Evidence on this point has been considered in a previous section of this chapter.

The transporter model has been considerably revised and extended by Koch (1967). Fig. 4 shows his conception of the process in permease-containing and in cryptic cells, with and without coupled metabolic energy. Koch postulates that "The transporter (T) is the substance, structure or channel that permits diffusion of the substrate (G) by its interaction, through the cell membrane." The generality of this description of the transporter must be regarded as a weakness of the model.

According to Koch's view, permease mediated *entry* (condition II in Fig. 4) does not require coupled metabolic energy. The permease protein catalyzes a reaction between transporter and sugar which is not energy-linked. In the accumulation process, in contrast, a sub-system in the cell may actively extract the substrate from the TG complex. In doing so, metabolic energy released as compound A (which may be ATP or its energetic equivalent) is converted via an exergonic process into B (Koch, 1967).

According to Koch's model, the association and dissociation of the TG complex on the inner face of the membrane in energy-poisoned cells is not catalyzed by permease, even if the cell contains permease (condition II). The sole pathway of exit of sugar from the cell is by way of an un-

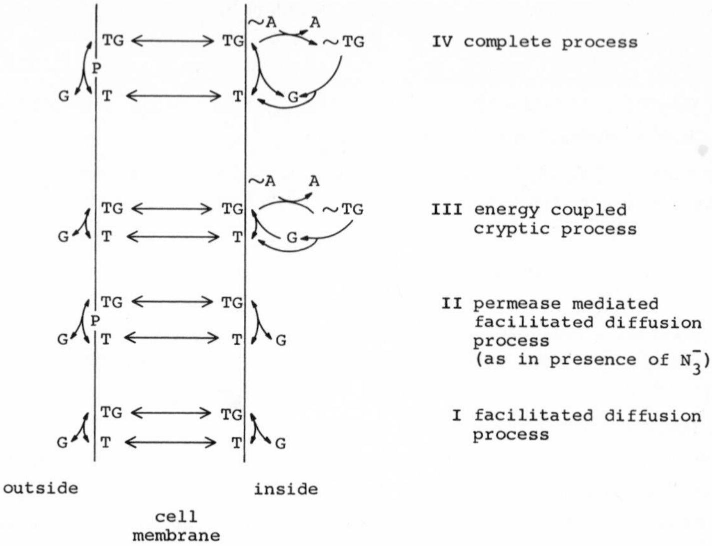

FIGURE 4. Model of the lac transport system proposed by Koch (1964, 1967). G = galactoside. P = permease (inducible, stereospecific, fixed in position). Several permeases of the same or different specificity may react with the same T. T = transporter or carrier element which crosses the barrier in unspecified manner with or without sugar. A = immediate energy source; reserves of A are not large. TG = "activated" transporter sugar. Chemical nature unspecified; although depicted as separate from membrane must be on or in membrane. There are very few or no pores, cracks, or fissures which may allow non-carrier mediated passage. Reprinted with permission of the author and publishers.

catalyzed reaction between T and G, both in condition II and in condition I. The rate of such a reaction would have to be fast, since exit of labeled sugars from permease-containing cells is fast. If the uncatalyzed reaction is fast, then it is not easy to understand why the rate of ONPG hydrolysis is very much faster in condition II than in condition I. Entry of ONPG in cells of condition I would be expected to be almost as fast as exit under condition II, but this is not the case.

THE M PROTEIN MODEL

The model proposed by Fox and Kennedy (1965) is of the second type, since it postulates a cycle of transformations of the carrier, and not of the substrate (Fig. 5). The carrier is the M protein, the product of the y gene. The model distinguishes sharply between two processes: (1) the facilitated entry of galactosides into the cell, and (2) their accumulation against a concentration gradient.

In *facilitated entry,* a molecule of β-galactoside in the medium combines with the *M* protein to form a complex of the Michaelis-Menten type.

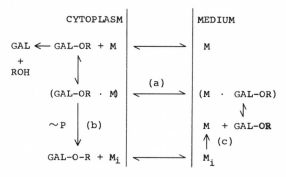

FIGURE 5. Working model of function of M protein in the *lac* permease system. From Fox and Kennedy (1965) with permission of the authors and publishers.

Thermal movement of the protein in the membrane exposes this sugar binding site alternately at the exterior and interior surfaces of the membrane. Recent studies by Hubbell and McConnell (1969) using spin-labeled lipids support the view that biological membranes are sufficiently fluid in character to permit rotational diffusion of this kind. On the inner face of the membrane, the complex may dissociate. If the sugar is a substrate for the enzyme β-galactosidase, its continuous hydrolysis by the enzyme leads to a substantial flow of galactoside from the medium into the cell. This process is not dependent upon coupled sources of metabolic energy. Since there is a large excess of β-galactosidase in fully-induced, wild-type cells, the transport process [step (a) in Fig. 5] is rate-making. ONPG hydrolysis in intact azide-poisoned cells would thus be transport-limited and according to this model, be dependent only on functional M protein.

In the *accumulation process*, the galactoside M complex on the inner face of the membrane may undergo a reaction, indicated as Step (b) of Fig. 5, in which the M protein is converted to an altered form, M_i, with greatly reduced affinity for galactosides. This transformation is coupled to sources of metabolic energy. On the external face of the membrane, the form M_i is converted once again to the M form in reaction (c) which may not require metabolic energy. The transport cycle then continues. The asymmetry of binding of galactoside by the M protein on the exterior as compared to the interior membrane is the primary cause of the internal accumulation of the galactoside.

This model differs from those proposed by Kepes (1960) and Koch (1964, 1967) in that it does not involve a generalized sugar carrier substance or transporter: the sugar binds directly to the M protein. To this extent the results of direct binding tests (Tables 4 and 5) are consistent with the M protein model.

The postulate that mediated entry and exit are the result of thermal diffusion of the carrier molecule seems to be the simplest possible hypothesis. The viscosity of the membrane phase must be markedly affected by the specific composition of its lipids. The viscosity (and hence the frictional coefficient limiting rotational diffusion) may be expected to undergo abrupt transitions at temperature intervals in which the lipids "set" or solidify. The observed changes with temperature in the rate of the mediated entry of ONPG into energy-poisoned cells are in general consistent with such a view, but quantitative correlations are not possible.

A major weakness of the M protein model is that the required cycle of transformations of the M protein has not been demonstrated in a cell-free system. If the transformations involve only alterations in the conformation of the protein, these may prove exceedingly difficult to detect. The development of in vitro binding assays may be of some help in this regard.

GRADIENT COUPLING AND THE ACCUMULATION OF SUGARS AND OTHER METABOLITES IN ANIMAL TISSUES

The fundamental role of the sodium pump in driving other coupled transport systems in animal tissues has been pointed out by Curran (1965) and by Crane (1965). There is evidence, reviewed by Crane (1968) that the up-hill concentration of amino acids, sugars, and other metabolites such as norepinephrine, by various tissues is dependent upon sodium transport. Crane (1968) has developed a general model for such *gradient coupling* (Fig. 6).

The up-hill accumulation of sugars by means of gradient coupling requires a carrier with affinity both for sugar molecules and for sodium ions. When the carrier binds sodium, its affinity for sugar is greatly increased. On the external face of the membrane, the carrier is saturated with sodium, since the content of sodium in extracellular fluids is high, and the carrier binds sugar with high affinity. On the inner face of the membrane, the sodium content is low, because of the efficient operation of the pump which continually removes sodium and replaces it with potassium. Hence the carrier on the interior of the membrane has little affinity for sugar, and an inward, up-hill flow of sugar takes place, driven by the outward pumping of sodium.

The gradient coupling model has many features which make it an attractive general solution for the problem of up-hill accumulation of any metabolite which does not undergo metabolism during transport. It is economical, since it requires that the cell have only one primary pump which will create a gradient to which the flow of other metabolites can be coupled. In the case of the systems in animal tissues reviewed by Crane (1968), the gradient coupling model is supported by considerable bio-

CELL MEMBRANE

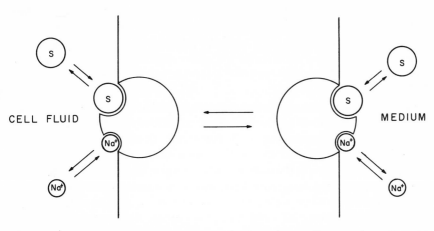

CELL FLUID   MEDIUM

FIGURE 6. Gradient coupling model of Crane. Carriers of a gradient couples system are postulated to have not one but two specific sites. One of these may bind sugars, amino acids or other metabolites. The other binds a specific ion. In the systems in animal tissues so far studied, this ion is the sodium ion. From Crane (1968) with permission of the author and publishers.

chemical evidence. Its relevance to bacterial permeases deserves serious consideration.

In *E. coli,* there is no evidence that the transport of sodium is a process of primary physiological function. The transport of potassium and the maintenance of a high internal potassium concentration are essential, however (Lubin, 1964). The concentration of galactosides by *E. coli* takes place even with high external concentrations of potassium, i.e., under conditions in which no potassium gradient exists, making it very unlikely that the *lac* permease is coupled to a potassium gradient. Gradient coupling in bacteria (if it exists) may perhaps be linked to the transport of hydrogen ions, which is probably a universal cellular process. Pavlasova and Harold (1969) measured the flow of hydrogen ions into cells treated with EDTA and valinomycin, an antibiotic which makes the cell membranes more permeable to potassium. [*E. coli* is ordinarily insensitive to valinomycin, but previous treatment with EDTA by the procedure of Leive (1968) induces sensitivity to the antibiotic.] Under these conditions (which are rather far removed from the physiological), uncoupling agents markedly increased the passage of hydrogen ions into the cells. The authors interpret this result as offering some support for the chemiosmotic hypothesis of Mitchell (1966) according to which a proton gradient across the membrane may be the primary source of energy for driving up-hill transport processes, and for ATP production. However, this interpretation of the mode of action of uncoupling agents has been vigorously challenged by Chance et al. (1967), who conclude that there is little evidence for the dissipation of a measurable proton gradient upon the addition of uncoupling agents to mitochondria.

ACKNOWLEDGMENTS

It is a pleasure to acknowledge the contributions of the following collaborators who worked on the lactose transport system in the author's laboratory: Drs. J. B. Armstrong, J. R. Carter, Jr., C. F. Fox, T. H. D. Jones, G. A. Scarborough, E. Schillinger, A. Tarlov, and Miss M. K. Rumley.

Experimental work in the author's laboratory on the *lac* permease system has been supported by grants from the U. S. Public Health Service, National Institute of Neurological Diseases and Blindness (NB-02946), General Medical Sciences (GM-13952) and the Life Insurance Medical Research Foundation.

REFERENCES

ASCENSIO, C., G. AVIGAD, and B. L. HORECKER. 1963. Preferential galactose utilization in a mutant strain of *E. coli*. Arch. Biochem. Biophys. *103:* 299.

BONIFACE, J. and A. L. KOCH. 1967. The interaction between permeases as a tool to find their relationship on the membrane. Biochim. Biophys. Acta *135:* 756.

BURSTEIN, C. 1968. Ph.D. thesis, Paris.

BUTTIN, G. 1968. Les systemes enzymatiques inductibles du metabolisme des oses chez *Escherichia coli*. Adv. Enzymol. *30:* 81.

CARTER, J. R., Jr., C. F. FOX, and E. P. KENNEDY. 1968. Interaction of sugars with the membrane protein component of the lactose transport system of *Escherichia coli*. Proc. Nat. Acad. Sci. *60:* 725.

CAVARI, B. Z., Y. AVI-DOR, and N. GROSSOWICZ. 1967. Effect of carbonyl cyanide *m*-chlorophenylhydrazone on respiration and respiration-dependent phosphorylation in *Escherichia coli*. Biochem. J. *103:* 601.

CHANCE, B., C. P. LEE, and L. MELA. 1967. Control and conservation of energy in the cytochrome chain. Fed. Proc. *26:* 1341.

COHEN, G. N. and J. MONOD. 1957. Bacterial permeases. Bacteriol. Rev. *21:* 169.

COHEN, G. N. and H. V. RICKENBERG. 1955. Étude directe de la fixation d'un inducteur de la β-galactosidase par les cellules d'*Escherichia coli*. Compt. Rend. *240:* 466.

COHN, M. and K. HORIBATA. 1959. Analysis of the differentiation and of the heterogeneity within a population of *Escherichia coli* undergoing induced β-galactosidase synthesis. J. Bacteriol. *78:* 613.

CRANE, R. K. 1965. Na^+-dependent transport in the intestine and other animal tissues. Fed. Proc. *24:* 1000.

———. 1968. Gradient coupling and the membrane transport of water soluble compounds: A general biochemical mechanism. *In* H. Peeters [ed.] Protides of the Biological Fluids (Proceedings of the XVth Annual Colloquim, Brugge, Belgium 1967). Elsevier Publishing Co., Amsterdam.

CURRAN, P. F. 1965. Ion transport in intestine and its coupling to other transport processes. Fed. Proc. *24:* 993.

DREYFUSS, J. and A. B. PARDEE. 1966. Regulation of sulfate transport in *Salmonella typhimurium*. J. Bacteriol. *91:* 2275.

FIELDS, K. L. 1968. Mechanism of colicin action and of abortive infection by bacteriophage. Dissertation, Massachusetts Institute of Technology.

FIELDS, K. L. and S. E. LURIA. 1969. Effects of colicins EI and K on transport systems. J. Bacteriol. *97:* 57.

FOX, C. F., J. R. BECKWITH, W. EPSTEIN, and E. R. SIGNER. 1966. Transposition of the *lac* region of *Escherichia coli*. J. Mol. Biol. *19:* 576.

FOX, C. F., J. R. CARTER, and E. P. KENNEDY. 1967. Genetic control of the membrane protein component of the lactose transport system of *Escherichia coli*. Proc. Nat. Acad. Sci. *57:* 698.

FOX, C. F. and E. P. KENNEDY. 1965. Specific labeling and partial purification of the M protein, a component of the β-galactoside transport system of *Escherichia coli*. Proc. Nat. Acad. Sci. *54:* 891.

FOX, C. F. and G. WILSON. 1968. The role of a phosphoenolpyruvate-dependent kinase system in β-glucoside catabolism in *Escherichia coli*. Proc. Nat. Acad. Sci. *59:* 988.

FRAENKEL, D. G., F. FALCOZ-KELLY, and B. L. HORECKER. 1964. The utilization of glucose 6-phosphate by glucokinaseless and wild-type strains of *Escherichia coli*. Proc. Nat. Acad. Sci. *52:* 1207.

GANESAN, A. K. and B. ROTMAN. 1966. Transport system for galactose and galactosides in *Escherichia coli*. J. Mol. Biol. *16:* 42.

GEL'MAN, N. S., M. A. LUKOYANOVA, and D. N. OSTROVSKII. 1967. Respiration and Phosphorylation of Bacteria. Plenum Press, New York.

GUTHRIE, P. and A. B. PARDEE. 1969. Discussion in a symposium on membrane proteins. J. Gen. Physiol. *54:* 93 s.

HERZENBERG, L. A. 1959. Studies of the induction of β-galactosidase in a cryptic strain of *Escherichia coli*. Biochim. Biophys. Acta *31:* 525.

————. 1961. Isolation and identification of derivatives formed in the course of intracellular accumulation of thiogalactosides by *Escherichia coli*. Arch. Biochem. Biophys. *93:* 314.

HEYTLER, P. G. 1963. Uncoupling of oxidative phosphorylation by carbonyl cyanide phenylhydrazones. I. Some characteristics of *m*-Cl-CCP action on mitochondria and chloroplasts. Biochemistry *2:* 357.

HOKIN, L. E. and M. R. HOKIN. 1963. Phosphatidic acid metabolism and active transport of sodium. Fed. Proc. *22:* 8.

HUBBELL, W. L. and H. J. MCCONNELL. 1969. Motion of steroid spin labels in membranes. Proc. Nat. Acad. Sci. *63:* 16.

ISHIKAWA, S. and A. L. LEHNINGER. 1962. Reconstitution of oxidative phosphorylation in preparations from *Micrococcus lysodeikticus*. J. Biol. Chem. *237:* 2401.

JACOB, F. and J. MONOD. 1961. On the regulation of gene activity. Cold Spring Harbor Symp. Quant. Biol. *26:* 193.

JONES, T. H. D. and E. P. KENNEDY. 1969. Characterization of the membrane protein of the lactose transport system of *Escherichia coli*. J. Biol. Chem. *244:* 5981.

KASHKET, E. R. and T. H. WILSON. 1969. Isolation and properties of mutants of *Escherichia coli* with increased phosphorylation of thiomethyl-β-galactoside. Biochim. Biophys. Acta *in press.*

KAWASAKI, T., I. MIYATA, K. ESAKI, and Y. NOSE. 1969. Thiamine uptake in *Escherichia coli*. I. General properties of thiamine uptake system in *Escherichia coli*. Arch. Biochem. Biophys. *131:* 223.

KENNEDY, E. P. 1969. Studies on the lactose transport system of Escherichia coli. J. Gen. Physiol. *54:* 91 s.

KENNEDY, E. P. and G. A. SCARBOROUGH. 1967. Mechanism of hydrolysis of o-nitrophenyl-β-galactoside in *Staphylococcus aureus* and its significance for theories of sugar transport. Proc. Nat. Acad. Sci. *58:* 225.

KEPES, A. 1957. Metabolismé oxydatif lie au fonctionnement de la galactoside-perméase d'*Escherichia coli*. Compt. Rend. *244:* 1550.

———. 1960. Études cinétiques sur la galactoside-perméase d'*Escherichia coli*. Biochim. Biophys. Acta *40:* 70.

KEPES, A. and G. N. COHEN. 1962. Permeation, p. 179. *In* I. C. Gunsalus and R. Y. Stanier [ed.] The Bacteria. Vol. IV. Academic Press, New York.

KEPES, A. and J. MONOD. 1957. Étude du fonctionnement de la galactoside-perméase d'*Escherichia coli*. Compt. Rend. *244:* 809.

KOCH, A. L. 1963. The inactivation of the transport mechanism of β-galactosides of *Escherichia coli* under various physiological conditions. Ann. N.Y. Acad. Sci. *102:* 602.

———. 1964. The role of permease in transport. Biochim. Biophys. Acta *79:* 177.

———. 1967. Kinetics of permease catalyzed transport. J. Theoret. Biol. *14:* 103.

KOLBER, A. R. and W. D. STEIN. 1966. Identification of a component of a transport 'carrier' system: Isolation of the permease expression of the *lac* operon of *E. coli*. Nature *209:* 691.

KUNDIG, W., F. D. KUNDIG, B. ANDERSON, and S. ROSEMAN. 1966. Restoration of active transport of glycosides in *Escherichia coli* by a component of a phosphotransferase system. J. Biol. Chem. *241:* 3243.

LEDER, I. G. and J. W. PERRY. 1967. Interrelated effects of cold shock and osmotic pressure on the pool of permease accumulated substrates in *E. coli*. Fed. Proc. *26:* 394.

LEIVE, L. 1968. Studies on the permeability change produced in coliform bacteria by ethylenediaminetetraacetate. J. Biol. Chem. *243:* 2373.

LUBIN, M. 1964. Cell potassium and the regulation of protein synthesis. *In* J. F. Hoffman [ed.] The Cellular Functions of Membrane Transport. Prentice-Hall, Englewood Cliffs, New Jersey.

MATSUI, H. and A. SCHWARTZ. 1966. Purification and properties of a highly active ouabain-sensitive Na^+ = and K^+ = dependent adenosine triphosphate from cardiac tissue. Biochim. Biophys. Acta *128:* 380.

MITCHELL, P. 1966. Chemiosmotic coupling in oxidative and photosynthetic phosphorylation. Biol. Rev. Camb. Phil. Soc. *41:* 445.

MONOD, J. 1956. Remarks on the mechanisms of enzyme induction, p. 7. *In* Enzymes: Units of Biological Structure and Function. Academic Press, New York.

NAONO, S., J. ROUVIERE, and G. GROS. 1965. Preferential transcription of the lactose operon during the diauxic growth of *Escherichia coli*. Biochem. Biophys. Res. Commun. *18:* 664.

NIKAIDO, H. 1962. Phospholipid as a possible component of carrier system in β-galactoside permease of *Escherichia coli*. *9:* 486.

NOSSAL, N. G. and L. A. HEPPEL. 1966. The release of enzymes by osmotic shock from *Escherichia coli* in exponential phase. J. Biol. Chem. *241:* 3055.

NOVICK, A. and M. WEINER. 1957. All or none induction and permease system. Proc. Nat. Acad. Sci. *43:* 553.

PARDEE, A. B. 1957. An inducible mechanism for accumulation of melibiose in *Escherichia coli*. J. Bacteriol. *73:* 376.

————. 1968. Membrane transport proteins. Science *162:* 632.

PAVLASOVA, E. and F. M. HAROLD. 1969. Energy coupling in the transport of β-galactosides by *Escherichia coli:* Effect of proton conductors. J. Bacteriol. *98:* 198.

PRESTIDGE, L. S. and A. B. PARDEE. 1965. A second permease for methyl-thio-β-galactoside in *E. coli*. Biochim. Biophys. Acta *100:* 591.

RICKENBERG, H. W., G. N. COHEN, G. BUTTIN, and J. MONOD. 1956. La galactoside-perméase d'*Escherichia coli*. Ann. Inst. Past. *91:* 829.

ROBBIE, J. P. and T. H. WILSON. 1969. Transmembrane effects of β-galactosides on thiomethyl-β-galactoside transport in *Escherichia coli*. Biochim. Biophys. Acta *173:* 234.

ROSEMAN, S. 1969. The transport of carbohydrates by a bacterial phosphotransferase reaction. J. Gen. Physiol. *54:* 138 s.

ROSENBERG, T. and W. WILBRANDT. 1957. Uphill transport induced by counterflow. J. Gen. Physiol. *41:* 289.

ROTMAN, B. 1959. Separate permeases for the accumulation of methyl-β-D-galactoside and methyl-β-D-thiogalactoside in *Escherichia coli*. Biochim. Biophys. Acta *32:* 599.

ROTMAN, B., A. K. GANESAN, and R. GUZMAN. 1968. Transport systems for galactosides in *Escherichia coli*. J. Mol. Biol. *36:* 247.

ROTMAN, B. and J. RADOJKOVIC. 1964. Galactose transport in *Escherichia coli*. The mechanism underlying the retention of intracellular galactose. J. Biol. Chem. *239:* 3153.

SCARBOROUGH, G. A., M. K. RUMLEY, and E. P. KENNEDY. 1968. The function of adenosine 5'-triphosphate in the lactose transport system of *E. coli*. Proc. Nat. Acad. Sci. *60:* 951.

SCHEUCH, D., C. KAHRIG, E. OCKEL, C. WAGENKNECHT, and S. M. RAPOPORT. 1961. Role of glutathione and of a self-stabilizing chain of SH-enzymes and substrates in the metabolic regulation of erythrocytes. Nature *190:* 631.

SENEZ, J. C. 1962. Some considerations of the energetics of bacterial growth. Bacteriol. Rev. *26:* 95.

SHAPIRO, A. L., E. VIÑUELA, and J. V. MAIZEL, Jr. 1967. Molecular weight estimation of polypeptide chains by electrophoresis in SDS-polyacrylamide gels. Biochem. Biophys. Res. Commun. *28:* 815.

SIMONI, R. D., M. LEVINTHAL, F. D. KUNDIG, W. KUNDIG, B. ANDERSON, P. E. HARTMAN, and S. ROSEMAN. 1967. Genetic evidence for the role of a bacterial phosphotransferase system in sugar transport. Proc. Nat. Acad. Sci. *58:* 1963.

SISTROM, W. R. 1958. On the physical state of the intracellularly accumulated substrate on the β-galactoside permease in *Escherichia coli*. Biochim. Biophys. Acta *29:* 579.

STEIN, W. D. 1969. Discussion in a symposium on membrane proteins. J. Gen. Physiol. *54:* 93 s.

TANAKA, S., D. G. FRAENKEL, and E. C. C. LIN. 1967. The enzymatic lesion of strain MM-6, a pleiotropic carbohydrate-negative mutant of *Escherichia coli*. Biochem. Biophys. Res. Commun. *27:* 63.

TARLOV, A. R. and E. P. KENNEDY. 1965. The β-galactoside permease system and the metabolism of phospholipids in *Escherichia coli*. J. Biol. Chem. *240:* 49.

VAN GRONINGEN, H. E. M. and E. C. SLATER. 1963. The effect of oligomycin on the (Na^+ and K^+)-activated ATP-ase of brain microsomes and erythrocyte membranes. Biochim. Biophys. Acta *73:* 527.

WEST, I. C. 1969. The site of action of adenosine-5'-triphosphate on β-galactoside transport in *Escherichia coli*. FEBS Letters *4:* 69.

WILSON, T. H. and E. R. KASHKET. 1969. Isolation and properties of thiogalactoside transacetylase-negative mutants of *Escherichia coli*. Biochim. Biophys. Acta *173:* 501.

WINKLER, H. H. and T. H. WILSON. 1966. The role of energy coupling in the transport of β-galactosides by *Escherichia coli*. J. Biol. Chem. *241:* 2200.

———, ———. 1967. Inhibition of β-galactoside transport of substrates of the glucose transport system in *E. coli*. Biochim. Biophys. Acta *135:* 1030.

WU, H. C., W. BOOS, and H. M. KALCKAR. 1969. Role of the galactose transport system in the retention of intracellular galactose in *Escherichia coli*. J. Mol. Biol. *41:* 109.

ZABIN, I. 1963a. Crystalline thiogalactoside transacetylase. J. Biol. Chem. *238:* 3300.

———. 1963b. Galactoside transport and protein synthesis. Fed. Proc. *22:* 27.

ZABIN, I., A. KEPES, and J. MONOD. 1959. On the enzymic acetylation of isopropyl-β-D-thiogalactoside and its association with galactoside-permease. Biochem. Biophys. Res. Commun. *1:* 289.

———, ———, ———. 1962. Thiogalactoside transacetylase. J. Biol. Chem. *237:* 253.

ZWAIG, N. and E. C. C. LIN. 1966. A method for isolating mutants resistant to catabolite repression. Biochem. Biophys. Res. Commun. *22:* 414.

Chapter V

The Lactose Repressor

WALTER GILBERT

Harvard University, Cambridge, Massachusetts

BENNO MÜLLER-HILL

Institute for Genetics, Cologne, Germany

The repressor for the lactose operon has been the paradigm for negative control. The Jacob and Monod (1961) hypothesis proposed that control genes would make repressors which would turn off other genes. Regulatory genes, as distinct from "structural" genes, were to make substances that could directly affect a rate-determining step in the synthesis of the functional products of other specific genes. This rate-determining step defines a target for the control: a specific point of interaction for the controlling substance. Such a target, named an "operator," could be a specific point on a DNA molecule. The binding of a substance to the region of the DNA molecule that serves as an initiation point for the synthesis of messenger RNA clearly could block (or affect or enhance) the synthesis of that messenger. Alternatively, the target for control could be a region on a messenger RNA molecule. The binding of a control substance to such a messenger could easily be imagined to block the attachment of ribosomes and hence the synthesis of proteins. The term "bind" simply supplies a specific physical picture. As far as any genetic arguments are concerned, any biochemical process that leads to the same result would serve. The control substance could modify bases, achieving the same ends through a chemical alteration of structure. The isolation of several repressors (Gilbert and Müller-Hill, 1966; Ptashne, 1967a; Riggs and Bourgeois, 1968; Pirrotta and Ptashne, 1969) and the demonstration that the operator is a region on a DNA molecule to which they bind (Ptashne, 1967b; Gilbert and Müller-Hill, 1967; Riggs, Bourgeois, Newby, and Cohn, 1968; Ptashne and Hopkins, 1968) now has given an explicit biochemical realization to those suggestions.

The particular model for genetic control put forward by Jacob and Monod

93

(1961) contains two essential ideas: one is the concept of separate, specific genes involved in the control of other genes, the existence of specific regulatory genes; the other is the notion that the product of the regulatory gene, the controlling substance itself, will act as an intermediate to make a connection (a physical interposition) between a small molecule—a compound acting as a signal—and the target for the control. A biochemical realization of this second idea would be that the molecule serving as a signal could bind to the control substance to alter the affinity of the control substance for the operator. This proposal was a complete shift away from instructive theories of control, which require that there be a way in which the signal is like the act controlled: the enzyme called forth by the substrate (even formed upon the substrate in the primitive form of such theories), the antibody shaped by the antigen, or the sperm to contain a homunculus. The interposition between signal and act of a controlling substance, which interacts separately with a small molecule and the operator, permits the relationship of the small molecule to the enzyme evoked to be dictated only by evolutionary accident; there is no necessary structural relationship. The explicit mechanism that Jacob and Monod suggested, that the control should involve a gene product that represses gene function, is an accident of the systems that were analyzed originally. It is true for phage λ, the enzymes of lactose utilization, galactose, glycerol, the tryptophan bio-synthetic enzymes, and others, that the controlling gene makes a gene product that behaves as a repressor. (This has an explicit genetic meaning: in the absence of the control gene, if the gene is deleted for example, the structural genes run at full rate. In a genetic complementation experi-ment, a cytoplasmic product of the control gene turns off the structural genes. General reviews of the various systems are Epstein and Beckwith, 1968, and Dove, 1968.) However there are a number of other cases, genes *N* and *Q* of phage λ, which turn on the early and late functions of that phage, or the enzymes for the metabolism of arabinose and maltose, in which the structural genes will not function in the absence of the product of the control gene. These are examples of positive control, the regulatory gene product being necessary for expression. How such genes act is unknown. If such control is exerted at the DNA level, a positive control gene might make a factor (like the sigma factor, Burgess, Travers, Dunn and Bautz, 1969) that binds to the RNA polymerase and permits that enzyme to initiate on a new region of DNA, or make a factor that binds to DNA, to open it for reading, or act negatively to prevent a stopping of the reading of DNA by interfering with an RNA stop signal. Alternatively, a variety of steps at the RNA-to-protein level could be affected. In many cases, however, it is not clear yet that these positive control genes do not act in a more trivial way by generating or shaping a small molecule that acts to interfere with a repressor made by some still unidentified gene.

If the cell is to respond to a chemical signal coming from outside, a number of steps will intervene before that signal affects the synthesis of proteins. The chemical signal must penetrate, be concentrated, possibly be altered, possibly trigger the release of other chemicals which, in turn, serve as signals—each step requiring a specific enzyme or function and so requiring the product of a specific gene. Genetically, each of these genes can be altered by mutation, each such mutation can appear as a "control" or "regulatory" effect. Exhaustive genetic analysis can only suggest which control genes affect the transmission of the signal and which specify the actual way in which the process is controlled. Only biochemical analysis can ultimately prove the mechanism.

THE LACTOSE OPERON

Figure 1 shows a schematic genetic map of the lactose region of the *E. coli* chromosome. As described in detail elsewhere in this book, there are three structural genes: *z*, the gene for β-galactosidase, the enzyme that splits lactose into glucose and galactose; *y*, the gene producing a protein that is involved in the permeation (and active concentration) of lactose; and *a*, the gene for the thiogalactoside transacetylase, an enzyme which has no known in vivo function, strains deleted for the *a* gene behaving normally in all tests. These three contiguous genes are controlled together, the levels of the three products changing in a coordinate fashion. Such a set of genes is called an operon, and is thought of as being under the control of an operator.

Three controlling elements are shown on the map: the *i* gene, *p*, the promoter, and *o*, the operator. The *i* gene makes a controlling substance, a repressor. We know this through the variety of mutations that exist in this gene. The basic defining mutation is the change to *i⁻*: when no product

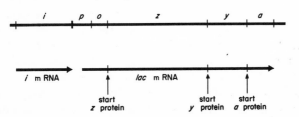

FIGURE 1. A Schematic Map of the Lactose (*lac*) Region of the E. coli Chromosome. The figure shows the order of the regions on the DNA making up the lactose operon. The products of the three structural genes, *z*, *y*, and *a* (β-galactosidase, permease and transacetylase) are synthesized coordinately under the control of a repressor gene, *i*, whose product works at the operator region, *o*, to prevent the synthesis of messenger RNA (mRNA) for the structural genes. The messenger for the *lac* enzymes is synthesized starting in the promoter region, *p*. The *i*-product (the *lac* repressor) is made from the *i* messenger RNA which is synthesized in the direction shown starting at an *i*-gene promoter at the far left of the gene.

is made by the *i* gene, if it were deleted, for example, then the structural genes function at full rate at all times; while in the wild-type (i^+) cell, the enzymes are made at only 1000th of the full rate in the absence of sugar. The crucial experiment that formed the basis of the Jacob and Monod theory was a genetic complementation experiment. If both a wild-type *i* gene and a defective *i* gene were put into the same cell, then the wild-type gene dominated and turned off, not only the piece of DNA adjacent, but also all other pieces of DNA carrying the lactose genes in the same cell. One infers that the *i* gene makes some product that acts through the cytoplasm to prevent the expression of the lactose genes. Thus, the i^- mutations are recessive constitutives, constitutive meaning that the enzymes are made without being induced by the sugar, and the distribution of these i^- mutations defines the *i* gene. The two other controlling regions do not appear to make any product; both are defined through mutations that have only *cis* effects, changing the behavior only of the piece of DNA bearing the mutation. The operator, conceptually the target for the *i* gene product, is a site for *cis*-dominant constitutive mutations. These o^c (operator constitutive) mutations permit a partial escape from the control by the product of the *i* gene, but in a complementation experiment only the structural genes physically adjacent to the mutation function. The promoter is defined genetically by mutations that prevent the expression of all three structural genes simultaneously. These mutations, p^-, occur outside the structural genes and affect only the physically adjacent genes in the *cis* position (Jacob, Ullman and Monod, 1964; Ippen, Miller, Scaife, and Beckwith, 1968). The order of genes is *p-o-z-y-a*. RNA for this operon is read in the direction from *z* to *a* (Kumar and Szybalski, 1969). It is generally believed, although there is no explicit biochemical proof as yet, that the promoter region provides the starting site of the RNA for the operon, read out as one piece, and thus that the p^- mutations change the rate of initiating RNA synthesis, for example, by being base changes that change the affinity of the RNA polymerase for this special region.

How does the sugar induce? The hypothesis of Jacob and Monod was that the sugar, or an analog of the sugar, would block the action of the repressor, prevent the attachment of the repressor to the operator, and so leave the genes open to function. The inducer might bind to the repressor in order to make it physically unable to interact with the operator. Such a model is supported by the existence of another class of mutants of the *i* gene, mutants in which the *i* gene product behaves as if it has lost its affinity for the inducer. Such a defective repressor should only be able to bind to the operator; a cell containing such repressors should never be induced. Such i^s mutations were found—mutations to a trans-dominant uninducible phenotype. Because the i^s cells could be induced at a 1000-fold greater concentration of inducer than was needed for the wild type, and because one could supply an argument based on the interaction between i^s and o^c in complementation to show that no more repressor was synthesized in the i^s than in the wild type, one would believe that these mutations were adequately explained as a loss of affinity of the repressor for the inducer (Willson, Perrin, Cohn, Jacob and Monod, 1964).

The earlier comment about the penetration and modification of a small molecule signal has an explicit realization in the lactose operon. The sugar lactose itself is not an inducer (Burstein, Cohn, Kepes, and Monod, 1965). The sugar must be acted upon by β-galactosidase, which as a transgalactosidase transfers the galactose to some (unknown) receptor to make the inducer. Thus the basal level of β-galactosidase is needed to provide the first molecules of inducer. A z^- cell cannot be induced. Furthermore, a y^- cell cannot be induced by lactose. The permease must be functional to keep a high enough level of lactose in the cell for the induction by the sugar to be maintained. Thus, if only the "natural" inducer were known, both z^- and y^- mutations would appear to have some "regulatory" properties. These complexities are avoided by the use of unmetabolized inducers such as IPTG (isopropyl-thio-galactoside), which cannot be split by β-galactosidase.

THE NATURE OF THE REPRESSOR

In 1961, the general view was that repressors would turn out to be RNA molecules. That thought was based on an explicit experiment, a chloramphenicol inhibition experiment (Pardee and Prestidge, 1959) which was believed to show that the *lac* (lactose) repressor could be made in the presence of chloramphenicol and thus was an RNA molecule. The experiment is wrong; many years later, it was shown that the repressor cannot be made in the presence of inhibitors of protein synthesis (Horiuchi and Ohshima, 1966; Barbour and Pardee, 1966). However, during that period, people talked themselves into the view that repressors were RNA molecules, overcoming the attitude that the easiest way of providing a connection between a small molecule and nucleic acid sequence was to use a well-shaped protein molecule, and ever since, one wondered whether the control molecule would turn out to be RNA or protein, or both.

Further reasons for believing that the active structure required protein were that one found a variety of temperature-sensitive mutations of the *i* gene, both thermolabile (i^{TL}) and temperature-sensitive synthesis (i^{TSS}) mutations (described in detail in Sadler and Novick, 1965). More convincing, however, were the isolations of nonsense mutations in the *i* gene (changes to the nonsense codon UAG which interrupts polypeptide synthesis), which produce an inactive repressor (Müller-Hill, 1966; Bourgeois,

Cohn and Orgel, 1965). Ultimately, the proof of the nature of this control substance waited upon its isolation and purification as a protein.

We (Gilbert and Müller-Hill, 1966) isolated the product of the lactose *i* gene by using only that one property most central to the picture of repressor control, that the repressor should bind to the inducer. The experiments were not biased by any requirement as to the composition of the repressor, nor did they depend on any model for its action. The inducer that was used is an analog of the sugar, IPTG, the best inducer known. The binding of radioactive IPTG to the repressor was followed by equilibrium dialysis: 0.1 ml samples of protein solutions being dialysed in an ordinary dialysis sack against a solution of radioactive IPTG. Although the interaction is rather tight, a dissociation constant of 1.3×10^{-6} M, there is so little repressor in the wild-type cell that the molecule must be purified blindly before its presence in the protein solution put into the dialysis sack can be detected (even directly in the bacterial cell, only a few per cent excess of IPTG can be bound). However, after an ammonium sulfate fractionation of the bacterial extract, we observed material that bound IPTG. This material could be purified and turned out to be protein. But, was this material, which bound the inducer, relevant? What is the proof that this substance is, in fact, the product of the *i* gene? Even though the affinity of binding is comparable to that which one would estimate the repressor to have from an in vivo argument, this is not sufficient identification. Only the variety of mutant forms of the *i* gene yields the necessary proof. The original tests to show that the binding material was the *i* gene product were that the material was not made in i⁻ cells (nonsense i⁻'s in which no gene product would be made), although all the lactose enzymes were being made at a high level, and that the material was not observed in iˢ cells, which differ from the uninduced wild type only by a point mutation in the *i* gene that abolishes the affinity of the repressor for IPTG. (The various mutant forms of the *i* gene were put into identical genetic backgrounds, so that unknown variations from strain to strain could not confuse the issue.) These tests, although successful, were negative in character; a better test would be to show that a modification in the *i* gene would yield a modified (but identifiable) product. We had a further mutation available, a mutant strain which induced more easily than does the wild type and thus, which had a repressor with a different affinity for the inducer. In vitro this mutant repressor bound IPTG with a different dissociation constant than that of the wild type.

More recently, a number of further proofs have appeared. Ohshima, Tomizawa and Horiuchi, 1968, have shown that temperature-sensitive mutations of the *i* gene produce an IPTG-binding protein that has a different temperature stability than does the wild type. Furthermore, there are mutations in the *i* gene that change the amount of gene product both as estimated from in vivo tests and as determined physically. The amount of repressor made by the wild-type cell is very small, about 0.002% of the cell's protein: about ten copies per haploid genome. (The amount of repressor follows gene dosage, rising appropriately in diploid and triploid cells.) Benno Müller-Hill (Müller-Hill, Crapo and Gilbert, 1968) sought and found mutant forms of the *i* gene which made more repressor (i^Q, Q for quantity, mutations). These were obtained by reverting a temperature-sensitive repressor (an i^{TSS}) to a wild-type phenotype at high temperature by growth on a medium that killed constitutives. Rather than revert the original amino acid change that led to the temperature-sensitive protein, the cell could mutate more readily to provide more repressor and thus to overcome the deficit at the restrictive temperature. This produced an $i^{Q,TSS}$ repressor, containing both the overproducing and the temperature-sensitive mutation. The i^Q mutation can be recovered separately by recombination. The original i^Q makes 10-fold more repressor. The mutation lies at the end of the *i* gene furthest from the *z* gene (at the left in Fig. 1); the *i* gene is read from left to right (Miller, Beckwith and Müller-Hill, 1968; Kumar and Szybalski, 1969); we believe that this i^Q mutation is most likely a promoter mutation, producing a 10-fold faster synthesis of *i* gene messenger.

The technology has now reached the point that the *lac* repressor is an easily obtainable protein. The very low level in the wild-type cell, 0.002% of the protein, has been raised more than 1000-fold. The i^Q mutation raised the level by a factor of 10, to 0.02% (or 0.05% in a diploid). To get still more repressor, we put the i^Q on a defective phage, a derivative of phage λ carrying the *lac* genes as a replacement of the late phage functions. This phage can be triggered by heat to multiply within the cell. Several hundred copies of the phage genome are made, but the phage is unable to lyse the cell. These multiple copies of the *i* gene make, in practice, about 25-fold more repressor so that these cells are harvested with 0.5% of their protein *lac* repressor. Very recently, Jeffrey Miller (unpubl.) isolated a new mutant, an $i^{Super\ Q}$ that makes 5-fold more repressor than does the i^Q parent. This is 50 times the basal level. When this mutation is placed upon the phage, cells can be harvested with 2.5% of their protein *lac* repressor. This is a yield of several grams per kilogram of cells. Large amounts of repressor have been made in Cologne, and work on the amino acid sequence is being started there.

The material is purified easily by ammonium sulfate fractionation, elution from a phosphocellulose column at pH 7.5, and, if necessary, a DEAE column step. The *lac* repressor is an acidic protein (but it has a basic region capable of binding to phosphocellulose at neutral pH). There is nothing unusual about its amino acid composition. It is a tetrameric protein, 150,000 in molecular weight, with four identical subunits of 38,000. It binds four molecules of IPTG. How does it work?

THE REPRESSOR BINDS TO OPERATOR DNA

Ultimately, to understand how a repressor works, we wish to know what the physical target is and how the interaction of the repressor with that target blocks protein synthesis. The experiments that are presently feasible are to examine the interaction of the repressor with candidates for the operator. One can show that the *lac* repressor binds specifically to the *lac* operator DNA (Gilbert and Müller-Hill, 1967; Riggs et al., 1968). Such an experiment is done most easily by using DNA from the defective variant of phage λ that carries the *lac* genes. This phage will yield DNA molecules of a uniform size, each about 30×10^6 in molecular weight and each carrying one copy of the *lac* operator. (This is about a 70-fold higher gene dosage than would be true for bacterial DNA. Nonetheless, a 3 γ/ml solution of such DNA is only 10^{-10} M in operators.) The DNA sediments at 40 S; the *lac* repressor itself sediments at 7 S. Thus if we mix radioactive *lac* repressor made by purifying the *lac* repressor protein from radioactively-labeled *E. coli* with the purified phage DNA, and sediment the two together on a glycerol gradient, then if the protein binds to the DNA, it sediments obviously faster, moving in a band with the DNA.

Such experiments can show that the *lac* repressor binds only to DNA carrying the *lac* region. If one uses phage DNA that does not have the *lac* region, the protein will not bind. Neither will it bind to denatured *lac* DNA. But far more specifically, if the phage DNA carries an o^c mutation, a point or small deletion mutation in the operator, that mutation will abolish or weaken the binding. Thus we infer that the protein is binding only to a single sequence occurring only in the operator (as defined genetically).

INDUCTION IN VITRO

What does the inducer, IPTG, do to the binding? It prevents the binding. Or more specifically, if the repressor is first bound to the DNA, then the inducer, IPTG, will cause the complex to fall apart. These experiments directly support the notion that the repressor, on binding to the operator sequence on the DNA, prevents the functioning of the promoter. The inducer weakens the binding to the operator, the repressor comes off, and the operon can function. However, we do not know explicitly that the repressor blocks (sterically) the attachment of the RNA polymerase to the promoter.

THE AFFINITY OF THE REPRESSOR FOR THE OPERATOR

We estimated how tightly the repressor interacts with the operator by asking how low a concentration of components could be used before the complex fell apart as the DNA moved down the centrifuge tube. That estimate for the dissociation constant is 2×10^{-12} M or tighter in 10^{-2} M Mg^{++} and 10^{-2} M monovalent salt. At higher salt concentrations, the affinity weakens to 10^{-10} M in 0.15 M KCl. These salt concentrations span the physiological range and yield affinities in the range of in vivo estimates.

Such in vivo estimates can be made by arguing that the rate of enzyme synthesis depends only on the number of operators free from repressors. If the concentration of free operators is governed by a mass-action formula:

$$[O] [R] = K [OR]$$

relating the concentrations of free operators and repressors to the concentration of complexes of operators with repressors, then one can estimate K from the statements that there are about 10 repressors per cell (and thus [R] 10^{-8} M) and that the basal level of enzyme synthesis is 1000th the full level ([O]/[OR] is 1/1000). The dissociation constant, K, would then be on the order of 10^{-11} M. (The argument depends on the basal level reflecting the maximal amount of repression. If the basal level is due to some escape process, then the actual affinity could be much higher.)

A more accurate in vitro approach has been developed and exploited by Arthur Riggs and Suzanne Bourgeois (Riggs et al., 1968; Riggs, Suzuki and Bourgeois, 1969). They discovered that the repressor can cause the trapping of DNA molecules on cellulose nitrate filters. In the absence of repressor, the entire native DNA molecule will pass through the filter. When one repressor molecule binds to a DNA molecule, that DNA molecule will adhere to the cellulose nitrate filter base. (Possibly, since the repressor protein itself binds to the filter, the DNA molecule is glued to the filter material by the repressor.) By labeling the DNA and varying the concentration of repressor, they can observe a saturation curve and estimate a binding constant. Their estimates are now that the dissociation constant is 10^{-13} M in low salt (0.01 Mg^{++}, 0.01 KCl, 0.01 Tris pH 7.4, 5% DMSO). One can measure such high affinities directly because of the amplification resulting from the size of the DNA molecules, the binding of one repressor being measured by the fixation of 30×10^6 mol wt of DNA (or 10^5 phosphates). Gene concentrations in the range of 10^{-14} M are easily measurable.

The in vitro and in vivo estimates for the affinity are so high that they raise an immediate question about the rates of formation and dissociation of the repressor-operator complex. The dissociation constant might be thought of as the ratio of two rates—the ratio of the rate of decay of the complex, k_d, to the forward rate of formation, k_f: $K = k_d/k_f$. The repressor has to diffuse up to the DNA, has to find a particular point on the DNA molecule, and might have to adjust its shape or wait for the operator to assume the correct shape before the complex can form. This overall process cannot go any faster than the repressor can diffuse up to the neighborhood of the operator. If we are generous with our estimate, the diffusion limit for a molecule the size of the *lac* repressor to hit the surface of a 20A sphere would be 1 to 2 times 10^9/mole-sec. Thus one would expect the decay rate to be about 10^{-4}/sec, if the dissociation constant is to be 10^{-13} M. A characteristic time for decay of 10^4 seconds (which is several hours) would be quite an appreciable time for the components to stay together before the complex falls apart, but this is an immediate consequence of the tight binding.

Is it possible to detect this slow decay experimentally? Yes, it has been seen by Riggs and Bourgeois (unpubl.) using the filter binding assay. They complexed the *lac* repressor to radioactive *lac* DNA. Then they mixed that solution with a great excess of unlabeled *lac* DNA. As the repressor came off a labeled molecule and went onto an unlabeled one, that labeled molecule no longer could be trapped on the filter. Thus by filtering samples of such a mixture at different times, they could observe the loss over time of the label that could be trapped, and this loss reflects directly the decay of the original repressor-operator complex. Their actual estimate for the half-time is 30 min, a rate of about 5×10^{-4}/sec. The complex is indeed slow to decay in vitro.

THE NATURE OF INDUCTION

This slow decay immediately raises a problem because we know that in vivo one can induce promptly upon adding the inducer, with no detectable lag before the inducer-triggered event. If the kinetic process of induction were for the repressor to fall off the operator and then to be caught by the inducer, then one should not be able to induce any faster than the repressor can leave the operator: a thirty minute delay. However, there is no reason to accept this picture unless we would wish to believe that the inducer and the operator use the same site on the repressor, for only then must competition be the method of induction. If the inducer and operator use different sites, then the induction can be a two-step process in which the inducer first binds to the repressor stuck to the DNA and only after does that complex dissociate. Rather than blocking the reformation of the complex, the inducer could bind to and change slightly the repressor moiety of the repressor-operator complex, producing a fast decay of the complex. Such a change in the decay can be seen experimentally in vitro. Riggs and Bourgeois (pers. commun.) have examined the decay of the repressor-operator complex in the presence of inducer and see a faster decay. There are also compounds which are competitive inhibitors of induction—molecules analogous to the sugar but which prevent induction. Such molecules like ONPF (ortho-nitro-phenyl-fucoside) bind to the repressor and, in fact, prevent the dissociation: experimentally one sees a slower decay for the complex. We can understand these effects by thinking of the bound IPTG changing the repressor so that its affinity to the DNA is less, the binding is weaker, leading to a faster decay. With ONPF the binding is actually stronger, the decay, slower. Since the inducer changes the decay rates, a ternary complex is actually formed through which the inducer pushes the repressor off the operator.

There is a catch in these numbers because they require that the forward rate of formation of the complex be 5×10^9/mole-sec. This is, in fact, a very high rate constant. Riggs and Bourgeois (pers. commun.) have also measured this rate directly by diluting the components to the level that the complex takes tens of minutes to form. They observe, over these long times, a rate consistent with this 5×10^9/mole-second figure. This rate is so fast that one begins to expect that the critical object, up to which the repressor diffuses to be eventually trapped, is some region on the DNA molecule appreciably bigger than the operator. The repressor may need to hit only within several thousand A of the operator and then can move along the DNA to find the correct region. This is not too unreasonable because the repressor has a general affinity for DNA, for the phosphate backbone. (This affinity in the case of the *lac* repressor can be enhanced by leaving out the magnesium ion to the extent that the non-specific binding to the phosphates completely dominates the specific binding to the operator.)

The picture of induction as passing through a ternary complex would argue that there should be an interaction between the repressor-inducer complex and the operator. One should be able to detect the interaction between the "fully-induced" form of the repressor and operator DNA. So far this has not been seen in vitro but in vivo we can estimate an affinity. If there is a residual affinity of the repressor-inducer complex for DNA, then, if there is enough of that complex in the cell, it will bind to the operator and keep the genes from functioning. This actually happens in vivo in those mutants that make more and more repressor. The i^Q is inducible only to 65% of the full rate; the $i^{Super\ Q}$ only to 25% (Jeffrey Miller, pers. commun.). The argument that the rate of expression should be proportional to the concentration of free operators can be used to show that the affinity of the operator for the fully-induced complex is a factor of 2×10^4 weaker than that for the uncharged repressor. In the wild-type cell, these numbers mean that the amount of repressor which is 10^3 times the dissociation constant, and which keeps the operator closed 99.9% of the time, after full induction is only $1/20,000$ effective and keeps the operator closed 5% of the time.

THE NATURE OF THE OPERATOR

We do not yet know the structure of the operator or the details of the interaction between the operator and the repressor. The experiments so far only show that double-stranded DNA is required—and thus that the interaction sees either the outside of the native helix or requires the participation of both strands. There is enough information available, visible in the large groove, to distinguish all of the base pairs from the outside, while the DNA is double-stranded. It is not necessary to separate the strands to see the hydrogen bonds used in the Watson-Crick pairing in order to read a sequence. How big is the operator? To the extent that this region is a stretch along the DNA to which a protein molecule the size of one subunit of the *lac* repressor (38,000 mol wt) or of the size of the λ repressor (30,000 mol wt) can bind, it can be only between one and two turns of the DNA molecule (35 to 70 A, 10 to 20 bases). There is a general argument as to how large such a region must be based simply on the realization that there are very few *lac* repressors in an *E. coli* cell. These repressors bind to one site on the *coli* DNA with very high affinity. They must not find other regions of the DNA with equally high affinity or they will be sopped up and unable to function. This means that the region to which they bind must be unique in the chromosome (3×10^6 base pairs) and thus must have *at least* the specificity of 12 bases. Thus, we might think of a region 12 to 15 bases long, 40 to 50 A long, associated with a binding energy in the range of 16–18 kilocalories. These are not unreasonable numbers to associate with one another. An interaction with this specificity, "seeing" 12 to 15 bases, must make about 12 to 15 contacts; to the extent that each contact yields between 1 and 2 kilocalories the energetics (i.e. the tightness of binding) and the specificity are commensurate. The change in binding energy involved on induction, a change by 2×10^4 in affinity, or 6 kilocalories is brought about by the binding of up to four IPTG's each one of which can bind with about 8 kilocalories. Clearly there is enough free energy available in the binding of the IPTG's to produce a distortion in the repressor capable of weakening its total binding to the operator by 6 kilocalories.

Phenotypic Complexities

There are two dominance effects in vivo that are simply explained in terms of a mixing of subunits of a tetrameric repressor (see Müller-Hill et al., 1968). These are the interaction between the i^s and the i^Q genotypes and the existence of dominant i^- mutations. The i^s mutation is a change in the repressor so that IPTG can no longer take the molecule off the operator. Such changes could be changes in the IPTG binding site, so that the affinity for the inducer was effectively abolished, as is the case with the i^s that was used as a control in the original isolation of the *lac* repressor, or they could be changes in the structure of the repressor so that the binding of the inducer-shaped ligand no longer triggers the change in the affinity for the operator needed for induction. (Molecules such as ONPF, or ONPG, bind to the repressor but do not decrease its affinity for the operator.) Clearly if there is in the cell a mixture of i^s and i^+ repressors, then the i^s repressors will bind to and cover the operators whether or not any inducer is present; this was the dominance observed by Willson et al., (1964). However, if an i^Q/i^s heterozygote is constructed, the phenotype is *lac* plus; such heterozygotes can be induced to about 25% of the full level. How is this to be understood? Even the great excess of good repressor serves no role after the cell has been fully induced—under these conditions all the good repressor is removed from the operator, leaving the operator open to be covered in turn by the i^s repressors present. The heterozygote with i^Q must contain fewer i^s molecules than that with i^+. This could be explained either by the i^s being repressed by the i^Q or by a complementation caused by the mixing of subunits. The first explanation is that the *lac* repressor should set its own level by some feedback control, the i^Q would have escaped such a control in *cis* but would exercise such control in *trans*, turning down the production of *i*-product by the normal *i*-gene. This control could not be through the usual inducible interaction, because IPTG does not induce the formation of more repressor. That this hypothetical control does not exist can be argued since the level of either wild type or i^Q repressor shows a direct gene dosage; in diploid and triploid cells the level of repressor approximately doubles and triples as shown directly by the yields on purification or as shown in vivo by complementation against o^c's. Thus each copy of the *lac* repressor gene seems to function independently and is not turned off by the greater concentration of repressor in the cell. The behavior of i^Q/i^s diploids, therefore, should be explained as subunit mixing: the i^Q allele will make a great excess of wild-type subunits; these will combine with the i^s subunits to make various hybrid repressors. Both the hybrids with three i^+ subunits and those with two i^+ subunits must be at least partially inducible. If the same subunit mixing occurs in the i^+/i^s diploid, there will still be enough hybrids with four or three bad (i^s) subunits to account for all the repression.

That there are dominant i^- (i^{-d}) mutations can also be attributed to the interaction between subunits. Although the original defining characteristic of the i gene was that constitutive mutations were recessive, a few years ago a further class of i^- point mutations in the i gene was found, which were later shown to be *trans*-dominant constitutives. These mutations, however, are recessive to the i^Q: ten-fold more repressor overcomes this effect. The i^{-d} can be interpreted as having bad subunits which go together to form an IPTG binding but inactive repressor and which can mix with good subunits to form hybrid, inactive molecules; the bad subunits distorting the good so that the molecule will no longer bind to the operator.

GENERAL IMPLICATIONS

The control in *lac* is exercised by a small number of molecules made by a gene that appears to run at a fixed rate under the control of a promoter changeable only by mutation. These control molecules, acidic proteins, interact with a very specific site on the DNA with very high affinity. These properties may occur again in higher cells, but the volume of the cell and the amount of DNA increases about a 1000-fold; thus the specificity and affinity should also increase a 1000-fold.

The control is simple. Negative control is simple because it is stripped down to the bare elements: the recognition of a specific place, a region of a nucleic acid, and the recognition of a ligand, a small molecule that will serve as a signal by binding to and changing the control element. Steric hindrance can do the rest—the recognition of a specific region by the control protein can be associated with a tight binding to that region; such tight binding means that that region is physically inaccessible to polymerases or to ribosomes. Positive control in general must call upon some further shape specificity in the control substance beyond these minimal requirements because the control substance must activate some step; it must bind not only to a specific region of a nucleic acid but also, say, to a polymerase.

The control is efficient. One *lac* repressor of 150,000 mol wt controls about 4×10^6 mol wt worth of DNA; the control material bound to the DNA is about 3% by weight of the genes controlled. Phage λ provides a still more vivid example of efficiency because 30×10^6 mol wt of DNA is controlled by a repressor of 30,000 mol wt, only 0.1% by weight of the DNA that is controlled. This is a better analog for higher cells: control through elements of high specificity but there, in the chromosome, in trace acounts. But not

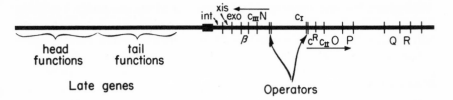

FIGURE 2. Schematic Map of the Genes of Phage Lambda. On the right half of the phage genetic map lies the gene for the phage repressor, C_I, and the early genes that function when the repressor is inactivated. One operon is read to the left containing genes N (early positive control) and a set of genes, *beta, exo* (early positive control), *cis* (excision), *int* (integration) involved in recombination and in the integration of the phage DNA into the host chromosome. To the right of C_I another operon is read to the right containing genes O and P involved in phage DNA replication. Gene Q turns on late function: R (lysozyme) and the other late genes.

only does λ provide an example of efficiency, the control of the many phage genes is more sophisticated than the simple lactose operon.

Eisen, da Silva, and Jacob (1968) have shown that there is a specific separate control of the amount of λ repressor. While the repressor is present it shuts off the two operators controlling the two early operons of the phage (see Fig. 2). However, once the repressor has been inactivated and the operon to the right of the C_I gene begins to run, no further C_I repressor can be made. The most recent experiments by Harvey Eisen suggest that the first product made by this operon is a repressor of the repressor ($C^{Repressor}$) which turns off any further synthesis of the C_I repressor. The phage can have two stable intracellular states which can be displayed if the phage genes that kill the cell are removed. Either it makes the C_I and never the C^R product, or it makes the C^R (and other enzymes from the right-hand operon) and not the C_I.

There are further steps of positive and negative control. The other operon under direct C_I control of the C_I gene makes the gene N product which is required for the high-level expression of all the early phage functions. The N product is a positive control element; if the left-hand operator is open, the N product turns on a further set of genes to the left, involved in recombination, integration and excision functions. If the right-hand operator is open, the N product enhances the level of gene products made to the right: genes involved in phage DNA synthesis, so that phage can multiply. The level of the N product, and of the genes in the left-hand operon, are controlled negatively by the C^R product (also called *tof;* Pero, 1970). This further negative loop turns down the level of recombination and integration functions and presumably produces some balance between these functions and those of DNA replication and maturation. There is a further separate control of the late phage functions. The *N* product also turns on gene *Q* which itself turns on the late functions—such as coat proteins, tail structures, and a lysozyme. Already in this simple organism control loops interact in a complex way.

ACKNOWLEDGMENT

This work was supported in part by NIGMS, grant #GM 09541.

REFERENCES

BARBOUR, S. D. and A. B. PARDEE. 1966. The establishment of β-galactosidase repression in the mating system of *Escherichia coli* K12. J. Mol. Biol. *20:* 505.

BOURGEOIS, S., M. COHN, and L. E. ORGEL. 1965. Suppression of and complementation among mutants of the regulatory gene of the lactose operon of *Escherichia coli*. J. Mol. Biol. *14:* 300.

BURGESS, R. R., A. A. TRAVERS, J. J. DUNN, and E. K. F. BAUTZ. 1969. Factor stimulating transcription by RNA polymerase. Nature *221:* 43.

BURSTEIN, C., M. COHN, A. KEPES, and J. MONOD. 1965. Role du lactose et de ses produits metaboliques dans l'induction de l'operon lactose chez *Escherichia coli*. Biochim. Biophys. Acta. *95:* 634.

DOVE, W. 1968. The genetics of the lambdoid phages, p. 305. *In* H. Roman [ed.] Ann. Rev. Genet. Annual Review, Inc., Palo Alto, Calif.

EISEN, H., L. H. PEREIRA da SILVA, and F. JACOB. 1968. The regulation and mechanism of DNA synthesis in bacteriophage lambda. Cold Spring Harbor Symp. Quant. Biol. *33:* 755.

EPSTEIN, W. and J. BECKWITH. 1968. Regulation of gene expression, p. 411. *In* P. Boyer [ed.] Ann. Rev. Biochem. Annual Review, Inc., Palo Alto, Calif.

GILBERT, W. and B. MÜLLER-HILL. 1966. Isolation of the *lac* repressor. Proc. Nat. Acad. Sci. *56:* 1891.

———, ———. 1967. The *lac* operator is DNA. Proc. Nat. Acad. Sci. *58:* 2415.

HORIUCHI, T. and Y. OHSHIMA. 1966. Inhibition of repressor formation in the lactose system of *Escherichia coli* by inhibitors of protein synthesis. J. Mol. Biol. *20:* 517.

IPPEN, K., J. MILLER, J. SCAIFE, and J. BECKWITH. 1968. New controlling element in the *lac* operon of *E. coli*. Nature *217:* 825.

JACOB, F. and J. MONOD. 1961. Genetic regulatory mechanisms in the synthesis of proteins. J. Mol. Biol. *3:* 318.

JACOB, F., A. ULLMANN, and J. MONOD. 1964. Le promoteur, element genetique necessaire a l'expression d'un operon. Compt. Rend. Acad. Sci. *258:* 3125.

KUMAR, A. and W. SZYBALSKI. 1969. Orientation of transcription of the *lac* operon and its repressor gene in *Escherichia coli*. J. Mol. Biol. *40:* 145.

MILLER, J. H., J. BECKWITH, and B. MÜLLER-HILL. 1968. Direction of transcription of a regulatory gene in *E. coli*. Nature *220:* 1287.

MÜLLER-HILL, B. 1966. Suppressible regulator constitutive mutants of the lactose system in *Escherichia coli*. J. Mol. Biol. *15:* 374.

MÜLLER-HILL, B., L. CRAPO, and W. GILBERT. 1968. Mutants that make more *lac* repressor. Proc. Nat. Acad. Sci. *59:* 1259.

OHSHIMA, Y., J. TOMIZAWA, and T. HORIUCHI. 1968. Isolation of temperature-sensitive *lac* repressors. J. Mol. Biol. *34:* 195.

PARDEE, A. B. and L. S. PRESTIDGE. 1959. On the nature of the repressor of β-galactosidase synthesis in *Escherichia coli.* Biochim. Biophys. Acta *36:* 545.

PERO, J. 1970. Location of the phage λ gene responsible for turning off λ-exonuclease synthesis. Virology *40:* 65.

PIRROTTA, V. and M. PTASHNE. 1969. Isolation of the 434 phage repressor. Nature *222:* 541.

PTASHNE, M. 1967a. Isolation of the λ phage repressor. Proc. Nat. Acad. Sci. *57:* 306.

————. 1967b. Specific binding of the λ phage repressor. Nature *214:* 232.

PTASHNE, M. and N. HOPKINS. 1968. The operators controlled by the λ phage repressor. Proc. Nat. Acad. Sci. *60:* 1282.

RIGGS, A. D. and S. BOURGEOIS. 1968. On the assay isolation and characterization of the *lac* repressor. J. Mol. Biol. *34:* 361.

RIGGS, A. D., S. BOURGEOIS, R. F. NEWBY, and M. COHN. 1968. DNA binding of the *lac* repressor. J. Mol. Biol. *34:* 365.

RIGGS, A. D., H. SUZUKI, and S. BOURGEOIS. 1970. The *lac* repressor-operator interaction. I. equilibrium studies. J. Mol. Biol. *48:* 67.

SADLER, J. and A. NOVICK. 1965. The properties of repressor and the kinetics of its action. J. Mol. Biol. *12:* 305.

WILLSON, C., D. PERRIN, M. COHN, F. JACOB, and J. MONOD. 1964. Non-inducible mutants of the regulator gene in the "lactose" system of *Escherichia coli.* J. Mol. Biol. *8:* 582.

Chapter VI

Transcription of the Lactose Operon in *E. coli*

GÉRARD CONTESSE, MICHEL CRÉPIN and FRANÇOIS GROS

Institut de Biologie Physico-Chimique
Paris, France

For the past ten years, the lactose system of *E. coli* has served as a reference model to study gene expression and its control in microorganisms. Most of our knowledge about the functioning of this classical system stems from pure genetic studies or chemical or immunological analyses of the enzymes coded for by the structural genes that compose the *lac* operon.

Relatively little work has been focused on *lac*-specific mRNA, in spite of the fact that much of our understanding about the regulation of the *lac* system would benefit from a clear picture about the mechanism whereby it is transcribed into messenger RNA in normal as well as in physiologically or genetically altered conditions.

This latter remark not only applies to the formal study of enzymatic repression mechanisms but to problems such as catabolite repression, polarity effects, role of the promoter sequence as an initiation signal for gene expression and possible coupling between translational and transcriptional processes.

The purpose of this chapter is to survey some of the general properties of the RNA transcription product, resulting from the expression of the lactose region in *E. coli* and to examine if, and how, we can correlate many of the classically-known effects at the enzyme level, with changes at the messenger RNA level.

PROPERTIES OF *LAC*-SPECIFIC RNA FROM INDUCED WILD TYPE

Numerous approaches have been used for detecting RNA corresponding to the *lac* region, some involving direct hybridization techniques, others taking advantage of the enzyme forming capacity of the preinduced messenger. Although this latter technique has been extensively used and appears particularly well suited for studying the kinetics of synthesis and breakdown of operon transcription products, annealing techniques are more direct. They can provide information on molecular weights and might potentially lead to isolation and sequence analysis of the pure RNA transcript.

EARLY STUDIES ON *lac* mRNA DETECTION

RNA produced in response to the induction of the *lac* operon was first detected in a series of annealing studies involving purified DNA's from *lac* transducing bacteriophages or from F'*lac* episomes. In work by Hayashi et al., (1963) for instance, the *lac* messenger was identified chromatographically among total pulse-labeled RNA from an induced wild type and distinguished from other *E. coli* messengers by virtue of its homology with DNA from bacteriophage P_1d1.

Attardi et al., (1963) used a stepwise hybridization procedure inspired from a former approach developed by Bautz and Hall (1962) for the purification of the T_4r_{II} specific RNA. Total pulse-labeled RNA fractions from an IPTG-induced or non-induced culture, as well as from a regulatory constitutive mutant, were first purified by zone sedimentation on sucrose gradients and they were adsorbed on agar gel columns containing heat denatured *E. coli* DNA from a *lac*-deletion strain. After suitable incubation at 63°C the non-hybridized portion enriched in material complementary to the *lac* region was assayed for its *lac* RNA content in a second hybridization step involving purified F'*lac*-DNA.

Table 1 recalls some of these former results. Most of the strains used as sources for *lac*-specific RNA were diploid heterogenotes in respect to the *lac* region. As can be seen quite clearly, while no more than 0.3–0.4% of F'*lac* complementary chains are present among total *E. coli* hybridizable RNA from a non-induced culture, this figure amounts to about 4% in an i^+ fully induced diploid, and is close to 5.6% in an i^- strain.

Different authors have attempted to estimate the molecular weight of the RNA complementary to the *lac* region. Using a MAK column, Hayashi et al. (1963) observed that the fraction which, after induction, can be annealed to P_1dlac DNA behaves as a high molecular weight component being eluted after the 23 S ribosomal RNA. Similarly Attardi et al., (1963) found for instance that pulse-labeled RNA from cells initiating a diauxic growth on lactose can be chromatographically resolved into a series of fractions, one of which was able to specifically anneal with total DNA from a Serratia-F'*lac* diploid strain and appeared to elute late from the column. Sucrose gradient fractionation has also been used to detect chains of highest sedimentation velocities among *lac*-specific RNA from induced

Table 1. Synthesis of *lac*-specific mRNA in inducible E. coli (F'*lac*$^+$) and in a heterogenote regulator constitutive mutant of the lactose system.

DNA in agar gel	First run				Second run			
	1000 × 74 DNA				F'*lac* DNA			
P^{32} RNA (cpm) Source of mRNA	Total applied × 10^{-4}	Eluate I (2 × SSC) × 10^{-4}	Eluate II (0.01 × SSC) × 10^{-4}	II/I × 100	Total applied × 10^{-4}	Eluate I (2 × SSC) × 10^{-4}	Eluate II (0.01 × SSC) × 10^{-4}	F'*lac* hybr. RNA Total hybr. RNA × 100
200 PS (F'*lac*$^+$) induced	19.8	13.2	2.10	15.9	8.50	5.77	520	3.84
200 PS (F'*lac*$^+$) non-induced	22.0	14.5	1.98	13.8	8.85	6.35	51	0.42
i$_3$ − 2310e (Fi$_3^-$) induced	24.7	16.7	2.60	15.5	8.60	6.23	750	5.60

For the labeling of messenger RNA 250 ml of each culture were allowed to grow up to an OD (at 420 mμ) of 0.75, in a low phosphate mineral medium. In the non-induced cultures glucose was added as a carbon source; induced cultures were grown in the presence of glycerol + 2 × 10^{-4}M IPTG. In all cases the cultures were exposed to 20 to 25 mC P^{32} for 0.3 − 0.7% of the generation time. P^{32} labeled messenger RNA from 200 PS (F'*lac*$^+$) was purified as described by Attardi, et al., (1963); in order to reduce the specific activity of any irrelevant mRNA which could interact with the other E. coli genes of the F'*lac* episome or with residual Serratia DNA, the labeled cells were mixed before extraction with a 5 to 10-fold excess of unlabeled non-induced cells, grown on glucose. In the case of strain i⁻ 2310$_e$ (Fi$_3^-$) the cells were extracted by the duponolphenol method without addition of carrier cells and total RNA was employed for hybrid formation. In order to adsorb out the "non-relevant" messenger RNAs the P^{32} pulse labeled RNA was passed first through an agar-gel column containing a large excess of DNA of strain Δ1000 × 74 carrying a deletion in the *lac* region. The material eluted by 2 × SSC was concentrated by ethanol precipitation and run through a DNA agar column containing partially purified F'*lac* DNA.

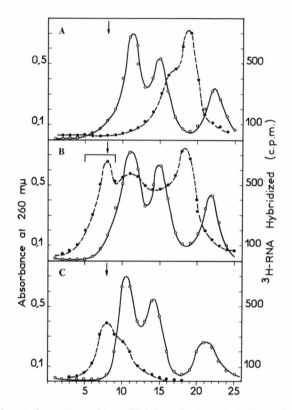

Figure 1. Sedimentation pattern of *lac*-mRNA from the *lac*⁺ strain Hfr H: Cells were grown at 37°C on 63 medium supplemented with B_1 and glycerol. When the optical density measured with a Zeiss spectrophotometer was 1 at 420 mµ, the cells were pulse-labeled for 2 min with 2 µ Ci/ml ³H uridine (16 Ci/mM) and poured on iced 63 containing 0.02 M sodium azide. Cells were lysed by the lysozyme freezing and thawing technique and RNA deproteinized by cold phenol treatment.

Tritiated RNA preparations were sedimented on 5%–30% linear sucrose gradient containing 0.01 M tris buffer pH 7.3 and 0.05 M KCl for 4 h 30 at 36,000 rpm, using a cold SW 39 rotor. After the centrifugation the bottom of the tubes were punctured and fractions collected. A portion of each fraction (100 µl) was hybridized with 1 µg φ 80 d*lac* DNA on membrane filter (Sartorius MF 50). Hybridization takes place in 2 ml 4xSSC at 66°C for 18 hr.

––•–– Amount of ³H RNA hybridized (c.p.m.)
––○–– Absorbance at 260 mµ
 ↓   determine the 30 S region in each gradient.

RNAs were prepared either from a non-induced culture (A) or from a culture induced by 5 × 10⁻⁴ M IPTG for 5 min (B). (C) depicts the sedimentation profile of purified *lac* mRNA obtained by ethanol precipitating the fractions around the 30 S region of a gradient similar to (B); cold RNA was added to the purified *lac* mRNA.

E. coli. Thus Guttman and Novick (1963), by mixing the C^{14} pulse-labeled RNA from an IPTG, induced culture with the H^3 labeled RNA from a non-induced one and centrifuging the mixture through a sucrose gradient found that the ratio C^{14}/H^3 remained relatively constant across the gradient except for a very sharp increase in a region corresponding to material sedimenting at 30 S. The presence of a 30 S specific component among the rapidly labeled RNA synthesized at the onset of diauxic growth and identified by hybridization was also observed by Naono et al. (1965). By using annealing tests with ϕ_{80} d*lac* as a detector (see next section) Contesse and Gros (1968) observe that the 1 min pulse-labeled *lac*-specific RNA from a 5 min preinduced wild type is in fact heterogeneous in size. As can be seen from Fig. 1, the centrifugation pattern from non-induced cells reveals the existence of relatively low sedimenting material (8-10 S). The pattern from induced cells is clearly different and chains of high apparent sedimentation velocities accompany the (8-10 S) material. Worthy of notice is the 30 S peak (a region shown by the arrow on Fig. 1). One likely interpretation is that the 30 S fraction corresponds to completed *lac* RNA transcripts while chains of lower size (around 20 S) represent *lac* mRNA in its growing state. Figure 1C shows an attempt to fractionate the 30 S RNA by a rerun on a sucrose gradient.

Although it has not yet been proved that the 30 S RNA actually represents the polycistronic transcription product of the whole, functionally active *lac* operon, this appears likely. A messenger RNA chain sedimenting at 30 S should weigh, according to Kurland's formula (1960), about 1.7×10^6 daltons which represents clearly more information than what is needed for the β-galactosidase monomer (130,000), even if a portion of the RNA chain corresponded to the operator complementary region.

In keeping with the polycistronic nature of messenger RNA made during induction of the *lac* system is the observation by Kiho and Rich (1965) that part of the nascent β-galactosidase molecules found in lysates from β-thiogalactoside induced wild-type *E. coli* are attached to long-size polysomes. By contrast, β-galactosidase polysomes from induced *y-deletion* or *y-amber* mutants are sensibly shorter in size.

DETECTION OF *lac* SPECIFIC RNA BY HYBRIDIZATION WITH ϕ80 d*lac* DNA LEVEL OF *lac* mRNA IN INDUCED CELLS

In many of the studies, to be described below, the synthesis of mRNA complementary to the *lac* region of *E. coli* has been followed by hybridizing pulse-labeled RNA from IPTG-induced cells with the alkali denatured DNA prepared from a purified suspension of the transducing phage ϕ_{80} d*lac*. The nitrocellulose filter technique described by Gillespie and Spiegelman (1965) has been used. Figure 2 shows typical titration curves of *lac*-specific

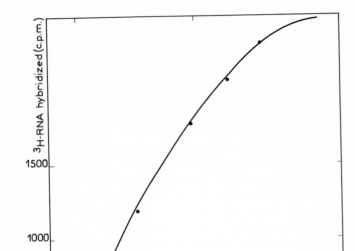

FIGURE 2. *Saturation of 1 μg φ₈₀ dlac DNA by 1 min pulse labeled ³H RNA:* The RNAs were extracted from two *lac⁺* MO subcultures.

———•——— ³H-RNA from a 5 min 5 × 10⁻⁴ M IPTG.
———o——— ³H-RNA from a non induced culture.

The cells were grown and treated as in Fig. 1; the hybridization conditions are also the same.

material in pulse-labeled RNAs derived from an induced or a non-induced culture of the wild-type diploid strain MO. At DNA excess, a 7- to 10-fold difference in the initial slopes is usually observed. Background values due to ϕ_{80} hybridizable material have not been deduced as they are very small (seldom exceeding 0.01%).

The ϕ_{80} *dlac* hybridizable RNA from a non-induced culture could represent, at least in part, the product from gene *i*—which codes for the repressor. However, it is unlikely that the figure of 0.05% which corresponds to the percent RNA hybridized before induction is entirely ac-counted for by the *i* gene expression since studies by Kumar and Szybalski (1969) show that, in *lac*-repressed cells of a homozygous diploid strain with an i^Q mutation, the fraction of the total pulse-labeled RNA which is transcribed from the *i* gene does not exceed 0.02% of the total pulse-labeled RNA. The figure corresponding to the i^+ strain used in our experiments is probably at least one half this value. Moreover, the pulse-labeled RNA from a strain carrying a total deletion of the *lac* region including the *i* segment still hybridizes to quite an appreciable extent (about 80% the level of an uninduced wild-type) with denatured ϕ_{80} d*lac* DNA. One is, therefore, led to conclude that the non-induced level of hybridization must chiefly reflect the constitutive expression of genes extraneous to the *lac* region of the *E. coli* chromosome and lying adjacent to *lac* in the DNA of the transducing phage.

If one takes this interpretation into account one can explain why the relative increase in *lac*-specific RNA consecutive to induction appears, at first sight, considerably smaller than the relative increase in enzyme activity which currently represents a factor of about 1000-fold the basal level (Gilbert and Müller-Hill, 1966).

One way to improve the annealing specificity (that is to reduce the contribution of extraneous genes) may lie in the use of specific DNA *strands* since Kumar and Szybalski (1969) using the purified *L* strand from ϕ_{80} d*lac* observe a difference of 60- to 200-fold in the amount of *lac*-specific RNA between induced and non-induced populations.

The recent isolation (Shapiro et al., 1969) of *lac* transducing phages of the λ series carrying part of the *lac* region *at the exclusion* of non-*lac* chromosomal material (λp *lac* 5) should permit even greater improvements in the *lac*-specific RNA detection. However, the best *lac* RNA detector should in principle be the pure *lac* operon DNA duplex, which Shapiro, et al., (1969) have succeeded in obtaining after suitable enzymatic digestion of heteroduplexes structures which result from annealing the H strands from denatured λp *lac* 5 and from ϕ_{80} p*lac* 1 DNA's.

By calculating the difference between the level of hybridization in fully induced and non-induced cultures the fraction of total pulse-labeled RNA which can be estimated to be *lac*-specific in normal induced cultures ranges between 0.4% (Attardi et al., 1963; Contesse et al., 1966) and 1.2% (Kumar and Szybalski, 1969).

In our hands the 0.4% figure does not significantly vary for pulse lengths from 20 sec to 2 min. To really appraise the meaning of this figure the hybridization efficiency of phage specific RNA using the nitrocellulose filter technique should in fact be taken into account.

ORIENTATION OF TRANSCRIPTION OF THE *lac* OPERON AND ITS REPRESSOR GENE IN *Escherichia coli*

By using the separated DNA strands of ϕ_{80} d*lac* phage in which, in the prophage state, the *i* gene and the elements of the *lac* operon are oriented with the same polarity as at the normal location on the *E. coli* chromosome, and by determining which DNA strand hybridizes with the pulse-labeled *lac* mRNA, Kumar and Szybalski (1969) have shown that transcription of the *lac* operon is counterclockwise. As schematized in Fig. 3 from Kumar and Szybalski, radioactive mRNA from *lac*[+]-induced cultures hybridizes only with strand L from denatured ϕ_{80} d*lac* DNA, that is with the strand which is transcribed leftward on the vegetative map of λ or ϕ_{80} and whose 5' terminus is on the left. Results from these annealing experiments are in good accordance with those derived from studies of pleiotropic mutations, which also suggest that transcription proceeds from the promoter in the direction of tfr A (Jacob, Monod, 1961; Ippen et al., 1968).

A similar orientation of transcription (namely counterclockwise) has in fact been demonstrated for all the *E. coli* genes tested so far (Kumar and Szybalski, 1969).

Since the *i* gene, which codes for the *lac* repressor is closely linked to, but not functionally coordinated with the *lac* operon, it was of interest to find out if its transcription was differently oriented or not. Two distinct approaches have been used to test this point. In the one followed by Miller, Beckwith, and Müller Hill (1968), *E. coli* strains were constructed in which

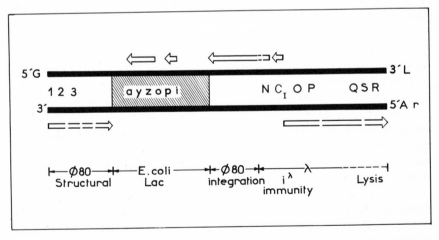

FIGURE 3. Map of the *lac*-transducing hybrid coliphage λ $C_{I\ 857}$ h_{80} d*lac* (ϕ_{80} d*lac*) (After Kumar and Szybalski, 1969).

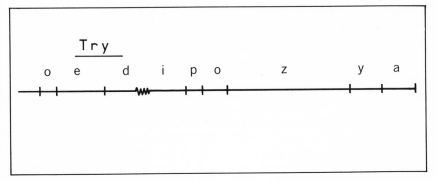

FIGURE 4. Diagram depicting how the *trp* operon may be joined to the *"i"* gene (after Miller, Beckwith, and Müller-Hill, 1968).

the right-hand end of the *i* gene (see Fig. 4) was fused by a long deletion to the left end of the *trp* operon. R⁻*trp* derivatives of such deletions were obtained and a diploid was constructed by introducing a F'*lac* episome which is *i⁺z⁻*. Upon derepression of the *trp* operon, the basal level of *lac* operon expression (as measured by β-galactosidase activity) was found to increase about twentyfold. This increase proved to be due to the derepressed synthesis of a repressor fragment which negatively complemented the wild-type *i* gene product of the episome. It was thus concluded that expression and, therefore transcription, of the regulatory gene proceeds from the *trp* promoter region in the direction of the right end of *i* (from left to right) or, if one prefers, with the same orientation as that previously determined for the *lac* operon. This conclusion was also supported by results of the mapping of the *i*^Q mutation, a mutation which increases the rate of synthesis of the *lac* repressor and is likely to reside in some sort of promoter segment of this regulatory gene. Accordingly, the *i*^Q mutation was found to map on the left end of the *i* gene. Kumar and Szybalski (1969) have arrived at the same conclusion, by means of the ϕ_{80} d*lac* DNA hybridization technique described above. Total pulse-labeled RNA from derepressed cells of a diploid strain with *i*^Q mutation was purified by a two-step hybridization technique so as to retain the H³ labeled mRNA corresponding to the *i* gene while eliminating the *lac* mRNA. The purified *i* mRNA hybridized prominently with the L strand of ϕ_{80} d*lac* DNA.

Transcription of the *i* gene is, therefore, oriented in the same direction as transcription of the 5 other genetic elements (*p o z y a*) which constitute the *lac* operon. This is not, however, the case for all systems since in the λ chromosome for instance, transcription of the C_I regulatory gene proceeds in the same direction as that of N and C_{III} (on the L strand) but opposite in direction to that of the x C_{II} O P cluster, whose activity is also directly controlled by the C_I gene product (Kourilsky et al., 1968; Kumar et al., 1969).

KINETICS OF INDUCED *LAC* RNA SYNTHESIS IN NORMAL STRAINS FOR *Escherichia coli*

Most of the conclusions pertaining to the kinetics of synthesis and breakdown of the *lac*-specific mRNA have so far been based upon measurements of the short-lived precursor of β-galactosidase that is built after induction and is rapidly converted into active enzyme molecules upon removal of the inducer.

PRINCIPLES AND RESULTS OF DEINDUCTION EXPERIMENTS

When saturating amounts of an inducer for β-galactosidase, such as IPTG, are added to an exponentially growing population of *Escherichia coli*, no increase in enzyme activity is detected until after 3 to 4 min (Pardee and Prestidge, 1961). Part of this lag period is due to the time required for manufacturing the specific mRNA for β-galactosidase, for converting its genetic information into specific protein monomers and for assembling the monomers into oligomers. That specific *lac* messenger RNA is formed during the latency is quite simply shown by the following experiment: a pulse of IPTG (4 × 10⁻⁴ M) is given and 20 sec later (at a time where no increase of enzyme activity is yet detectable), one dilutes the culture so that *no further* induction can be sustained. If we measure the enzyme activity in the pulse-induced population by the conventional ONPG procedure (Pardee et al., 1959), we see (Fig. 5) that, about 1 to 2 min later, β-galactosidase begins to be synthesized at an autocatalytic rate which decreases after 2 min to become negligible after 5 min. By supposing that the decreasing rate of synthesis reflects the decay of a relatively synchronized population of mRNA molecules one can plot, on a semi-log scale, the remaining synthesizing ability versus time. The exponential decay curve thus obtained allows one to calculate the half-life of the messenger: it is equivalent to 1 min. These simple pulse-induction studies, therefore, lead to a first conclusion: namely, *that soon upon repression release, the cells pile up a short-lived precursor for β-galactosidase, the metabolic unstability of which is very reminiscent of that of the whole messenger RNA fraction.*

Further support to the idea that the enzyme-forming capacity which develops upon induction can be equated to the specific messenger RNA transcript is provided by the fact that no such an increase in enzyme-forming capacity is observable in the presence of specific inhibitors of RNA

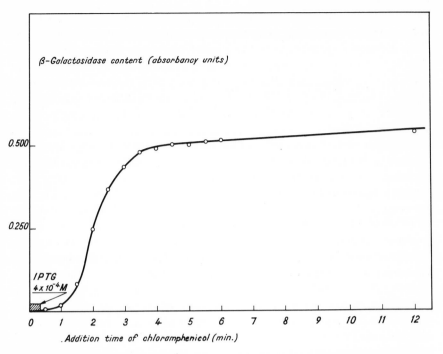

β-Galactosidase content (absorbancy units)

0.500

0.250

IPTG
4×10⁻⁴M

0   1   2   3   4   5   6   7   8   9   10   11   12

Addition time of chloramphenicol (min.)

FIGURE 5. *Characterization of the z messenger by its capacity to synthesize β-galactosidase:* A culture of strain ML 3 was induced by 4×10^{-5} M IPTG during 20 sec and diluted 50-fold in prewarmed medium. β-galactosidase synthesis was measured in 4 ml aliquots withdrawn at various times and mixed with 50 μg/ml chloramphenicol (after Kepes, 1963).

synthesis, such as proflavine or of analogs known to alter the coding properties of messenger RNA. This latter criterion has been followed quite closely by Nakada and Magasanik (1964). They found that if 5 fluorouracil is present during the induction period representing the lag before the first appearance of enzyme activity, subsequent expression of the enzyme forming potential (in a medium without 5 Fu) leads to very little β-galactosidase production as compared to the control sample pulse-induced without 5Fu; the decrease in β-galactosidase formation is partly compensated by the synthesis of a serologically cross-reacting protein. The presence of 5 Fu during the period of *expression* proper does not affect enzyme synthesis. In view of the miscoding resulting from the incorporation of 5 Fu into RNA (Bussard et al., 1960; Gros et al., 1961), it is likely that the enzyme-forming potential which is elicited by induction must be largely the messenger RNA derived from the genes induced.

Experiments involving differential labeling of β-galactosidase with radioactive or heavy isotopes and separation by the equilibrium density gradient centrifugation of enzymes molecules initiated during induction and after reestablishing repression (inducer removal) have shown that a large portion of the β-galactosidase activity expressed from the enzyme-forming potential involves chain initiation as well as termination. In other words, the enzyme synthesized after the removal of IPTG represents largely the initiation of new protein products and consequently reflects the expression of intact messengers rather than the finishing of half completed polypeptides (Fan, 1966).

Measurement of the *lac* messenger RNA from the pulse induction studies of the type described above has made possible a precise determination of its early kinetics of synthesis.

If one examines Fig. 5, it is clear that the plateau level of enzyme activity consecutive to an elementary wave of expression in a pulse-induced culture gives an estimate of the *amount* of specific messenger that was present in the population at the time inducer was removed. Figure 6 permits one to appraise the kinetics of specific mRNA synthesis throughout induction by simply plotting the plateau levels reached when IPTG is diluted at the

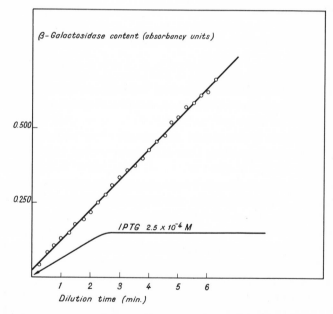

FIGURE 6. *Kinetics of "z messenger" synthesis during induction:* IPTG (2.5×10^{-5} M) was added to an exponentially growing culture of strain *E. coli* ML 3 and 0.1 ml aliquots were removed at various times and diluted in 5 ml prewarmed culture medium. Each dilution was toluenized 18 min after the sampling time and the final amount of β-galactosidase was plotted in function of the time of dilution (from Kepes, 1963).

times shown in abscissa. The curve obtained expresses the sum of the enzyme activity at the time inducer was removed and of the surplus activity developed upon full enzyme expression (20 min) (Kepes, 1963).

One very interesting and clear-cut conclusion from Graph 6 is that induction of messenger RNA synthesis starts without any detectable lag period. Genes for β-galactosidase synthesis thus seem to be turned on immediately at maximal rate by induction.

HYBRIDIZATION STUDIES

We have just seen that use of the enzyme-forming potential as a tool for measuring *lac*-specific RNA leads one to conclude that transcription of genes for β-galactosidase would be turned on immediately at maximal rate by induction.

However, a series of published data from Baker and Yanofsky (1968) and from Imamoto (1968) based upon hybridizations with the DNA's from appropriate transducing phages did indicate that derepressed transcription of another bacterial operon, the one involved in tryptophan biosynthesis, is not immediately at maximal rate but rather occurs *in steps*, as if a fixed period had to elapse between successive rounds of *trp* RNA synthesis.

Figure 7 shows still unpublished results concerning the kinetics of *lac* RNA synthesis, which also somewhat conflict with the data from enzyme deinduction studies described in the preceding section. In the present experiment, very short pulses of H^3 uridine (20 sec) are given at 10 sec intervals and, at the end of each pulse, the total *lac*-specific RNA present in the sample is estimated by the ϕ_{80} d*lac* hybridization technique. The maximal rate of *lac* RNA synthesis appears to be reached in three successive steps, each one being of sensibly equal height, and increases in rate occurring at regularly spaced intervals, namely every 50 sec–60 sec at a temperature of 32°C.

One way to interpret this rhythmic pattern is to suppose (as have done Baker and Yanofsky (1968) in the case of the trp operon) that one molecule of RNA polymerase (or a finite number of molecules) binds to the promoter region every minute and that, in the meantime, nascent RNA chains continue to grow. In such an hypothesis, the steady state expression of the *lac* operon would be compatible with three equally spaced molecules (or groups of molecules) of RNA polymerase moving along the length of the operon at the same rate, and in such a way that, as the first one entering would be ready to pass the distal region of the operon (or to be released), a new one would be ready to initiate a round at the promoter site.

At present, it is not yet clear why such rythmicity phenomenon is not detected when the rate of messenger RNA is determined by measuring

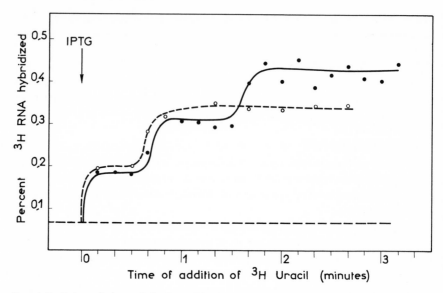

FIGURE 7. *Rate variations of the lac mRNA synthesis during the early stage of induction:
E. coli MO is grown at 32°C on 63 medium supplemented with B₁ vitamin, charcoal-filtrated
vitamin-free casaminoacids and glycerol. When the optical density is 1.0 the culture is
induced (cf. figure 1) with 5 × 10⁻⁴ M IPTG. From the induction onset, series of 5 ml aliquots
were pulse-labeled for 20 sec. with 20 μ Ci/ml ³H uridine (20 Ci/mM) and poured on 5 ml
frozen medium containing 20% sucrose and 0.02 M sodium azide.
The percent hybridization of each aliquot was determined, after annealing with 1 μg φ₈₀
dlac DNA ——●—— and 1 μg φ₈₀ EZ₁ DNA ——○—— (φ₈₀ EZ₁ is deleted for the y and a genes).
The background level due to non-lac mRNA was determined by two 20 sec pulse-labeling
performed before adding IPTG and is materialized by the dotted horizontal line. Each percent
value is plotted against the time at which labeling was begun in the corresponding sample.*

the β-galactosidase-forming potentials in cultures during the first minutes
of induction (see Fig. 6). A possibility is that the translation yield of each
individual messenger transcribed is not constant. Obviously more experiments will be needed to settle this point.

POLARITY AND TRANSCRIPTION OF THE *LAC* OPERON

Polarity [i.e., the reduced expression of genes from an operon distally
located in respect to a nonsense codon (Jacob and Monod, 1961; Franklin
and Luria, 1961)] has been the subject of considerable investigation during
the last years, both at the genetic and biochemical levels. Numerous
models have been proposed to explain the polarity effect (Martin et al.,
1966; Imamoto et al., 1966) and the reader will profitably consult Chapter
10 for general discussions on this phenomenon. In the forthcoming

sections we will restrict ourselves to the incidence of polarity on *lac* mRNA synthesis.

SYNTHESIS OF TRUNCATED RNA TRANSCRIPTS IN POLAR MUTANTS

Both Yanofsky and his coworkers (1966) (1967) with the trp system, as well as ourselves with the *lac* system (1966), have shown that gene expression in nonsense polar mutants results in the synthesis of *truncated* messenger RNAs.

Figure 8 recalls some of the previous results obtained by Contesse et al., (1966) 2 min pulse-labeled RNAs from 5 min induced cultures of various non-permissive *E. coli* strains, carrying "ochre" or "amber" mutations at various sites of the z or y cistrons, were prepared. Contents in *lac*-specific RNA chains were comparatively tested by carrying out hybridization saturation experiments using a constant amount of ϕ_{80} *dlac* DNA. The respective genetic locations of the mutated sites and the acetylase-forming capacities of maximally induced cultures are indicated on Fig. 8. Clearly all the hybridization curves corresponding to the z mutants, and one of those corresponding to the y mutants, display two linear portions with different slopes, the steeper one being the first. This tendency appears more pronounced when the mutations lie closer to the operator. Particularly significant is the fact that breakpoints are distributed in the same relative *order* as levels of acetylase production.

This has been interpreted as suggesting that mRNA populations, in the various mutants studied, comprise two classes of chains: some shorter than the full-length RNA transcript and others of the same size, or of a size close to the entire polycistronic mRNA. Low-size chains would constitute the prominent species and would thus preferentially anneal at low RNA inputs.

Zone sedimentation studies ought to permit testing such an hypothesis, since *lac* RNA fragments should be detectable, in addition to full-size messenger RNA. Moreover, the length of fragments should be related, to some extent, with the locations of the mutated sites in respect to the operator. That this prediction is borne out is illustrated on Fig. 9.

Particularly interesting is the case of YA 486, an operator proximal mutant producing 5% the maximal acetylase level upon induction; in addition to full-size mRNA (30 S)—and to the spurious material present before induction (8-10 S)—fractions with very low sedimentation values (3-4 S) have constantly been found. Preliminary purification of this low molecular weight RNA has been attempted. Figure 10 shows that B.D. cellulose chromatography can partly resolve the *lac* RNA fragments (which hybridize to ϕ_{80} *dlac* DNA) from non-specific material (tRNA-mRNA breakdown products) annealable with DNA from a *lac*-deletion strain. Such

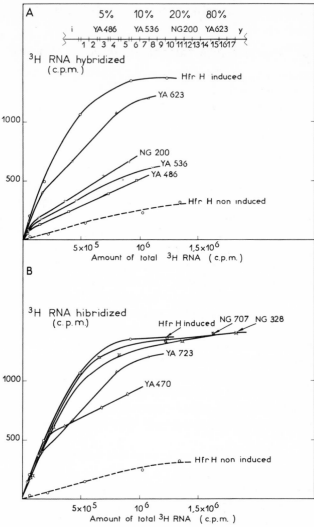

FIGURE 8. *Saturation of* ϕ_{80} *dlac DNA by pulse-labeled RNAs from lac⁻ nonsense polar mutants:* Each mutant was grown at 37°C on 63 medium supplemented with B_1 and glycerol. When the exponentially growing cultures reached an optical density of 1 (at 420 mμ), they were divided into two equal portions, one of which was induced by 5×10^{-4} M IPTG during 5 min. while the other remained uninduced. After this period each subculture was pulse labeled 2 min. with 2 μ Ci/ml ^{3}H uridine and RNA extracted as usual.

To establish this graph a correction was applied to the hybridization values such that all the curves corresponding to the non-induced samples would superimpose to the one given by the *lac⁺* non-induced control.

Genetic locations of the nonsense codons, and levels of transacetylase production by the z⁻ mutants are shown in the upper part of the diagram.

YA 470, NG 328 and NG 707 are y⁻ polar mutants and Hfr H is the wild-type control.

a material might be of value for analyzing the 5' proximal sequence of the *lac*-specific RNA.

Using another strain, NG-200, which bears a more distally-located nonsense triplet and synthesizes 20% the normal acetylase amount upon induction, the sucrose gradient pattern obtained suggests the accumula-

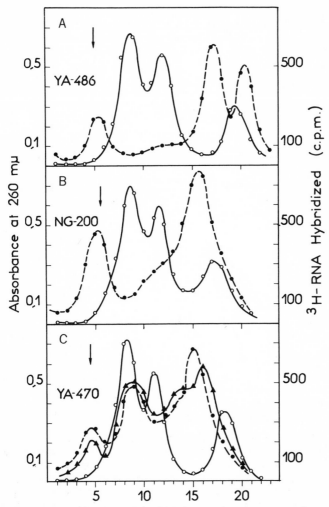

FIGURE 9. *Sedimentation patterns of lac mRNA from various nonsense polar mutants:* (Cf. Fig. 8 and Fig. 1.)

--●-- ³H-RNA hybridized with 1 μg ϕ₈₀ d*lac* DNA

--▲-- ³H-RNA hybridized with 1 μg ϕ₈₀ EZ₁ DNA

--○-- Absorbance at 260 mμ
  determines the 30 S region in each gradient.

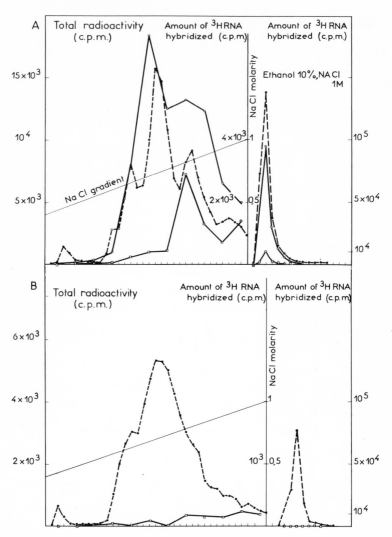

FIGURE 10. *B.D. cellulose chromatography of YA 486 ^{32}P labeled lac mRNA:* Two 300 ml cultures of YA 486 (one induced with IPTG and the other not) were labeled with 30 mCi ^{32}P for 4 min. The extracted RNAs were centrifuged on a 25 ml 5 to 25% sucrose gradient for 15 hr. at 20,000 rpm in a SW 25 rotor of the Spinco Model L ultracentrifuge. Fractions from the gradients corresponding to material sedimenting at 5 S or less were precipitated with ethanol and resuspended in a 0.01 M acetate buffer pH 4.5 containing 0.01 M $MgCl_2$. The two RNA preparations were passed twice through a millipore filter to get rid of poly-phosphates, and chromatographed on two benzoylated DEAE cellulose columns. Elution was carried out with a linear gradient of NaCl (0.4 M to 1 M) in buffer. After the gradient, each column was washed with a 1 M NaCl, 10% ethanol containing buffer. Total radioactivity was measured in each fraction of the eluate (---●---) and hybridization was performed with ϕ_{80} dlac (—□—) and *E. coli lac* DNA (—○—).

tion of 8 to 10 S fragments, superimposed to the non-specific peak fraction detectable before induction (Fig. 9B). Zone centrifugation pattern of lac-specific, pulse-labeled RNA from YA 470, a y polar mutant, which synthesizes 25% of the maximal acetylase activity is also interpretable on the basis of mRNA fragment production. A 22 S component which presumably corresponds to the z gene predominates while a small amount of 30 S chains is also detectable. Furthermore, hybridization with ϕ_{80} EZ_1 DNA carrying only the z gene and a little portion of y shows that the material of the two peaks contains sequences complementary to the β-galactosidase gene (Fig. 9C).

CASE OF THE EXTREME POLAR MUTANTS (0°)

Special mention has to be made of a class of polar mutants bearing a nonsense triplet in a region very close to the operator right-hand end. These have for some time been referred to as operator negative (0°) (Jacob and Monod, 1961), as no acetylase activity could be detected in

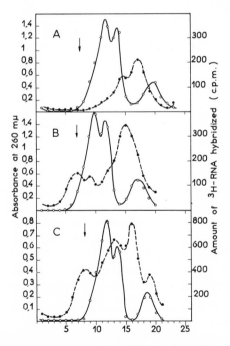

FIGURE 11. Effect of chloramphenicol on lac RNA synthesis in various polar mutants: (A)—Lac RNA sedimentation pattern in hyperpolar mutant cells, 2320_e (FO°$_2$), i⁻. (B)—Lac RNA sedimentation pattern obtained with the same cells, treated 2 min with 200 μg/ml chloramphenicol before labeling. (C)—Sedimentation pattern of lac RNA from YA 486 cells treated 2 min with 200 μg/ml chloramphenicol, after a 5 min induction period (compared with pattern of Fig. 9).

such mutants after induction. Further studies by Beckwith (1964) have proved that such organisms are of the suppressible class and do, in fact, represent extreme polar mutants of the z proximal region. Previous studies by Attardi et al., (1963) had shown that no *lac*-specific material was identifiable by annealing tests in the RNA from these steady state induced organisms. This has been confirmed by Contesse et al. (1966), who observed in addition that, under permissive conditions, such strains manufacture appreciable amounts of *lac*-specific RNA (Fig. 11).

Effect of Chloramphenicol on *lac* RNA Synthesis in Nonsense Mutants

Addition of chloramphenicol markedly increases the proportion of full length, *lac*-specific transcription products, among the RNA synthesized in induced nonsense mutants. This effect is particularly striking in the case of $0°$ type mutants: when 2320_e ($FO°_2$) (a diploid with two *lac* operator proximal mutations, one in the chromosome and the other in the episome) is pulse-labeled, the sedimentation pattern of the ϕ_{80} d*lac* hybridizable RNA does not significantly differ from that of a *lac*$^+$-induced culture (Fig. 11A). In contrast, when chloramphenicol is added for 2 min, after a 5-min IPTG treatment, the pulse-labeled RNA contains some ϕ_{80} d*lac* hybridizable 30 S material in significant amounts. This suppressible effect is also visible on strain YA 486 (Fig. 11C) (Contesse and Gros, 1968).

Distal Nucleolytic Breakdown of mRNAs from Nonsense Mutants—A Possible Cause for Fragment Production

Two clearly distinct mechanisms could possibly account for the prominence of RNA fragments among the transcription products from induced nonsense mutants: one could, for instance, hypothesize some type of coupling between DNA transcription and the translational movement of ribosomes along the growing RNA chain. Premature interruption in message reading, a process known to cause ribosomal release at the nonsense codon (Webster and Zinder, 1969), would then inhibit further progression of the RNA polymerase, past the mutated site. According to the other hypothesis, transcription would proceed to completion but a nucleolytic attack would trim away the region in mRNA which remains uncovered by ribosomes beyond the nonsense triplet.

If the exonuclease action overtakes the RNA polymerase before this latter enzyme reaches the beginning of the distal gene, transcription would continue with a sterile path and this would generate polarity (Morse and Yanofsky, 1969). If, on the other hand, the RNA growing point enters the beginning of the next gene *before* the endonuclease comes into play, a new stock of ribosomes would bind the newly-transcribed (internal) "starter" on the truncated messenger RNA and save the distal mRNA region from exonucleolytic cleavage.

To choose between the coupling or destroying hypotheses, experiments have been done, both with the tryptophan (Morse and Yanofsky, 1969) and the lactose systems (Contesse et al., 1969), the principle of which is as follows: lack of propagation of the RNA growing point beyond the nonsense triplet would imply that the segment in mRNA distal to the mutated site would very seldom be detected in hybridization tests, whatever the length of the pulse labeling. In contrast, would ribosome detachment not cause the RNA growing point to stop, but rather generate some nucleolytic breakdown of the unprotected region, important differences would be found in the hybridization patterns of *distal* RNA portion, depending on the *length* of the pulse. Results obtained with strain YA 486 are in favour of this latter expectation.

A culture of this strong polar mutant was induced for a time sufficiently long to get a random distribution of the RNA growing points along the *lac* operon region. The induced culture was exposed to pulses of H^3 uracil for different lengths of time (varying from 20 sec up to 3 min) and, at the end of each pulse, the ratio of ϕ_{80} EZ_1 to ϕ_{80} d*lac* hybridizable radioactivity was determined. Strain MO, a normal *lac*+ haploid, was similarly treated to serve as a control. It is clear that with YA 486, the shorter the duration of the pulse, the greater the ratio; whereas in the case of MO, the ratio does not significantly vary with pulse lengths (Fig. 12). Since one is dealing with steady state induced cultures and since hybridization ratios are sensibly equal for very short-pulse labeling in the control and the mutant, this clearly suggests that the distribution of polymerases among the whole *lac* operon region is sensibly the same in both types of strains. Thus, the occurrence of a nonsense triplet does not cause RNA growing points to stop at or near this triplet.

As the pulse length increases, greater RNA stretches become labeled. The observable decrease in the ϕ_{80} EZ_1/ϕ_{80} d*lac* hybridization ratio in YA-486 would reflect the increasing probability for the RNA region comprised between the nonsense codon and the next start signal to undergo a nucleolytic attack, with a reduced rate of transcription in this particular region.

It thus appears likely that, even in strong polar mutants, such as YA-486, transcription of the operon goes to completion but the segment of newly-transcribed RNA beyond the nonsense codon is susceptible to degradation. This would account for the large proportion of fragments among the transcription products.

The favorable effect of chloramphenicol on transcription in *lac* polar

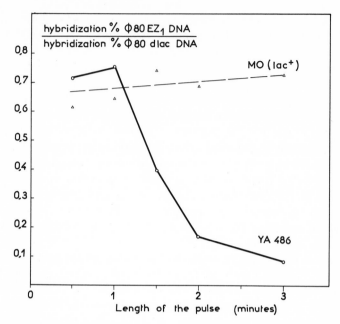

FIGURE 12. *Effect of pulse lengths on the hybridizability properties of lac RNA in a strong polar mutant:* Samples of a 20 min. IPTG-induced culture of YA-486 were labeled with 10 μ Ci/ml ^{3}H-uridine (20 Ci/mM) for various times and the percent hybridization ratios ϕ_{80} EZ$_1$ DNA/ϕ_{80} d*lac* DNA for each ^{3}H-RNA sample were measured and plotted as a function of pulse lengths.
The same experiment was done with the MO (*lac*$^+$) cells.

———o———o——— YA 486
———△———△——— MO

mutants and the increased proportion of long-size RNA chains would fit the degradative model just outlined. As is known from studies with starved amino acid auxotrophs (Morris and De Moss, 1966), the drug permits artificial ribosomal reattachment and such an effect would reduce the probability with which discharge of ribosomes at the nonsense codon does occur.

STUDIES WITH PROMOTER NEGATIVE MUTANTS

Induction of strains L$_{37}$ and L$_8$, two promoter negative mutants which synthesize no more than 8% the normal β-galactosidase level gives rise to only a very limited increase in *lac*-specific RNA (Fig. 13), (Contesse et al., 1969). Contrary to the operator negative mutant situation this marked reduction in RNA-forming capacity is not compensated by the

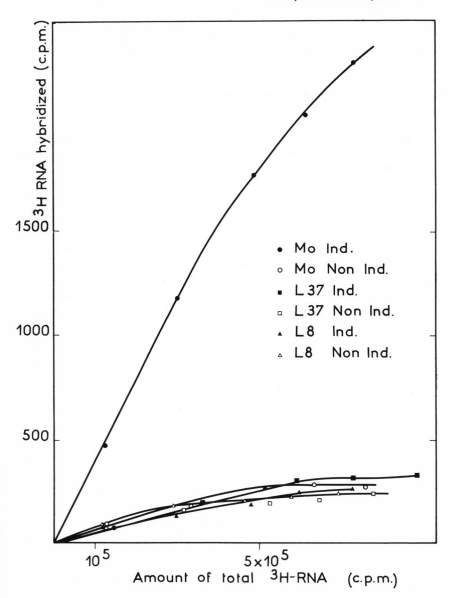

FIGURE 13. *Saturation of ϕ_{80} dlac DNA by pulse labeled RNA from lac⁻ promoter mutants:* Increasing amounts of 1 min. pulse-labeled RNA from 5 min. induced or non-induced subcultures were annealed with 1μg alkali denatured ϕ_{80} dlac DNA using the nitrocellulose filter technique (cf. Fig. 2). MO is the wild type, L8 and L37 are the promoter mutants.

addition of chloramphenicol. This leads one to think that the promoter mutant specific defect in RNA synthesis would reflect a direct transcriptional effect rather than accelerated message breakdown.

CATABOLITE REPRESSION AND SYNTHESIS
OF *LAC*-SPECIFIC RNA

It is well known that intermediary substances (catabolites), the production of which accompanies the metabolic conversion of energy-yielding compounds, act as corepressors for many *inducible* systems. This is the phenomenon of catabolite repression (Magasanik, 1961) of which the glucose effect (Epps and Gale) is a special case. Still little is understood about the precise molecular mechanism of this phenomenon (Magasanik, this volume).

Recent studies by Perlman, et al., (1969) and by Silverstone, et al., (1969) have shown that mutation within the promoter site of the *lac* region could generate complete insensitivity to catabolite repression. Insofar as the promoter can be regarded as the region in DNA where message transcription begins, this strongly suggests that catabolite repression inhibits initiation of messenger RNA synthesis.

Another possible break-through might be in an early observation by Makman and Sutherland (1965) which showed that *E. coli* cells grown on glucose synthesise less 3'–5' cyclic AMP than those maintained in a nonglucose containing medium. Quite significantly, it has been established that, in the presence of cyclic AMP, the glucose effect on β-galactosidase synthesis is in great part overcome (Perlman and Pastan, 1968; Ullmann and Monod, 1968). That cyclic AMP also restores the normal level of *lac* RNA in cells induced in the presence of glucose has indeed been shown by Jacquet and Kepes (1969). Moreover, Fig. 14 illustrates an unpublished experiment from Contesse, et al., (1969) in which the comparative levels of *lac*-specific RNA were measured by the ϕ_{80} d*lac* annealing technique, in IPTG-induced cultures grown either on glucose, or glucose plus cyclic AMP. While the presence of glucose reduces induction of *lac* RNA to an appreciable extent, this effect is in great part overcome by cyclic AMP. Recent observations from Pastan's laboratory reach the same conclusion and show in addition that neither glucose, nor cyclic AMP, do affect the decay rate of *lac* RNA.

We have data suggesting that the catabolite repression effect at the transcriptional level might not simply lie on a blocking of message initiation at the promoter site. We observe that, in glucose repressed cultures, *abortive* cycles of *lac* RNA synthesis occur with low periodicity. Synthesis of fragmented messages could possibly account for the decoordination

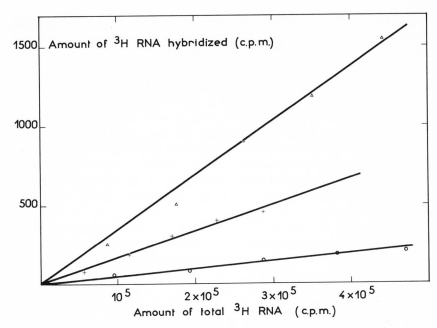

FIGURE 14. *Effect of catabolite repression and 3'–5' cyclic AMP on mRNA synthesis in 2 AY 36:* Cells were grown on glucose for many generations and pulse labeled 30 sec. with 4μCi/ml H^3 uracil (20 Ci/mM) after 5 min. induction either in the absence, or in the presence of 3'–5' cyclic AMP (5×10^{-3} M).

△ glucose + IPTG + Cy AMP
+ glucose + IPTG
○ glucose − non-induced

observed by Ullmann and Monod between the α peptide of β-galactosidase and β-galactosidase synthesis (1969) or between β-galactosidase and acetylase synthesis in catabolite repressed conditions.

STUDIES ON IN VITRO COUPLED φ_{80} d*lac* DNA TRANSCRIPTION

Many features of the *lac* operon transcription mechanism and of its regulation would be easier to study if an in vitro system was available. Important advances have been made in this direction due to the work of Zubay, who has reported on a DNA-directed cell-free system capable of producing β-galactosidase activity. The system uses ϕ_{80} d*lac* DNA as a template, a cell-free extract of *E. coli* bacteria, and the various components or effectors required for the transcription of the DNA and the translation of the mRNA. That such a system can successfully initiate transcription of the *lac* operon in vitro, is attested indirectly by measuring the first quarter of the β-galactosidase peptide chain, termed α, using the complementation system of Ullmann et al. (1967).

In some cases synthesis of active enzyme can also be made to occur even in the absence of the complementing protein, showing that the entire biologically active enzyme is formed de novo in the in vitro system.

In the presence of added *lac* repressor (Chambers and Zubay, 1969) the synthesis of α is inhibited about 2-fold but, quite remarkably, the presence of cyclic 3–5′ AMP both increases the synthesis of active enzyme and the effectiveness of repression which can then reach about 95%. It is postulated that cyclic AMP greatly improves the quality of transcription in such a way that a higher percentage of the transcription cycles are repressor sensitive.

Unfortunately, no work has as yet been published regarding the properties and mode of synthesis of ϕ_{80} d*lac* in vitro transcription products, in particular as far as *lac* complementary RNA is concerned.

CONCLUSION

Studies on the *lac* messenger RNA have by and large paralleled the investigations on the regulation of the lactose operon itself. They have proved to be of value for analyzing the early kinetics of induction and the mechanisms of phenomena such as the polarity effect or catabolite repression.

Much remains to be done, however, for improving the characterization of the *lac*-specific RNA or for studying its metabolism and the control of its synthesis.

So far, there have been relatively few attempts to purify the polycistronic product from the *lac* operon but the availability of DNA from new *lac*-transducing phage (λpd*lac* 5) and recent improvements of the DNA-RNA annealing procedures at low temperatures should permit such an approach. It would be of particular interest to undertake sequence analyses on the 5′ proximal region of the messenger in order to learn more about chemical punctuation for message initiation. This problem has much appeal in view of the large number of *lac*-promoter mutants which are presently available. However, it is likely that in vitro transcription of the pure *lac* operon DNA might more easily provide results.

We still know relatively little about the initiation step in message synthesis. There are good reasons to believe that message translation begins very soon after the message is transcribed (Kepes, 1967; Morse et al., 1968) and one interesting question is whether some type of mRNA ribosome interaction is involved for initiating (or reinitiating) message transcription in vivo. While it is clear that *lac* RNA synthesis can be induced in the absence of protein synthesis, presence of chloramphenicol (Nakada and Magasanik, 1964; Contesse and Gros, 1968), puromycin (D. Alpers and G. Tomkins, 1966), or amino acid starvation (Nakada and Magasanik, 1964), it still remains possible that reinitiation of RNA transcription is closely entangled with the very early steps in protein synthesis (Revel et al., 1968). Until the appropriate mutants for initiation factors are available, this point will be difficult to settle.

While the mean half-life of *lac* mRNA has been calculated with precision, using different techniques (Kepes, 1967; Leive and Kollin, 1967), information regarding the polarity of message destruction is still indirect: experiments by Kepes and by Alpers and Tomkins suggest that message breakdown normally occurs at the vicinity of the operator locus and sequentially proceeds towards the other distal end. This view is supported by Morikawa and Imamoto (1969) and Morse et al. (1969) whose studies indicate that, in the case of the tryptophan system, message destruction initiates before the synthesis of the operon specific transcript is completed and that it proceeds in the direction from E to A, that is from the operator proximal to the operator distal end.

Studies on in vitro transcription using DNAs from *lac*-transducing phages and the purified *E. coli* RNA polymerase have been somewhat disappointing so far. For instance, attempts to inhibit *lac* RNA transcription by highly purified preparations of *lac* repressor have always failed. The current belief is that this is related to the fact that during transcription of native DNA, from a phage such as ϕ_{80} d*lac*, other regions besides the *lac*-specific promoter are used as start signals for *lac* transcription. This view is supported by the observation that DNA from promoter mutants which synthesize no detectable *lac* RNA upon induction (Beckwith, 1969) can direct transcription of *lac* RNA in vitro.

What appears to be a much more fruitful approach to the in vitro analyzing of *lac* RNA transcription and its control is the coupled system developed by Zubay. In this system ϕ_{80} d*lac* transcription takes place in the presence of all the components required for protein synthesis as well as cyclic AMP. That active β-galactosidase can be formed and proves to be largely repressible must be regarded as an excellent criterion for correct recognition of the *lac*-promoter sequence by the RNA polymerase. It is not yet clear, however, which of the many component(s) present in the system is involved in the fidelity of DNA transcription.

ACKNOWLEDGMENTS

E. coli strains Hfr H, 2320_e (FO^2_0) were generously supplied by Dr. F. Jacob.

300 P and strain 2 AY 36 were gifts from Dr. A. Ullmann.

Dr. A. Newton kindly gave us the polar strains: YA 486, YA 536, NG 200, YA 623, YA 470, NG 707 and NG 328.

Phage ϕ_{80} d*lac* (λ_{857} h$_{80}$ d*lac*) was prepared from strain CA 5004 which was a gift from Dr. E. Signer. The strain EZ$_1$ (gift from Dr. J. Beckwith) was our source for phage ϕ_{80} EZ$_1$ (λ_{857} h$_{80}$ z$^+$ y$^-$ a$^-$). Doctor Beckwith kindly provided us also with strains MO, M 8003 (L8), M 8005 (L 37) and CA 8218.

The authors are grateful to Miss A. Malhié for her skillful technical help.

This work was supported by grants from the Fonds de Développement de la Recherche Scientifique et Technique, the Commissariat à l'Energie Atomique, the Centre National de la Recherche Scientifique, the Ligue National Française contre le Cancer, Fondation pour la Recherche Médicale Française.

REFERENCES

ALPERS, D. and G. TOMKINS. 1966. Sequential transcription of the gene of the lactose operon and its regulation by protein synthesis. J. Biol. Chem., *241:* 4434.

ATTARDI, G., S. NAONO, J. ROUVIERE, F. JACOB, and F. GROS. 1963. Production of messenger RNA and regulation of protein synthesis. Cold Spring Harbor Symp. Quant. Biol. *28:* 363.

BAKER, R. and C. YANOFSKY. 1968. The periodicity of RNA polymerase initiations: a new regulatory feature of transcription. Proc. Nat. Acad. Sci. *60:* 313.

BAUTZ, E. and B. HALL. 1962. The isolation of T$_4$ specific RNA on a DNA-cellulose column. Proc. Nat. Acad. Sci. *48:* 400.

BECKWITH, J. 1963. Restoration of operon activity by suppressors. Biochim. Biophys. Acta *76:* 162.

BUSSARD, A., S. NAONO, F. GROS and J. MONOD. 1960. Effets d'un analogue de l'uracile sur les propriétés d'une protéine synthétisée en sa présence. C. R. Acad. Sci. Paris *250:* 4049.

CHAMBERS, D. and G. ZUBAY. 1969. The stimulatory effect of cyclic adenosine 3'–5' monophosphate on DNA-directed synthesis of β-galactosidase in cell free system. Proc. Nat. Acad. Sci. *63:* 118.

CONTESSE, G., S. NAONO, and F. GROS. 1966. Effet des mutations polaires sur la transcription de l'opéron lactose chez *Escherichia coli.* C. R. Acad. Sci. Paris *263:* 1007.

CONTESSE, G. and F. GROS. 1968. Action du chloramphenicol sur la transcription de l'opéron lactose chez des mutants polaires d'*Escherichia coli.* C. R. Acad. Sci. Paris *266:* 262.

CONTESSE, G., M. CREPIN, and F. GROS. 1969. Transcription de l'opéron lactose chez des mutants promoteurs d'*Escherichia coli.* C. R. Acad. Sci. Paris *268:* 2301.

EPPS, H. and E. GALE. 1942. The influence of the presence of glucose during growth on the enzymic activities of *Escherichia coli:* Comparison of the effect with that produced by fermentation acids. Biochem. J. *36:* 619.

FAN, D. 1966. Decay of intact messengers in bacteria. J. Mol. Biol. *16:* 164.

FRANKLIN, N. and S. LURIA. 1961. Transduction of bacteriophage P₁ and the properties of the *lac* genetic region in *E. coli* and *S. dysenteriae.* Virology *15:* 299.

GILBERT, W. and B. MÜLLER-HILL. 1966. Isolation of the *lac* repressor. Proc. Nat. Acad. Sci. *65:* 1891.

GILLESPIE, D. and S. SPIEGELMAN. 1965. A quantitative assay for DNA-RNA hybrids with DNA immobilized on a membrane. J. Mol. Biol. *12:* 829.

GROS, F., W. GILBERT, H. HIATT, G. ATTARDI, P. SPAHR, and J. WATSON. 1961. Molecular and biological characterization of messenger RNA. Cold Spring Harbor Symp. Quant. Biol. *26:* 111.

GUTTMAN, B. and A. NOVICK. 1963. A messenger RNA for β-galactosidase in *Escherichia coli.* Cold Spring Harbor Symp. Quant. Biol. *28:* 373.

HAYASHI, M., S. SPIEGELMAN, N. FRANKLIN, and S. E. LURIA. 1963. Separation of the RNA message transcribed in response to a specific inducer. Proc. Nat. Acad. Sci. *49:* 729.

IMAMOTO, F., J. ITO, and C. YANOFSKY. 1966. Polarity in the tryptophan operon of *E. coli.* Cold Spring Harbor Symp. Quant. Biol. *31:* 235.

IMAMOTO, F. 1968. On the initiation of transcription of the tryptophan operon in *Escherichia coli.* Proc. Nat. Acad. Sci. *60:* 305.

IPPEN, K., J. MILLER, J. SCAIFE, and J. BECKWITH. 1968. New controlling element in the *lac* operon of *E. coli.* Nature *217:* 825.

JACOB, F. and J. MONOD. 1961. Genetic regulatory mechanisms in the synthesis of proteins. J. Mol. Biol. *3:* 318.

JACOB, F. and J. MONOD. 1961. On the regulation of gene activity. Cold Spring Harbor Symp. Quant. Biol. *26:* 193.

JACQUET, M. and A. KEPES. 1969. The step sensitive to catabolite repression and its reversal by 3'–5' cyclic AMP during induced synthesis of β-galactosidase in *E. coli.* Biochem. Biophys. Res. Comm. *36:* 84.

KEPES, A. 1963. Kinetics of induced enzyme synthesis, determination of the mean life of galactosidase specific messenger RNA. Biochim. Biophys. Acta *76:* 293.

KEPES, A. 1967. Sequential transcription and translation in the lactose operon of *Escherichia coli.* Biochim. Biophys. Acta *138:* 107.

KIHO, Y. and A. RICH. 1965. A polycistronic messenger RNA associated with β-galactosidase induction. Proc. Nat. Acad. Sci. *54:* 1751.

KOURILSKY, P., L. MARCAUD, P. SHELDRICK, D. LUZZATI, and F. GROS. 1968. Studies on the messenger RNA of bacteriophage λ. I. Various species synthesized early after induction of the prophage. Proc. Nat. Acad. Sci. *61:* 1013.

KUMAR, S., K. BOVRE, A. GUHA, Z. HRADECNA, V. MAHER, and W. SZYBALSKI. 1969. Orientation and control of transcription in *E. coli* phage λ. Nature *221:* 823.

KUMAR, S. and W. SZYBALSKI. 1969. Orientation of transcription in the *lac* operon and its repressor gene in *Escherichia coli.* J. Mol. Biol. *40:* 145.

KURLAND, C. 1960. Molecular characterization of ribonucleic acid from *Escherichia coli* ribosomes. I. Isolation and molecular weight. J. Mol. Biol. *2:* 83.

LEIVE, L. and V. KOLLIN. 1967. Synthesis, utilization and degradation of lactose operon mRNA in *Escherichia coli*. J. Mol. Biol. *24:* 247.

MAGASANIK, B. 1961. Catabolite repression. Cold Spring Harbor Symp. Quant. Biol. *26:* 193.

MAKMAN, R., E. SUTHERLAND. 1965. Adenosine 3'–5' phosphate in *Escherichia coli*. J. Biol. Chem. *240:* 1309.

MARTIN, R., H. WHITFIELD Jr., D. BERKOWITZ, and M. VOLL. 1966. A molecular model of the phenomenon of polarity. Cold Spring Harbor Symp. Quant. Biol. *31:* 215.

MILLER, J., J. BECKWITH, and B. MÜLLER-HILL. 1968. Direction of transcription of a regulatory gene in *E. coli*. Nature *220:* 1287.

MORIKAWA, N. and F. IMAMOTO. 1969. On the degradation of messenger RNA for the tryptophan operon in *Escherichia coli*. Nature *223:* 37.

MORISS, D. and J. DE MOSS. 1966. Polysome transitions and the regulation of ribonucleic acid synthesis in *Escherichia coli*. Proc. Nat. Acad. Sci. *56:* 262.

MORSE, D., R. BAKER, and C. YANOFSKY. 1968. Translation of the tryptophan messenger RNA of *Escherichia coli*. Proc. Nat. Acad. Sci. *60:* 1428.

MORSE, D., R. MOSTELLER, R. BAKER, and C. YANOFSKY. 1969. Direction of in vivo degradation of tryptophan messenger RNA. A correction. Nature *223:* 40.

MORSE, D. and C. YANOFSKY. 1969. Polarity and the degradation of mRNA. Nature *224:* 329.

MOSES, V. and M. YUDKIN. 1968. Catabolite repression in *Escherichia coli*. A study of two hypotheses. Biochem. J. *110:* 135.

NAKADA, D. and B. MAGASANIK. 1964. The roles of inducer and catabolite repressor in the synthesis of β-galactosidase by *Escherichia coli*. J. Mol. Biol. *8:* 105.

NAONO, S., J. ROUVIERE and F. GROS. 1965. Preferential transcription of the lactose operon during the diauxic growth of *Escherichia coli*. Biochem. Biophys. Res. Commun. *18:* 664.

PARDEE, A., F. JACOB and J. MONOD. 1959. The genetic control and cytoplasmic expression of inducibility in the synthesis of β-galactosidase by *E. coli*. J. Mol. Biol. *1:* 165.

PARDEE, A. and L. PRESTIDGE. 1961. The initial kinetics of enzyme induction. Biochim. Biophys. Acta *49:* 77.

PERLMAN, R., B. DE CROMBRUGGHE and I. PASTAN. 1969. Cyclic AMP regulates catabolite and transcient repression in *E. coli*. Nature *223:* 810.

PERLMAN, R. and I. PASTAN. 1968. Cyclic 3'–5'-AMP: Stimulation of β-galactosidase and tryptophanase induction in *E. coli*. Biochem. Biophys. Res. Commun. *30:* 656.

REVEL, M., M. HERZBERG, A. BECAREVIC and F. GROS. 1968. Role of a protein factor in the functional binding of ribosomes to natural messenger RNA. J. Mol. Biol. *33:* 231.

SHAPIRO, J., L. MacHATTIE, L. ERON, G. IHLER, K. IPPEN and J. BECKWITH. 1969. The isolation of pure *lac* operon DNA. Nature *224:* 768.

SILVERSTONE, A., B. MAGASANIK, W. REZNIKOFF, J. MILLER and J. BECKWITH. 1969. Catabolite sensitive site of the *lac* operon. Nature *221:* 1012.

ULLMANN, A. and J. MONOD. 1968. Cyclic AMP as an antagonist of catabolite repression in *Escherichia coli.* F.E.B.S. Letters *2:* 57.

ULLMANN, A., F. JACOB and J. MONOD. 1967. Characterization by in vitro complementation of a peptide corresponding to an operator-proximal segment of the β-galactosidase structural gene of *Escherichia coli.* J. Mol. Biol. *24:* 339.

WEBSTER, R. and N. ZINDER. 1969. Fate of the message-ribosome complex upon translation of termination signals. J. Mol. Biol. *42:* 425.

YUDKIN, M. and V. MOSES. 1969. Catabolite repression of the *lac* operon. Repression of translation. Biochem. J. *113:* 423.

ZUBAY, G., M. LEDERMAN and J. de VRIES. 1967. DNA-directed peptide synthesis. III. Repression of β-galactosidase synthesis and inhibition of repressor by inducer in a cell-free system. Proc. Nat. Acad. Sci. *58:* 1669.

Chapter VII

Complementation in β-galactosidase

AGNÈS ULLMANN and DAVID PERRIN

Département de Biologie Moléculaire
Institut Pasteur, Paris

INTRODUCTION

The term "complementation" has been generally used to define the phenomenon by which a biological function which has been lost or altered by a mutation can be restored through mutual compensation by differently altered mutants. It is generally accepted that the repair of function occurs at the level of the protein molecule and involves the interaction of differently altered polypeptide chains.

Since Benzer's definition of the cistron as the functional unit of genetic structure (Benzer, 1958), complementation tests have been used in many systems to distinguish between genes involving one or several cistrons. The distinction between inter- and intracistronic complementation is straightforward. Two cistrons should give two separate groups of complementation; the enzymes formed should be wild type, and all mutants of one group should complement all mutants of the other group. Actually the situation may be more complex (for instance, in the case of polar mutants or deletions) and in these cases, more stringent analyses are needed to draw the correct conclusion.

The purpose of studying complementation between z gene products was to determine the structure of the gene (whether it involves one or several cistrons), and thus to contribute to the elucidation of the structure of the protein controlled by the z gene. Much conflicting evidence has been reported concerning the subunit structure of β-galactosidase (i.e., whether the protomer involves one or several polypeptide chains). The study of complementation was of great help in solving this problem in a satisfactory way.

Since intracistronic complementation is mediated by protein-protein interactions, the study of this phenomenon may be of great interest in

143

our understanding of the mechanism of specific recognition and reassociation of proteins.

COMPLEMENTATION BETWEEN POINT MUTANTS

IN VIVO COMPLEMENTATION

It has been shown by Jacob and Monod (1961) that heterogenotes carrying different z^- point mutants may become lac^+ due to the formation of β-galactosidase by complementation.

Early observations using in vivo systems (Perrin, 1963) strongly suggested that the z gene involves only one cistron. This was supported by the following evidence:

(1) The different complementing z^- mutants do not form homogeneous topographically distinct linear groups on the genetic map.

(2) The enzyme formed by complementation exhibits different properties than the wild type.

Quantitative tests for in vivo complementation were performed on various diploids. Figure 1 shows the map positions of the z^- mutants

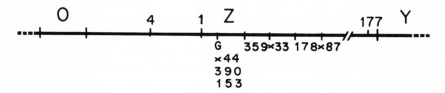

FIGURE 1. Map position of z^- mutants used in Table 1. Mutants G, X44, 390 and 153 are non-allelic, although extremely closely linked. All distances are arbitrary.

used as recipients. The heterozygotes were constructed using three different z^- mutants carried on the episome. Table 1 shows the specific activity of the β-galactosidase obtained in the various diploids. It can be seen from the table that positive complementation of a mutant with a given donor does not depend in any simple way on its position on the genetic map. Another observation is that the level of specific activity of β-galactosidase never exceeds 25% of the wild-type level.

Furthermore, when enzyme obtained by in vivo complementation is tested for its sensitivity to heat inactivation, it can be shown in every case to be much more rapidly inactivated than the wild-type enzyme. Figure 2 shows the thermal inactivation of two different complemented enzymes as compared to the wild type.

Table 1. β-galactosidase activity of $z_a^-/F'z_b^-$ diploids. β-galactosidase activity (expressed in units/mg dry wt bacteria) was measured in crude extracts. The specific activity of a z^+/Fz^+ homogenote in the same conditions is of the order of 20,000 U/mg.

z^- recipients in map order $o \longrightarrow y$	F'lac z^- donors		
	z_1^-	z_4^-	z_{177}^-
4		<11	1170
1	<3	<20	4450
G	400	1600	350
×44	<3	58	1220
390	131	2290	49
153	<3	30	1700
359	<3	869	188
×33	<3	305	250
178	2500	5070	<20
×87	25	130	74

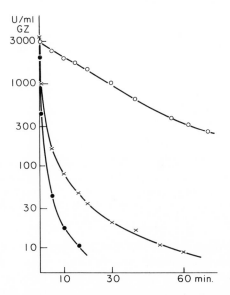

FIGURE 2. Heat inactivation of wild-type and complemented β-galactosidase. Crude extracts of wild-type (o—o), and in vivo complemented z_{177}^-/z_1^- (x—x) or z_{178}^-/z_1^- (●—●) β-galactosidase were incubated at 57°C in PM$_2$ buffer. (For technical references, see Materials and Methods: Ullmann, Jacob, and Monod, 1968.)

IN VITRO COMPLEMENTATION

In vitro complementation studies were performed using either crude bacterial extracts, or highly purified preparations of z^- mutants.

The purification of z^- proteins was based on the fact that many of these mutants (lacking the ability to form active enzyme) produce an altered protein (CRM) which cross-reacts immunologically with β-galactosidase. These purified CRM proteins could be shown to complement in vitro. For instance, the purified z^-_{178} protein has a mol wt of about 100,000 indicating that it has probably a monomeric structure (the protomer of active β-galactosidase having a mol wt of 135,000). The z^- protein even in a pure form has not been obtained as a single molecular species. Several peaks are always obtained in the ultracentrifuge indicating an association-dissociation equilibrium.

One can follow the kinetics of complementation by mixing the extracts or pure preparations of the two z^- mutants and measuring the appearance of β-galactosidase activity. The time course of complementation is very slow: half yield is obtained around 400 min at 28°C (Fig. 3). Using an excess of one component and a limited amount of the other one, the plateau values of complementation are linear with respect to both components.

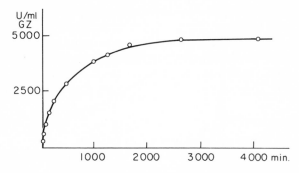

FIGURE 3. Kinetics of complementation reaction. z^-_1 and z^-_{178}-purified proteins were mixed at t = 0. Incubation was carried out at 28°C in PM_2 buffer. At different times samples were taken and assayed for β-galactosidase activity.

The β-galactosidase formed by complementation has a sedimentation coefficient S = 16, like the wild-type one. But studying the thermal sensitivity of the active protein, it has been found that it is as heat labile as the in vivo-produced enzyme. Moreover, the inactivation curves reveal a great heterogeneity of the enzyme, indicating that different types of molecules are involved (Fig. 4).

Restoration of enzyme activity by reassociation of differently altered subunits is not unique for z gene products. Similar phenomena were

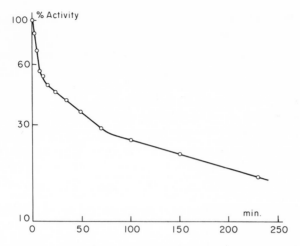

FIGURE 4. Thermal inactivation of an in vitro-complemented mixture of z_1^- and z_{178}^- at 46°C in PM_2 buffer.

reported for many oligomeric proteins (*N. crassa* glutamic dehydrogenase, *E. coli* alkaline phosphatase among others; for reference, see Schlesinger and Levinthal, 1965). The mechanism proposed by Crick and Orgel (Crick and Orgel, 1964) accounts well for this type of complementation.

As it had been earlier suggested by Brenner (1959) and Fincham (1959) intracistronic complementation may be due to interaction between protein subunits, neither of which can, by itself, give rise to any appreciable enzyme activity. The assumptions made by Crick and Orgel in order to account for the phenomenon of intracistronic complementation are the following:

(a) Certain mutations can produce a local misfolding of the protein; which in its turn prevents enzyme activity.

(b) This can be corrected by interacting with an adjacent region which has the correct (wild-type) folding.

There is thus little doubt that a mechanism of this kind must be invoked to account for certain types at least of complementation between point mutants in the *z* gene. However, as we shall see presently, an entirely different interpretation must be sought for other kinds of complementation which are observed in this system.

COMPLEMENTATION BETWEEN DELETION MUTANTS

The isolation of deletion mutants of the *z* gene involving quite large segments of the genetic structure led to the discovery of a new type of complementation.

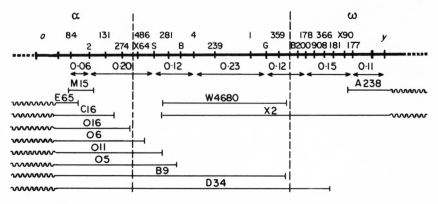

FIGURE 5. Diagrammatic representation of the z gene. The figures and letters above the solid line indicate the position of point mutations in the z gene: o, operator; y, structural gene of β-galactosidase permease. The figures below the line represent recombination frequencies, as determined by crosses between two point mutants. The lines below indicate the extent of various deletions: M 15, isolated by Beckwith (1964); A 238 and W 4680, isolated by Cook and Lederberg (1962); all others by Jacob, Ullmann, and Monod (1964).

Actually, it was found (Ullmann et al., 1965) that large deletions, covering *o, i, pro*$_2$ and *ph,* and extending to various sites of the z gene would complement all operator distal mutants of the z gene, up to a "barrier" which is thus defined (hereafter called the ω barrier); all deletions not extending beyond this barrier would complement all mutants of the ω region (see map, Fig. 5). The length of the deletion towards the operator end does not influence the complementation pattern. Small deletions within the operator proximal part of the z gene also give positive complementation with ω mutants. This type of complementation is called ω complementation and has been studied in vivo as well as in vitro.

Another type of complementation involving deletion mutants has been described (Ullmann, Jacob, and Monod, 1967): extracts of partial deletions of the operator-proximal segment of the z gene will complement with extracts of various β-galactosidase negative mutants having their operator-proximal segment intact. This type of complementation is called α complementation.

It has been shown (Ullmann, Jacob, and Monod, 1968) that both types of complementation represent non-covalent reassociation of peptide fragments, leading to the active enzyme.

CHARACTERIZATION OF THE COMPLEMENTING PEPTIDES

(a) ω donors and ω acceptors.

We call ω donors all mutants having their ω region intact and producing a peptide which will complement with the products of ω mutants. These latter we call ω acceptors.

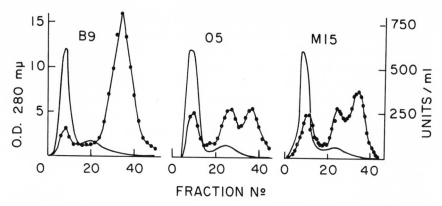

FIGURE 6. Distribution of ω activities from different deletion mutants on a Sephadex G-100 column. The different extracts were precipitated with $(NH_4)_2SO_4$ (40% saturation), dialyzed, and layered on the Sephadex column. ———: absorption at 280 mμ; ●——●: ω activity, measured after 1 hr of complementation with an extract of S 908. The values are expressed in U/ml β-galactosidase.

The ω region represents $\frac{1}{3}$ to $\frac{1}{4}$ of the total genetic length of the z gene; thus the expected mol wt of the complementing peptide would be around 40,000. In sucrose density gradients, the ω peptide has an S value of 3.2 and is retained in a Sephadex G-100 column. These data refer specially to ω peptides produced by deletions W4680 and B9; other ω producers have a more complicated pattern. In fact, if one compares the Sephadex G-100 elution patterns of three different ω donors [namely a large deletion (B9) and two smaller ones (0 5 and M 15)], it can be seen that in the case of the large deletion practically the totality of the complementing activity is retained on Sephadex, while in the case of the smaller deletions ω activity can be found in three positions (Fig. 6). One corresponds to the light fraction present in B9, while the other two activity peaks appear to be associated with heavier fractions. We do not know whether the "heavy ω" represents the ω peptide associated to other protein fractions coded by the intact part of the z gene or different aggregated forms of the ω peptide itself.

The ω peptide has been purified 500 times from deletion mutants, but at this stage it was not sufficiently homogeneous in order to perform physical chemical measurements. The ω peptide can be obtained in pure form from in vivo-complemented enzymes after dissociation with urea or guanidine, and as it has been shown by Goldberg and Edelstein (1970) it has a mol wt of 40,000.

The ω peptide can be reversibly renatured from 8 M urea or 6 M guanidine HCl, virtually without any loss in complementing activity. It is a highly heat-labile protein: its half life of thermal inactivation is 4 min at 41.5°C.

The ω peptide is present in all mutants of the z gene not affecting the ω region, as well as in the wild-type enzyme. We will return later in more detail to this question.

No ω acceptor has been obtained in pure form. Some of the properties of the acceptors have been studied in crude bacterial extracts (Ullmann and Monod, 1969). It has been found that, depending upon the ionic strength, the acceptor can exist in different forms of aggregation. At low ionic strength it is associated, probably into a tetramer, which at high ionic strength dissociates most likely into monomers. Both forms are active in complementation.

(b) α donors and α acceptors.

All mutants having their operator proximal segment (α segment) intact are α donors. All partial deletions not extending beyond a barrier (which can be situated between mutants 274 and X 64 in Fig. 1) can serve as α acceptors, when their extracts are mixed with an extract of an α donor. Table 2 summarizes results of complementation tests performed with different mutants. It can be seen that the α peptide represents an operator proximal segment of the gene extending from the operator to about $\frac{1}{5}$ or $\frac{1}{4}$ of the genetic length.

Figure 7 shows a sucrose density gradient sedimentation profile of a mixture of α and ω peptides. As it could be expected from the difference

Table 2. Screening tests for different donor and acceptor activities were performed on crude extracts. In some cases α donor activities were tested on guanidine treated extracts (Ullmann et al., 1967).

Mutant	α Donor	α Acceptor	ω Donor	ω Acceptor
W 4680	+	−	+	−
X 2	+	−	−	−
3310	+	−	+	−
200 B	+	−	−	+
S 908	+	−	−	+
X 90	+	−	−	+
A 238	+	−	−	+
YA 486	+	−	Not tested	
U 131	−	−	Not tested	
B 9	−	−	+	−
O 5	−	−	+	−
O 6	−	−	+	−
O 11	−	−	+	−
O 16	−	+	+	−
M 15	−	+	+	−
C 16	−	+	+	−
E 65	−	+	+	−
D 34	−	−	−	−

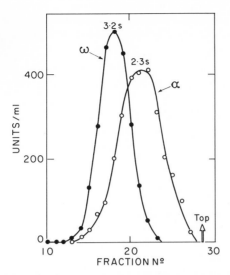

FIGURE 7. Sedimentation of α and ω in a sucrose density gradient 0.1 ml containing a mixture of α and ω peptide was centrifuged in a linear sucrose gradient (5 ml of 5 to 20% sucrose) for 17 hr at 39,000 rev/min α and ω activities were tested by complementation. The S values were calculated assuming an S value of 6.3 for alkaline phosphatase used as marker.

of the genetic length of the two segments, the α-peptide sediments with a velocity (2.3) lower than ω suggesting a smaller mol wt of the former.

Treatment of extracts at 0°C or 20°C with 6M guanidine or 8 M urea, followed by dialysis against buffer results in no significant loss of α-donor activity, but completely abolishes α-acceptor activity.

The most peculiar property of the α-peptide is its high temperature resistance in the presence of 6 M guanidine HCl. Fig. 8 shows the behavior of the α-peptide as compared to the ω peptide during a treatment at 100°C in the presence of 6 M guanidine HCl. While the ω peptide is inactivated very quickly, the activity of the α-peptide does not only remain stable, but its amount increases with time, suggesting that some covalent bonds have to be broken in order to liberate the free peptide. One should note, that after guanidine treatment at high temperature the S value of α (measured in sucrose density gradients) diminishes to a value = 1.3.

Zipser has shown (Morrison and Zipser, 1970) that if α-donor bacterial extracts are boiled in the absence of guanidine at temperatures ranging between 100°C to 120°C, the α-peptide can be quantitatively extracted. Using this technique, he has found that the smallest α peptide still retaining complementing activity has a molecular weight of about 7,000.

As we will see later, the wild-type enzyme contains a certain amount of free α as well as ω peptides and we will discuss their possible origin. At this point we should like to make one comment which specifically

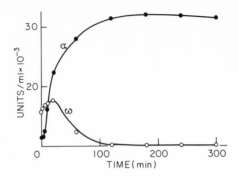

FIGURE 8. Heating of α and ω peptides in the presence of guanidine. Heating was performed at 100°C in the presence of 6 M guanidine in TVNS buffer (for buffer compositions see Ullmann, Jacob, and Monod, 1968). At different times samples were taken, dialyzed against TVNS buffer, and assayed for α and ω activities, using M 15 extract as α acceptor and S 908 extract as ω acceptor.

concerns a property of the α peptide. It is known that carboxymethylated β-galactosidase is completely devoid of enzymatic activity. After carboxymethylation in 8 M urea followed by dialysis when no enzymatic activity can be detected, α activity is still present, indicating that either the α peptide does not contain SH groups or that they are not required for complementation.

The properties of α acceptors have not been yet studied.

KINETICS AND STOICHIOMETRY OF THE COMPLEMENTATION

The kinetics of complementation between deletion mutants are faster compared with those between point mutants. Fig. 9 shows a time course

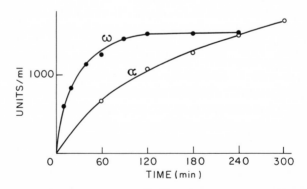

FIGURE 9. Time course of α and ω complementation. An extract of W 4680 was divided in two and equal volumes of acceptor extracts were added to each (S 908 in order to test ω complementation and M 15 for α complementation). At different times samples were taken and assayed for β-galactosidase activity.

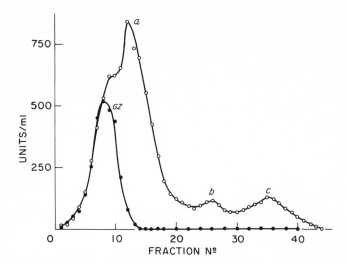

FIGURE 10. Distribution of β-galactosidase (GZ) and complementing activity on a Sephadex G-100 column. A crude extract of z_1^- was layered on a Sephadex column. ●——● represents the residual activity of β-galactosidase; ○——○ complementing activity, assayed with S 908 as acceptor.

of α and ω complementation and it can be seen that the plateaus are reached in about 2 to 3 hr.

One can easily distinguish a Crick-Orgel-type complementation from a complementation between peptide fragments. If an extract of z_1 (a point mutant in the middle part of the z gene) is mixed with an extract of S 908 (ω mutant), enzyme activity appears and a plateau is reached after 48 hr. The kinetics of this complementation are quite peculiar, as if one would deal with two different types of reactions. In fact, if the extract of the z_1 mutant is chromatographed on a Sephadex G 100 column, the complementing activity is found in three different positions (peak a, b and c on Fig. 10). If the time course of complementation of each peak is analyzed, it can be shown that the kinetics of the heavy fraction are "normalized" and the light fractions have typical ω-type complementation kinetics (Fig. 11).

Two conclusions can be drawn from this experiment:

(a) The two types of complementation can be distinguished by simple kinetic analysis

(b) The z_1 mutant contains free ω peptide; but this fact is not very surprising because, as we will see later, even the wild-type enzyme contains some free ω.

The stoichiometry of complementation has been studied in the case of ω complementation.

154 *Ullmann and Perrin*

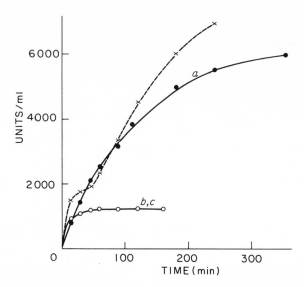

FIGURE 11. Time course of complementation of different z_1^- fractions. Fractions a, b, and c separated on a Sephadex G-100 column shown in Fig. 10 were pooled and assayed for complementing activity, using S 908 extracts as acceptor. x—x—x crude extract of z_1^-; ●—●—● heavy fraction obtained after Sephadex chromatography (a in Fig. 10); ○—○—○ trailing fractions obtained after Sephadex chromatography (b and c in Fig. 10).

The stoichiometry of ω complementation turned out to be a complex function of several conditions, namely:

(a) the state of aggregation of the acceptor which, in turn, depends on the ionic strength

(b) both the relative and absolute concentrations of the two interacting peptides

(c) the presence or absence of a β-galactoside analog which under certain conditions may increase the yield by a factor 10 or more.

These observations suggest that several distinct pathways may lead from acceptor + ω to active enzyme. (See also Ullmann and Monod, this vol.)

THE NATURE OF THE ACTIVE PRODUCT

At this point we do not wish to discuss the subunit structure of the complemented enzyme. We will return later to this question.

In this section only a few properties of the complemented enzyme will be mentioned:

(a) the active complemented enzyme, assayed by its enzymatic activity, whether it is the result of α or ω complementation and whether obtained in vivo or in vitro, appears in sucrose gradients as a homogeneous product with an S value of 16, suggesting very strongly that in all these different

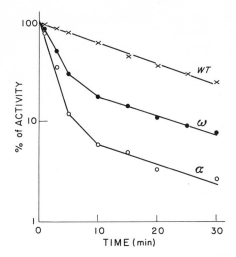

FIGURE 12. Heat inactivation of wild-type and complemented β-galactosidase. Crude extracts of 2 EO1 [wild-type β-galactosidase (WT)], U366/F B9 (ω-complemented β-galactosidase) and W 4680/F M 15 (α-complemented β-galactosidase) were incubated at 57°C in PM2 buffer. The activity is expressed as a percentage of the initial activity.

conditions activity is associated exclusively with a tetrameric structure like that of the wild-type enzyme. In a few cases enzyme produced in vivo by complementing diploids has been highly purified and the sedimentation coefficients determined in the analytical ultracentrifuge. The values obtained were virtually the same as measured in sucrose density gradients.

(b) The K_M values measured for two different ω-complemented enzymes are the same as for the wild-type enzyme.

(c) All complemented enzymes are much more rapidly inactivated by heat, than the wild-type enzyme. Fig. 12 shows a heat inactivation of an α-complemented and ω-complemented enzyme compared to a wild-type β-galactosidase.

(d) α- and ω-complemented enzymes cannot be renatured after treatment with 8 M urea.

COMPLEMENTATION AND STRUCTURE OF β-GALACTOSIDASE

The study of complementation between various point mutants or deletion mutants of the z gene leads to a better understanding of the subunit structure of β-galactosidase.

The main conclusions drawn from these studies may be summarized as follows:

(a) The z gene represents one cistron.

(b) The protomer of the wild-type β-galactosidase involves a single covalent polypeptide chain.

(c) Complementation between deletion mutants involves noncovalent association between peptides corresponding to different fragments of the wild-type chain.

In this chapter we shall summarize a few different types of studies which allowed us to draw the above conclusions.

UREA DENATURATION

It was first shown by Zipser (1963) that active enzyme could be recovered in good yield after treatment with 8 M urea. Perrin and Monod later showed (1963) that fairly good recovery (12% to 25%) could be obtained also after treatment by heat or 6 M guanidine.

The results of similar experiments are shown in Table 3. The only significant difference between these experiments and those mentioned above was the use of a buffer containing 10^{-2}M EDTA and no Mg^{++}. As it can be seen from the Table, the recoveries were very high but the presence of divalent cations during the dialysis prevents the recovery of activity (Ullmann and Monod, 1969).

The high recoveries of activity obtained with the wild-type enzyme do not depend on the state of purity of the enzyme preparation.

If preparations of complemented enzymes were submitted to the same urea treatment, the recoveries never exceeded a few per cent of the original activity (Table 4).

Table 3. Recovery of β-galactosidase after different treatments. Pure crystalline β-galactosidase was treated with urea and guanidine (Ullmann and Monod, 1969).

Treatment	U/ml β-Galactosidase	% Recovery
None	270,000	
Dialysis against 8 M urea then TVNS	280,000	104
+ 2.10^{-2} M Mg^{++} during dialysis	0	0
1 min at 100°C	0	0
1 min at 100°C, dialysis against 8 M urea, then TVNS	267,000	99
Dialysis against 6 M guanidine HCl, then TVNS	2,050	0.75
Dialysis against 6 M guanidine, then 8 M urea, then TVNS	202,000	75

Table 4. Recovery of β-galactosidase activity after urea treatment of wild-type and complemented enzymes. Urea treatment was performed on crude extracts (Ullmann et al., 1968). The extracts contained between 35 to 40 mg protein/ml. protein/ml.

Extract		β-Galactosidase (units/ml)		% Recovery
		Before urea	After urea	
3300		1,440,000	1,750,000	120
2E01		244,000	245,000	100
A238/F B9	(ω)	45,000	925	2
S908/F B9		61,000	1,348	2.2
S908/F Z1		127,500	8,000	6.2
U336/F B9		70,000	4,620	6
W4680/F M15	(α)	19,900	662	3.3
U281/F M15		28,700	2,280	8
U239/F M15		9400	450	4.7

These observations summarized above, therefore, show that 90% to 95% or more of the enzyme present in complementing diploids (or in the in vitro-complemented enzyme) must have a structure different from that of the wild type.

If the difference towards urea treatment between the two enzymes reflects a different subunit structure, the analysis of the products recovered after dialysis following the urea treatment should give a straightforward answer.

Extracts of wild-type and ω-complemented enzymes have been treated with 8 M urea, followed by dialysis against buffer, and then passed over a column of Sephadex G-100. As it can be seen in Fig. 13, there is a substantial difference in distribution profiles of the two enzymes:

(a) With the wild-type extract, only one kind of activity peak is found— β-galactosidase enzyme activity, eluted with the front of the column.

(b) In the case of the ω-complemented enzyme, there is some β-galactosidase activity found in the excluded fraction (corresponding to about 5% of the enzyme activity before treatment with 8 M urea). But as it can be seen in the Figure, more than 90% of the initial activity is found in the trailing fraction of the column, in the form of free ω peptide. On a sucrose gradient the sedimentation constant of this ω fraction was 3.15 S.

If the same experiment is performed with an α-complemented enzyme, after the urea treatment, β-galactosidase activity is not renatured whereas free α-peptide is liberated.

These results therefore suggest that in the wild type, as opposed to the

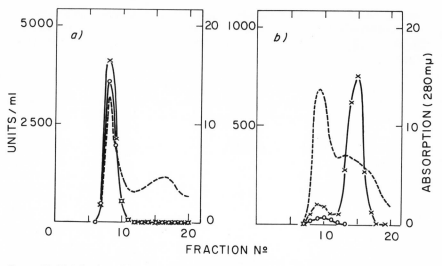

FIGURE 13. Distribution of β-galactosidase (GZ) and ω activities on a Sephadex G-100 column before and after urea treatment of the complemented enzyme. A crude extract of S 908/F B9 in TVNS buffer (containing about 40 mg protein/ml) was treated with 8 M urea (as described in Ullmann, Jacob and Monod, 1968). The extracts were passed over Sephadex columns: (a) before and (b) after urea treatment. — — —, ultraviolet absorption at 280 mμ; o—o—o, β-galactosidase activity; x——x——x——, ω activity.

complemented enzymes, the α and ω peptides are covalently associated with the rest of the chain.

THE ACTION OF PROTEOLYTIC ENZYMES

As the urea experiments suggested, in the complemented enzyme the association of the peptides is noncovalent, whereas the protomer of the wild-type enzyme involves a covalent polypeptide chain. If this is the case, one might expect to liberate some α and ω peptides by treating the wild-type β-galactosidase with proteolytic enzymes. As shown in Table 5, treatment of pure wild-type β-galactosidase with various proteolytic enzymes results, under our conditions, in only a very moderate loss of enzymatic activity (first column). In order to test for the presence of free α and ω in these preparations, this activity must be eliminated. This has been performed by a treatment with 6 M guanidine HCl. Since α and ω are resistant to this treatment, whereas β-galactosidase activity is virtually abolished under the same conditions, the protease-treated preparations were dissolved in 6 M guanidine, and thereafter dialyzed against buffer. After the elimination of the large precipitate which is formed during dialysis, the supernatant which contains virtually no β-galactosidase ac-

Table 5. Treatment of pure wild-type β-galactosidase with different proteolytic enzymes. Pure wild-type β-galactosidase (800,000 units/mg) was dissolved in TVNS buffer. The incubation was performed at 28°C with a proteolytic enzyme/GZ ratio of 1:50. After the time of treatment indicated in the table, GZ activity was measured and, immediately after, 2 vol of 7.5 M guanidine in TVNS buffer were added to 1 vol of the mixture. The samples were kept in guanidine for 3 hr at 20°C, and then dialysed against TVNS buffer, α and ω activities were measured in the supernatant fraction of the dialysed samples.

Exp.	Proteolytic enzyme	Time of treatment (hr)	Units/ml.		
			GZ	ω	α
1	None		370,000	445	400
	Chymotrypsin	4	325,000	9,000	800
	Trypsin	4	380,000	1,240	600
	Pronase	2	340,000	3,320	4,280
2	None		176,000	225	500
	Papain	4	135,000	6,300	12,800
3	None		123,000	240	200
	Subtilisin	0.5	116,000	4,550	1,620
	Subtilisin	2	113,000	8,700	1,650
	Subtilisin	5	109,000	18,500	2,350

tivity was assayed for the presence of α and ω. As it can be seen in the Table 5, even in the absence of proteolytic treatment one can find traces of α and ω activity but their amount is considerably increased after the treatment.

The presence of small amounts of free α and ω in the wild-type enzyme even in the absence of any proteolytic treatment will be discussed later.

At this point we should like to describe some aspects of the action of proteases on native β-galactosidase. In our experimental conditions (see legend of Table 5) the loss of enzymatic activity was negligible, and moreover some stringent tests (heat inactivation, polyacrylamide gel electrophoresis) showed that the enzyme treated with proteases has the same properties as the nontreated control. But once the quaternary structure was disrupted (for instance, dissociation with 8 M urea), many breaks in the covalent polypeptide chain can be revealed. Figure 14 shows a set of polyacrylamide gel electrophoresis in 8 M urea performed with the nontreated β-galactosidase, where one single band can be seen, and the same enzyme after 2 hr of treatment with different proteolytic enzymes. As a result of the treatment a great number of bands can be seen, indicating that many peptide bonds have been broken. It is indeed a remarkable fact that the tightness of the quaternary structure masks these

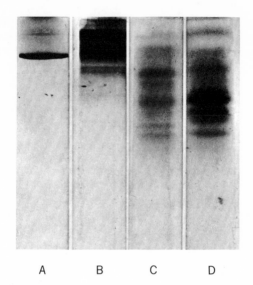

A   B   C   D

FIGURE 14. Polyacrylamide gel electrophoresis in 8 M urea. Pure β-galactosidase was treated with different proteolytic enzymes, as described in the legend of Table 5.
a—nontreated β-galactosidase; b—treated with chymotrypsin; c—treated with papain; d—treated with subtilisin. When the electrophoresis was performed in the absence of urea, only one band corresponding to active β-galactosidase is obtained following proteolytic treatment.

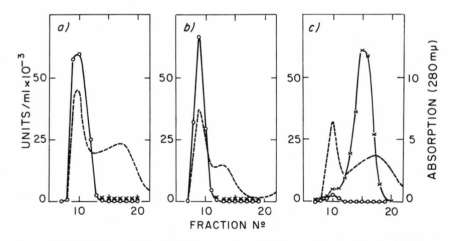

FIGURE 15. Distribution of β-galactosidase and ω activities on a Sephadex column before and after different treatments of the wild-type enzyme. A crude extract of wild-type enzyme in TVNS buffer (containing 40 mg protein/ml), was treated with: (a) 8 M urea; (b) chymotrypsin (for 90 min); (c) same as (b) followed by treatment with 8 M urea. 3 ml of the extract after each treatment was layered on a Sephadex G-100 column. — — —, Ultraviolet absorption at 280 mμ; —o—o—, β-galactosidase activity; —x—x—, ω activity.

breaks, showing that noncovalent interactions might be in some instances more important factors of stability than the continuity of a covalent chain.

As it has been shown in Table 5, proteolytic treatment liberates large amounts of α and ω peptides from the wild-type β-galactosidase. But these peptides cannot be liberated in a free state, unless the quaternary structure of the enzyme is disrupted. This can be demonstrated by the following experiment. As shown in Fig. 15, treatments of wild-type enzyme with urea alone or chymotrypsin alone do not allow the appearance of ω activity in the trailing fraction of a Sephadex G-100 column; whereas when both treatments are applied, a considerable amount of ω activity is recovered.

It has to be pointed out that ω-complemented enzyme has a radically different behaviour towards proteolytic treatment. As we already know, urea treatment alone of the complemented enzyme allows the recovery of ω activity in the trailing fraction of a Sephadex G-100 column (see Fig.

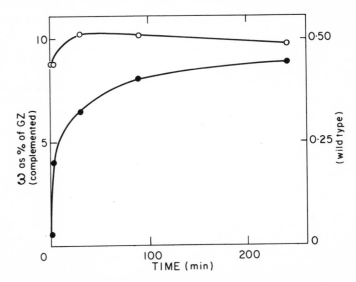

FIGURE 16. Time course of ω liberation from wild-type and complemented enzyme after chymotrypsin treatment. Crude extracts of 2 EO1 (wild-type β-galactosidase) and S 908/F B9 (ω-complemented β-galactosidase) in TVNS buffer were incubated with chymotrypsin at 28°C (1 mg proteolytic enzyme/50 mg bacterial extract). The proteolytic action was stopped by adding 2 vol of 7.5 M guanidine in TVNS buffer to 1 vol of incubation mixture. After 2 hr at 20°C, the guanidine was eliminated by dialysis against TVNS buffer. The precipitate formed after 16 hr of dialysis was eliminated and ω activity measured in the supernatant fraction. The ω activities are expressed as the percentage of the amount of β-galactosidase (GZ) present in the incubation mixture 30 sec before the addition of guanidine. (The loss of β-galactosidase activity due to the action of chymotrypsin is the same order in both extracts and represents 10% at 240 min). —o—o—, complemented enzyme; —•—•—, wild-type enzyme.

13). Moreover, treatment of the complemented enzyme with chymotrypsin does not increase significantly the yield of ω, when under the same conditions the recovery from the wild-type enzyme was increased about 20 times (Fig. 16).

RECOVERY OF "FREE" α AND ω PEPTIDES

The observations reported in the preceding sections show the different behaviour of wild-type and complemented enzymes towards urea and protease treatments, and very strongly suggest that the main difference between the two enzymes consists in their subunit structures.

As it has been shown in Table 5, guanidine treatment alone allows the recovery of small amounts of free α and ω from the pure wild-type enzyme. Therefore, the question had to be asked: how the yields of free peptides liberated from the wild-type enzyme by mild treatments, which are not supposed to break covalent bonds, can be compared to those obtained from a complemented enzyme, where presumably the peptides are non-

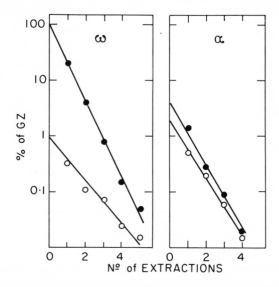

FIGURE 17. Extraction of α and ω from the pure wild-type and ω-complemented enzymes by repeated guanidine treatments. 3·3 mg of pure wild-type and ω-complemented enzyme were dissolved in 2 ml of 6 M guanidine in TVNS buffer at 0°C. The solutions were kept for 1 hr at 0°C and then dialysed against cold TVNS buffer for 12 hr. The precipitate formed during the dialysis was dissolved in cold guanidine, kept at 0°C for 1 hr and dialysed against cold TVNS buffer. The extraction procedure was repeated 3 more times. The supernatant fractions after each extraction were assayed for α and ω activities. The total amounts of α and ω after each extraction are expressed as the percentage of the β-galactosidase (GZ) activity initially present. ——•—•——, ω-complemented enzyme; —o—o— , wild-type enzyme.

covalently linked? The following experiment has been performed using pure wild-type and complemented enzymes: successive extractions at 0°C of α and ω by the guanidine procedure were carried out, using at each step the precipitate formed in the preceding one. As can be seen in Fig. 17, the successive extractions give exponentially decreasing yields of both α and ω, as expected if a constant fraction of each were extracted at each step. Extrapolation to the ordinate of the semi-logarithmic plots may be considered to give a rough estimate of the total amount of α and ω present in the preparation before treatment. In the case of wild-type protein the estimate for both α and ω amount to approximately 1%, whereas with ω-type complemented enzyme one can find about the same fraction of α as in the wild type, but the free ω extrapolates to 100%.

This result clearly shows that the totality of the ω peptide is "free" in the ω-type complemented enzyme, whereas the protomer of the wild-type protein contains approximately 1% noncovalent α and ω.

We will try to interpret this fact in the chapter concerning the origin of the complementing peptides.

ULTRACENTRIFUGE STUDIES

In some preliminary experiments (Ullmann, Jacob, and Monod, 1968) it has been shown that when the sedimentation profile of pure wild-type and ω-complemented enzymes were determined in the ultracentrifuge both in the presence and absence of 6 M guanidine HCl, the following results were being obtained:

(a) In the absence of guanidine both preparations appear homogenous and their sedimentation coefficient is the same within experimental errors, namely 16 S.

(b) In the presence of 6 M guanidine the wild-type preparation appears equally homogenous, showing a single symmetrical peak with an S_0 of 1.2 S.

(c) In the same conditions, the preparation of ω-complemented enzyme shows a non-symmetrical profile, which can be analyzed as indicating the presence of two components, one of which corresponds to approximately one-fourth of the total. The sedimentation coefficient of the major peak ($S_0 = 0.92$ S) is significantly lower than that of the single peak seen with the wild-type enzyme (Ullmann, Jacob, and Monod, 1968).

These experiments indicated that in contrast to the wild-type enzyme, the protomer of the complemented enzyme is built up of noncovalent unequal subunits.

In order to determine the precise tertiary and quaternary structure of the complemented enzyme, two questions had to be asked:

(1) How are the unequal subunits built up into the protomer?

(2) How is the proper quaternary structure of the enzyme achieved? These questions were answered in a satisfactory way by the recent work of Edelstein and Goldberg (1970) and Goldberg (1970).

These authors purified to homogeneity in vivo-complemented enzymes from two diploid strains: MU 366/F'B9 and X 90/F'B9. The specific activities (810.000 U/mg) did not differ in a significant way from the specific activities obtained currently with the pure wild-type enzyme (900.000 U/mg). The B9 mutant seems to be the largest deletion still having ω activity, indicating that it probably represents the shortest ω peptide. In contrast, the two ω acceptors MU 366 and X 90 are amber mutants and their chain-terminating codons occur in the ω region, far away from the ω barrier. Thus, the polypeptide chains coded by these mutants most probably contain an overlapping sequence of the ω region (longer in the case of X 90 than in that of MU 366); therefore, the prediction would be that the protomers of the two ω-complemented enzymes are larger than the wild-type one.

The authors determined the molecular weights of pure, native complemented enzymes, and on the other hand, they measured the molecular weights of ω and acceptor after the enzyme has been denatured by 6 M guanidine. The results are summarized in Table 6.

It can be seen from the table that:

(a) The protomers of the complemented enzymes have in fact a higher molecular weight than the wild-type one, showing that the genetic overlap between the amber acceptor and B 9 genomes is effectively translated in the polypeptide chains of the complemented enzyme.

(b) The molecular weights obtained for the native complemented enzymes clearly show that, like the wild type, they also have a tetrameric structure (see also Goldberg, this vol.).

The stoichiometry of the polypeptides was also determined and it was

Table 6. Two methods were used for mol wt measurements: (*a*) sedimentation equilibrium and (*b*) Archibald method. The mol wt of the protomer, acceptor, and ω were measured in the presence of 6 M guanidine. For further details see Goldberg and Edelstein (1970). The numbers marked with (c) represent calculated values.

		Molecular weight			
Strain	S_0	Native Enzyme	Protomer	Acceptor	ω
Wild type	16	540.000[a]	135.000[b]	—	—
MU 366/F B9	16	595.000[a]	150.000[c]	110.000[a]	39.000[a]
X 90/F B9	—	670.000[a]	166.000[c]	127.000[c]	

shown (Goldberg and Edelstein, 1970) that the protomer of the complemented enzyme is built up of one ω and one acceptor.

Thus it seems clear that the complemented enzyme is built up of four protomers, each one containing noncovalently-linked polypeptide chains in a ratio 1:1.

An additional problem was raised by these experiments, i.e., how the proper quaternary structure can be achieved in spite of the presence of four supernumerary polypeptide fragments of molecular weight 15,000 to 30,000 (depending upon the nature of the acceptor participating in complementation). It seems likely that these "extra peptides" must be positioned away from the association area between the protomers and do not interfere with the active site. It seemed likely that they were situated at the surface of the whole molecule and therefore susceptible to be removed by proteolytic treatments. In order to test this hypothesis, Goldberg digested the pure MU 366/F'B9 complemented enzyme with papain, using conditions described in the legend of Table 5. (It should be recalled, that there is no significant change in enzymatic activity during such a treatment.) the pure MU 366/F'B9 complemented enzyme with papain, using conditions described in the legend of Table 5 (It should be recalled, that there is no significant change in enzymatic activity during such a treatment). After this treatment, the mol wt of the enzyme was determined. It was found to have decreased from 595,000 to 535,000. This result indicates, that the "extra peptides" have been released from the enzyme as a result of the papain digestion, thus suggesting that these peptide fragments are in a highly accessible position.

THE ORIGIN OF THE ACTIVE PEPTIDES

Three hypotheses have been considered in order to account for the origin of the peptide fragments, produced not only by deletion or point mutants, but also by the wild-type strain.

(1) The α and ω peptides are products of different cistrons within the z gene.

(2) The fragments are produced by the action of some intracellular cathepsins, acting preferentially at certain points of the polypeptide chain.

(3) The peptides are produced during the synthesis of the polypeptide chain by the misreading of certain ambiguous codons, interpreted as restart points.

If the active peptides correspond to different cistrons, the enzymes produced by in vivo or in vitro complementation should exhibit the same properties as the wild type. The experimental facts described in the preceding chapters clearly show that this is not the case, and one has to conclude that the α and ω peptides are not coded by different cistrons. This conclusion is supported by chemical evidences (see Fowler and Zabin, this vol.): a single amino-terminal and a single carboxy-terminal per 135,000 mol wt protomer have been found in pure β-galactosidase.

As it has been shown, some proteases may liberate α and ω peptides from the wild-type enzyme; thus the interpretation of the origin of the peptides due to an intracellular cathepsin cannot be excluded. But certain experimental data, which will be described in this section, would rather support the third hypothesis, that is to say, the peptide fragments are the result of a few ambiguous restart points.

COORDINATION OF ω PEPTIDE AND THIOGALACTOSIDE TRANSACETYLASE

Under the "cathepsin hypothesis," one could expect the average frequency of hydrolytic cuts liberating ω peptide to depend on the structure of the whole polypeptide. Using deletion mutants of different length, we would not expect the frequency of liberation to be the same in all cases. Under the "ambiguous restart" assumption, by contrast, we would expect the frequency of such restarts to be invariant with respect to the structure of the product. These expectations may be tested, using the well-

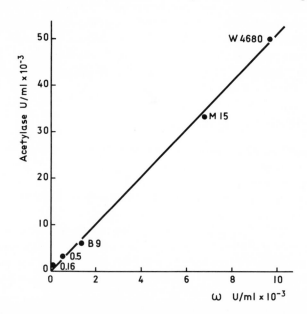

FIGURE 18. Coordination of ω and thiogalactoside transacetylase activities. Thiogalactoside transacetylase and ω activities were measured using crude extracts of different deletion mutants. The high values obtained for W 4680 and M 15 are due to the fact that for these two mutants diploid strains were used (W 4680/F W 4680 and M 15/F M 15).

established fact that under a great variety of conditions the production of β-galactosidase is strictly coordinated with that of transacetylase. Thus, measurements of transacetylase may serve as standard for comparison of ω production by different strains.

As we have seen, ω donors can be either small deletions in the z gene leaving the operator region intact, or large deletions, covering the operator and the promoter, and joining the remaining part of the z gene to another operon. In the first case, the production of transacetylase is under the control of the lac system; in the case of large deletions, the yield of transacetylase depends upon the properties of the promoter, to which the remaining genetic material of the lac operon happens to be joined. We know that these different deletions produce transacetylase, ranging from 2% to 50% of the wild-type level (Jacob, Ullmann, and Monod, 1965). Among these deletion strains we have chosen those which are ω donors, and compared their rates of ω and transacetylase synthesis. As it can be seen in Fig. 18, their production seems to be coordinated.

This finding is not easily compatible with the cathepsin hypothesis and it supports rather the restart hypothesis, if we suppose that certain ambiguous codons are misread with a low but constant frequency.

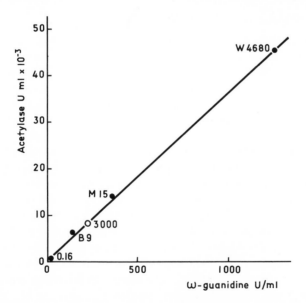

Figure 19. Coordination of guanidine-treated ω and thiogalactoside-transacetylase activities. Crude extracts of different deletion mutants and 3000 (wild-type) were divided in two. One part was treated with 6 M guanidine, and after elimination of guanidine by dialysis, ω activities were measured using S 908 extract as acceptor. Thiogalactoside-transacetylase activities were measured in the nontreated fractions.

As we have seen in a preceding chapter the wild-type enzyme contains about 1% of noncovalently-linked free ω peptide. If we assume that this number represents the frequency of misreading, one should find for all ω-producing mutants a yield of free peptide representing about 1% of the fully synthesized polypeptide chain.

In order to answer this question we extracted the free ω peptide from wild-type extracts, as well as from different deletion mutants with 6 M guanidine, and compared the amounts of guanidine-extractable ω with the corresponding transacetylase activities.

This is shown in Fig. 19. It can be seen from the figure:

(a) The coordination of transacetylase with ω can be observed even if the latter has been treated with guanidine.

(b) The amount of free ω produced by the wild-type strain (considering as basis of comparison the levels of transacetylase) is of the same order of magnitude as the amounts found in various deletion mutants.

These results seem to indicate that free ω is liberated with the same low frequency in all strains, suggesting that the sequence or length of the messenger translated prior to the ambiguous codon does not influence the frequency of misreading which would lead to ω restarts.

ω Peptide Produced by Amber Mutants

It has been described by Newton (Newton, 1966) that certain nonsense mutants, located in the middle section of the z gene, proximal to the ω barrier produce significant amounts of ω. Since ω-distal nonsense mutants show almost no activity, Newton concluded that there is a gradient of polarity for the expression of ω, similar to that observed for the expression of permease and transacetylase.

Analyzing the production of ω by different amber mutants under different conditions, we made a very striking observation: some nonsense mutants, situated in the middle section of the z gene and having extremely low in vitro ω activities under normal conditions, show a 2- to 25-fold increase in ω activity if a treatment with 8 M urea, followed by dialysis, is performed on the extracts. Table 7 shows the increase in ω activity of three different amber mutants, obtained after urea treatment.

It has to be remembered that the ω activity of deletion mutants can not be increased by urea treatment. In the same way the ω activity of an ω proximal amber mutant (NG 750, studied by Newton), producing high levels of ω is not affected by urea treatment.

These results show that even ω-distal nonsense mutants can reinitiate the translation of the ω peptide. However, the fact that the complementing activity can be revealed only after a treatment by urea shows that the ω peptide synthesized in these mutants is not in its correct conformation.

Table 7. Activities of different amber mutants before and after urea treatment. Urea treatment was performed on crude extracts. ω activities were measured before urea treatment and after elimination of urea by dialysis, using S 908 as acceptor.

	U/ml ω Activity	
Strain	Before urea	After urea
YA 486	80	486
U 281	90	2300
U 231	67	250
W 4680[x]	2700	2400

[x] Deletion mutant.

Not all amber mutants reveal ω activity after urea treatment. We do not know whether this means that there is no reinitiation of ω, or on the contrary, the peptide is synthesized, but the correct tertiary structure can not be obtained by a simple unfolding-refolding process.

This result suggests that reinitiation in these ω-distal nonsense mutants does not occur at or near the ω barrier but further up along the z gene. If so, we would expect the ω activity, revealed after urea treatment of extracts of these mutants, to turn up in a heavier fraction than those from ω-proximal amber mutants and deletions. This apparently is the case:

Studying the properties of the ω obtained after urea treatment from amber mutant U 281, we have found that the active fraction is not retained on Sephadex G 100; that is to say, it behaves like the "heavy ω," isolated from small deletions. On the other hand, chymotrypsin, which liberates ω from the wild-type enzyme, increases about 5-fold the yield of ω which can be revealed after urea treatment of the amber mutant.

Moreover, ambiguous reinitiation at two different points on the gene may not be expected to occur with the same frequency. This again is the case. The ω-proximal amber mutant NG 750 and the ω-distal amber mutant U 281 furnish, after urea treatment, a ratio of ω to transacetylase 5 times higher than observed with any deletion mutant.

It will be appreciated that the reactivation, following urea treatment, of ω activity in certain types of mutants may imply some consequences significant for theories concerned with the rules of protein folding and the thermodynamic stability of the native state.

SUMMARY AND CONCLUSIONS

Complementation studies of β-galactosidase reveal that the restoration of enzymatic activity may occur by at least two different mechanisms:

(1) Complementation between various point mutants, involving the repair of lesions by reassociation of differently altered subunits.

(2) Noncovalent reassociation of certain complementary fragments of the normally single polypeptide chain which forms the protomer of β-galactosidase can reassemble into an enzymatically active structure.

The first type of complementation has been found to occur not only in β-galactosidase but in several other systems involving oligomeric proteins. As a great deal of literature has been published on this subject, we do not want to discuss it in further details.

The second type of complementation has not yet been described in any other system. Therefore, we should like to discuss some implications of this phenomenon concerning the tertiary and quaternary structure of globular proteins.

The complementation studies lead to the following main conclusions:

(a) The protomer of wild-type β-galactosidase involves a single covalent peptide chain

(b) Complementation between deletion mutants of the z gene involves association between peptides corresponding to different fragments of the wild-type chain.

One of the most remarkable features of this complementation is the high affinity and specificity that the peptide fragments exhibit, being able to reassociate even at high dilution and in the presence of other proteins. A similar mechanism may be involved in the reconstruction of ribonuclease from different fragments produced under action of subtilysin (Richards and Vithayathil, 1959). But the restoration of ribonuclease activity has never been studied under conditions where "foreign" proteins might interfere with the reconstruction (Richards, private communication).

In order to account for the highly-specific reassociation of the peptide fragments, one has to suppose that both peptides are able separately to fold into a configuration close to the one which the corresponding segments achieve in the wild-type enzyme. If this can be confirmed it would be necessary to suppose that several independent nucleation centers are responsible for the folding of β-galactosidase (or in a more general way, for the folding of long polypeptide chains).

From mol wt and sedimentation coefficient measurements one can compute a frictional ratio value for the ω peptide ($f/f_0 = 1.1$), which supports the hypothesis that ω is indeed a globular protein. There is so far no reason to suppose that ω exhibits different tertiary structures in the complemented and wild-type enzymes.

The catalytic properties of wild-type and complemented enzymes are very similar: their turnover numbers and Michaelis constants for substrate are virtually identical; as we have seen, these functional similarities are reflected by structural similarities, in particular in their quaternary structure.

Concerning the mechanism of complementation between peptide fragments, we are not yet in a position to draw a definite conclusion. Further studies with pure proteins are needed for the better understanding of this phenomenon. From studies with crude extracts (Ullmann and Monod, 1969) it seems that the interaction is a complex one, and it may involve several pathways to achieve the native-like, enzymatically-active structure. It may be of great interest that the presence of a small molecule (actually a substrate analog of β-galactosidase) can influence specifically the pathway of formation of the tertiary and quaternary structure of the protein.

The origin of the peptide fragments, produced not only by deletion mutants, but also by the wild-type as well as amber mutants is not yet solved. Among the possibilities which have been considered we favor the hypothesis according to which the fragments are produced, during the synthesis of the peptide, by the misreading of certain ambiguous codons, interpreted with low frequency, as restart points.

ACKNOWLEDGMENTS

We express our gratitude to Dr. J. Monod for his unfailing advice and encouragement and for helpful criticism of the manuscript; and to Drs. F. Jacob, M. Goldberg and H. Buc for many stimulating discussions.

Research, in the Department of Molecular Biology, at the Pasteur Institute, has been aided by grants from the U.S. National Institutes of Health, the Délégation Générale à la Recherche Scientifique et Technique, the Centre National de la Recherche Scientifique, the Commissariat à l'Energie Atomique, and the Collège de France.

REFERENCES

BECKWITH, J. R. 1964. A deletion analysis of the *lac* operator region in *Escherichia coli.* J. Mol. Biol. *8:* 427.

BENZER, S. 1957. The elementary units of heredity, p. 70. *In* W. D. McElroy and B. Glass [ed.] The Chemical Basis of Heredity. Johns Hopkins Press, Baltimore.

BRENNER, S. 1959. Mechanism of gene action, p. 304. *In* G. E. W. Wolstenholme and M. O'Connor [ed.] CIBA Symposium on Biochemistry of Human Genetics. J. and A. Churchill, London.

COOK, A. and J. LEDERBERG. 1962. Recombination studies of lactose nonfermenting mutants of *Escherichia coli* K-12[1,2] Genetics. *47:* 1335.

CRICK, F. H. C. and L. E. ORGEL. 1964. The theory of inter-allelic complementation. J. Mol. Biol. *8:* 161.

FINCHAM, J. R. 1959. On the nature of the glutamic dehydrogenase produced by inter-allele complementation of the *am* locus of *Neurospora* crassa. J. Gen. Microbiol. *21:* 600.

GOLDBERG, M. E. 1970. Tertiary structure of *Escherichia coli* β-D-galactosidase. J. Mol. Biol. *46:* 441.

GOLDBERG, M. E. and S. EDELSTEIN. 1970. Sedimentation equilibrium of pauci-disperse systems. Subunit structure of complemental β-galactosidase. J. Mol. Biol. *46:* 431.

JACOB, F. and J. MONOD. 1961. On the regulation of gene activity. Cold Spring Harbor Symp. Quant. Biol. *26:* 193.

JACOB, F., A. ULLMANN, and J. MONOD. 1964. Le promoteur, élément génétique nécessaire à l'expression d'un opéron. Compt. Rend. Acad. Sci. Paris. *258:* 3125.

————, ————, ————. 1965. Délétions fusionnant l'opéron lactose et un opéron purine chez *E. coli.* J. Mol. Biol. *13:* 704.

MORRISON, S. and D. ZIPSER. 1970. The polypeptide products of nonsense mutations. J. Mol. Biol. (in press).

NEWTON, A. 1966. Effect of nonsense mutations on translation of the lactose operon of *Escherichia coli.* Cold Spring Harbor Symp. Quant. Biol. *31:* 181.

PERRIN, D. 1963. Complementation between products of the β-galactosidase structural gene of *Escherichia coli.* Cold Spring Harbor Symp. Quant. Biol. *28:* 529.

PERRIN, D. and J. MONOD. 1963. On the reversibility by treatment with urea of the thermal inactivation of *E. Coli* β-galactosidase. Biochem. Biophys. Res. Commun. *12:* 425.

RICHARDS, F. M. and P. J. VITHAYATHIL. 1959. The preparation of subtilisin-modified ribonuclease and the separation of the peptide and protein components. J. Biol. Chem. *234:* 1459.

SCHLESINGER, M. J. and D. LEVINTHAL. 1965. Complementation at the molecular level of enzyme interaction. Ann. Rev. Microbiol. *19:* 267.

ULLMANN, A., F. JACOB, and J. MONOD. 1967. Characterization by in vitro complimentation of a peptide corresponding to an operator-proximal segment of the β-galactosidase structural gene of *E. coli.* J. Mol. Biol. *24:* 339.

————, ————, ————. 1968. The subunit structure of wild-type versus complemented β-galactosidase of *Escherichia coli.* J. Mol. Biol. *32:* 1.

ULLMANN, A. and J. MONOD. 1969. On the effect of divalent cations and protein concentration upon renaturation of β-galactosidase from *Escherichia coli.* Biochem. Biophys. Res. Commun. *35:* 35.

ULLMANN, A., D. PERRIN, F. JACOB, and J. MONOD. 1965. Identification par complémentation in vitro et purification d'un segment peptidique de la β-galactosidase d'*Escherichia coli.* J. Mol. Biol. *12:* 918.

ZIPSER, D. 1963. A study of the urea-produced subunits of β-galactosidase. J. Mol. Biol. *7:* 113.

Chapter VIII

Transcription Starts and Stops in the *lac* Operon

JEFFREY H. MILLER

Harvard Medical School
Boston, Massachusetts

The levels of different proteins in single cell bacteria vary over a wide range. One example of a control mechanism which enables the cell to regulate the levels of different proteins under changing environmental conditions is provided by the Jacob-Monod theory (Jacob and Monod, 1961). The amounts of a given protein can be varied as much as 1000-fold by the use of specific inducers and repressors.

However, one finds that the maximal levels of different proteins also vary greatly (Pardee and Beckwith, 1962). A good example is the *lac* repressor, compared with β-galactosidase. Under conditions of full induction, β-galactosidase comprises as much as 3% of the soluble cell protein. In contrast the repressor, apparently synthesized constitutively, comprises only about 0.003% of the soluble cell protein (Müller-Hill, Crapo, and Gilbert, 1968; Gilbert and Müller-Hill, 1966). Since β-galactosidase (monomer) is 3.5 times the weight of the repressor (monomer), this corresponds to a difference, in terms of numbers of molecules, of several thousand-fold (Zabin, 1963). What types of control mechanisms exist which enable the cell to vary the maximal levels of different proteins over such a wide range?

Operons undoubtedly have discrete starting and stopping points for messenger-RNA synthesis. The starting point for transcription has been termed the *promoter*. By varying the nucleotide sequence of the promoter, the cell can fix the rate of transcription for any given operon. Alternatively, the level of various proteins could be governed by varying the efficiency of the ribosomal binding site on the mRNA. Also, different messengers might be degraded at different rates. Each of these mechanisms and others would give the cell great flexibility in controlling the maximal rates of expression of its numerous genes.

173

In this chapter the studies on the *lac* promoter will be reviewed, as will be the work on fused-operons involving the *lac* genes. Some preliminary results concerning messenger termination are also considered.

To avoid confusion it would be best if one defined the term "promoter" at the outset. The promoter, for a given operon, is the region in which transcription is initiated. Initiation here includes all of the processes involved in transcription up until the point at which the first RNA nucleotide is copied from the DNA. This includes recognition and binding of RNA polymerase, and the opening up of the DNA duplex. At some future date it may be possible to further subdivide the promoter into regions in which these different processes occur. Thus, the promoter governs the rate of transcription of a given operon. This rate can be altered by altering the promoter.

HISTORICAL BACKGROUND

The initiation of mRNA synthesis was first hypothesized to occur at the operator, in the original Jacob and Monod theory (Jacob and Monod, 1961). In this version of the model, the operator possessed a dual function: (1) interacting with the repressor and (2) serving as an initiation point for transcription.

This idea was supported by the existence of two types of mutations which appeared to map in the same small region. One, o^c mutations, rendered the operator partially insensitive to repressor and thus partially constitutive. These mutations are discussed in detail in other chapters. The second type of mutation was termed the o^o mutation. This mutation appeared to be an operator mutation which was defective in the initiation of transcription. o^o's were pleiotropically negative for all of the enzymes in the operon. They were *cis*-dominant, and they appeared to map in the operator region, between *i* and *z* (Jacob and Monod, 1961).

We now know, through the work of Beckwith, that these original o^o mutations are not operator mutations at all (Beckwith, 1964; Brenner and Beckwith, 1965). He was able to show by deletion mapping that these mutations do not map within the repressor sensitive site, but appear to lie within the *z* gene. In addition, both o_2^o and o_{U118}^o have been shown to be nonsense mutations which are suppressible by known nonsense suppressors (Brenner and Beckwith, 1965). Therefore, these are merely examples of extreme polar mutations. Some of the revertants of o^o mutations synthesize an altered β-galactosidase, which further proves that the mutations lie within the structural *z* gene (Jacob and Monod, 1961).

The term o^o was originally to describe lesions which "resulted in a permanent block of the transcriptional process" (Jacob and Monod, 1961). o^o mutations would exist if the operator is involved in transcription initiation. As far as I know, no single point mutation in the operator region of the *lac* operon has been found which severely lowers the levels of the enzymes. (One would not consider a large genetic insertion into the operator as an o^o mutation, even though it might result in the same phenotype, since this lesion results in the removal of the promoter from the rest of the operon.) For a diagram of this region see Fig. 3.

In 1964 Jacob, Ullman and Monod proposed that a distinct site for initiation of mRNA transcription existed, and was situated between *o* and *z*. (Jacob, Ullman, and Monod, 1964). They termed this region the promoter. The rationale for the location of the promoter was based on two lines of evidence. From the work done at the Pasteur Institute, it was known that among the operator constitutive mutants which were found there was a class of mutants which were also i^-. It seemed logical that these mutations were deletions extending from the *i* gene into the operator. Since the induced levels of β-galactosidase were unchanged, it was reasonable to assume that there was no essential element between *i* and *o*.

We now know from the work of Davies and Jacob that in fact these i^-o^c mutants are not deletions, but point mutants. Most of them are trans-dominant i^-'s which negatively complement a wild-type *i* gene (Davies and Jacob, 1968; Müller-Hill, Crapo and Gilbert, 1968). Others are double mutants (Beckwith, unpubl.; Davies, unpubl.).

The second line of evidence was the failure to find the *o-z* class of deletions (Class 1) depicted in Fig. 1. Sixty-seven z^-y^+ revertants of an i^s diploid, selected for growth on melibiose at 42°C, were characterized. All 67 were of Class 2 and appeared to fuse *z* and *y* to another operon. The apparent absence of Class 1 deletions suggested the existence of an essential element between the operator and the *z* gene (Jacob, Ullman, and Monod, 1964).

Quite recently, Jacob has isolated several *o-z* deletions (Eron, Beckwith, and Jacob, this volume). Some of their properties will be discussed later but their existence rules out this latter argument.

After the publication of the first promoter paper, (Jacob, Ullman, and

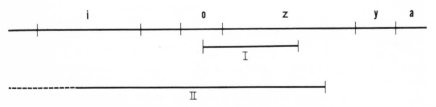

FIGURE 1. Deletions which result in constitutive production of permease.

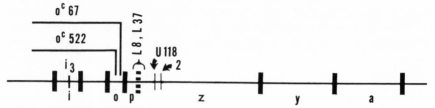

FIGURE 2. Original map of promoter mutations.

Monod, 1964), Scaife and Beckwith (1966) isolated several mutants which had the properties expected of promoter mutants. These mutations, which were cis-dominant pleiotropic negatives, were at first mapped between part of the operator and the z gene, and appeared to support the previous argument for an essential element in this region (Scaife and Beckwith, 1966). This mapping assignment was based solely on the fact that these mutants recombined with two i-o^c deletions, #67 and #522. Figure 2 shows how the assumption that 67 and 522 are deletions ending in the operator leads to this assignment. However, as previously mentioned, 67 and 522 are not deletions but point mutants. The fact that the promoter mutants recombine with them does not allow any conclusions as to their map position.

PROMOTER MUTANTS

The four mutants isolated were L1, L8, L29, and L37 (Scaife and Beckwith, 1966; Ippen, Miller, Scaife, and Beckwith, 1968). L8 and L37 appear to be identical. L1 has since been shown to be a deletion extending into the i gene (Miller, Ippen, Scaife, and Beckwith, 1968; Miller, Platt, and Weber, this volume).

The principle used in isolating these mutations was simply to screen UV-induced lac mutants for ones which were leaky. They assumed that some mutations, by altering but not abolishing the promoter, would lower the maximal levels of the lac enzymes. Table 1 shows that these mutants

Table 1. Enzyme Levels in Leaky lac-Mutants

% Induced wild-type mutant	% Induced wild type			
	β-galactosidase		galactoside permease +inducer	Thiogalactoside transacetylase +inducer
	−inducer	+inducer		
L1	1	2	2–5	1
L8	0.03	8	5–10	5
L37	0.03	6	5–10	5
lac+ (wild type)	0.1	100	100	100

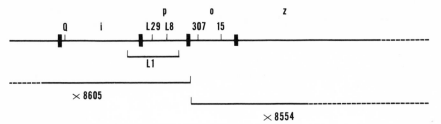

FIGURE 3. Deletion map of the promoter-operator region.

are pleiotropic in their effects. Also, the promoter mutants are *cis*-dominant (Scaife and Beckwith, 1966). The presence of an additional z^- operon (with an intact promoter) does not increase the level of β-galactosidase. And, an additional z^+ copy, introduced on an episome, is not affected by the presence of the promoter mutants on the chromosome.

Map Position. Figure 3 shows the map position of the promoter mutants. The use of deletions has enabled the absolute ordering of *p* with respect to *i* and *o* (Ippen, Miller, Scaife, and Beckwith, 1968; Miller, Ippen, Scaife, and Beckwith, 1968). Thus, deletion X8554 does not recombine with any operator mutant tested, but does with all of the promoter mutants. Also, deletions such as X8605 do not recombine with promoter mutants, but do with operator mutants.

The Promoter Deletion L1. L1 does not recombine with either of the two promoter point mutants (Miller, Ippen, Scaife, and Beckwith, 1968). It does recombine with several o^c mutants tested. At first glance, the levels of β-galactosidase in Table 1 are somewhat surprising. How can one account for the small but consistent 1.5- 1.8-fold induction ratio exhibited in strains with this lesion? Table 2 shows the result of an experiment which demonstrates that this induction ratio is due to a residual amount of repressor activity (Miller, Platt, and Weber, this volume). In this experiment one asks whether repression in *trans* can be detected in strains harboring L1 on an episome which is z^- and contributes no β-galactosidase. On the

Table 2. Repression by L1 in *trans* of an i^- z^+ strain

Episome	β-galactosidase	
	No IPTG	IPTG
i^+, p^+, z^-	0.6	550
(+), L1, z^-	300	550
(Q), L1, z^-	29	550
(Q, 115), L1, z^-	9	

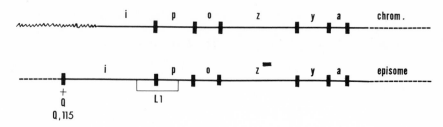

FIGURE 4. Diploid used for *trans* repression test of L1.

chromosome is a good z^+ gene, but an *i*-deletion (Fig. 4). Thus the only source of repressor is the episome which contains L1. In addition, the double mutant i^Q, L1 and the triple mutant i^Q, 115, L1 (all in the z^- form) were also tested. These latter mutations are in the *i*-promoter, and synthesize 10 and 35 times more repressor, respectively, than wild type. It can be seen that L1 exhibits the same 1.8-fold repression ratio in *trans*, and that one can increase the amount of repression by increasing the amount of the L1 repressor. This strongly suggests that the repressor in strains with L1 is altered.

Recently, the repressor from strains with L1 has been purified and shown to differ physically from the wild-type repressor (Miller, Platt, and Weber, this volume). It appears certain that L1 is a deletion extending from the *i*-gene into the *lac* promoter.

Revertants of Promoter Point Mutants. The work of Rita Arditti has shown that L8 and L29 are point mutants (Arditti, Scaife, and Beckwith, 1968). She analyzed the revertants of these mutants by selecting for growth on raffinose plus IPTG. Raffinose is a trisaccharide with a melibiose moiety. In *E. coli* K12 the *lac* permease transports raffinose into the cell (Schaefler, 1967). The levels of permease in a p^- mutant are too low, however, to allow growth on this sugar. Thus, this selective technique selects for strains which have at least 8–10% of the wild-type levels of *lac* permease. Arditti examined spontaneous revertants as well as those induced by 2AP, UV, and NG. Table 3 shows some of the revertants from L8 and L37. It appears that the revertants fall into three classes. Those with maximal levels which are less than 25% of the wild type, those between 50 and 75% and those with 100% of the wild type level. However, 2-aminopurine, which induces transitions, only induced reversions to wild type. Thus, for L29, 40/40 revertants are wild type with 2AP and for L37, 190/190. In contrast, for NG induced revertants of L37, 21/48 are wild type.

P1 mapping indicates that the wild-type revertants are at the same site as the original mutation. These results suggest that both L29 and L37

Table 3. Specific activity of β-galactosidase in revertants of L8 and L37

Strain		β-Galactosidase		Transacetylase induced
		uninduced	induced	
CA8000 (*lac*+)		0.1	100	100
CA8005 (L37)		0.02	6	3
	NG20	0.06	13	11
Intermediate	U89	0.05	14	10
	U82	0.08	21	18
level	U63	0.09	21	24
	NG11	0.1	28	21
revertants	NG27	0.1	58	51
	NG15	0.1	68	60
	NG18	0.1	72	68
	S2	0.1	75	71
Full	S1	0.1	100	100
level	NG4	0.1	100	100
revertants	U2	0.1	100	100
	2-AP64	0.1	100	100

were induced by transitions, and that the intermediate revertants were caused by transversions. In addition, P1 mapping has shown two intermediate level revertants are due to mutations at a second site, although very close to the original mutation.

Revertants of L1. No true revertants of this deletion have ever been isolated which have restored levels of repressor and also normal *lac* levels. However, mutations with partially restored *lac* promoter activity have been isolated (Scaife and Miller, unpubl.). Some of these are actually pseudo-revertants, resulting in an increased level of read-through from the *i* gene promoter. These mutations map at the far left extremity of the *i* gene. Other mutations appear to map within the remainder of the *lac* promoter. These revertants show a spectrum of levels ranging almost as high as wild type. Many of the spontaneous revertants appear to be unstable, and are probably insertions. It is conceivable that some nitroso-guanidine induced L1-revertants represent single base changes, but these mutants await further characterization.

A comprehensive study of base-analog induced revertants of L1 might reveal a great deal of information about the structure of the *lac* promoter.

FUSED OPERONS

Two operons are said to be fused if the genes of one operon are under the control of a second operon. The phenomenon of fused operons was first described by Jacob, Ullman, and Monod (1965). In this study they examined 16 deletions which ended in the *z* gene at one terminus (deleting the *lac* controlling elements), and within the purine operon at the other, leaving the pur controlling elements intact. In all deletions of this type, the remaining genes of the *lac* operon are now under purine control. Thus, IPTG has no effect. However, in the presence of excess adenine, the *lac* permease and transacetylase are repressed, and when adenine is limiting the synthesis of these enzymes is derepressed. Later, Signer and Beckwith succeeded in transposing the *lac* region to a new location on the *E. coli*. chromosome near the *trp* operon (Beckwith, Signer, and Epstein, 1966). By screening deletions of the T1 locus, now between *trp* and *lac,* they were able to isolate fusions of *lac* to *trp* (Fig. 6), which are completely analogous to the purine-*lac* fusions.

These are two examples of fusions in which the deletion ends in a structural gene of both operons. In the *trp-lac* fusions, it is thought that the synthesis of mRNA, which initiates at the *trp* promoter, proceeds into the *lac* operon because the end of the *trp* operon, which would contain any stop signal, has been deleted. The RNA-polymerase cannot recognize that it is now transcribing a different operon.

When *E. coli* is treated with lysates of colicin V, B, and ϕ80v, the only survivors are strains with mutations of the *trp*-linked T1 locus (Beckwith and Signer, 1966). A large percentage of these mutations are deletions (Franklin, Dove, and Yanofsky, 1965; Beckwith and Signer, 1966). How deep into the *lac* operon would a deletion have to cut in order to bring about a functional fusion to the *trp* genes? The *trp* operon is under the control of the threonine-linked *trp*R locus. In the R⁻ state the levels of the *trp* enzymes are 30–50-fold higher than in the R⁺ state (Morse and Yanofsky, 1969). Figure 5 shows some of the deletions which have been isolated with ends in *trp,* and Table 4 shows the R⁻ and the R⁺ level of β-galactosidase in these strains (Reznikoff, Miller, Scaife, and Beckwith, 1969). It is evident that one can isolate deletions which end within the *lac* operator and still fuse the two operons. However, when the deletion

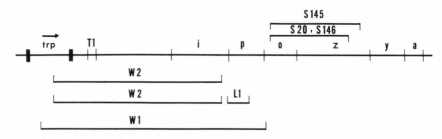

FIGURE 5. Deletions which fuse the *lac* genes to the *trp* operon; *o-z* deletions.

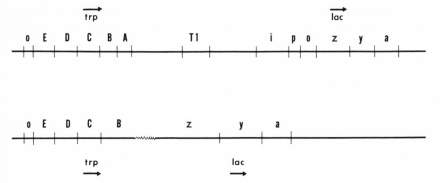

FIGURE 6. Fusion of the *trp* operon into the *z* gene.

ends in the *i* gene there is no observed increase in β-galactosidase when the *trp* operon is derepressed. Even when the background level of the *lac* enzymes is lowered by introducing a promoter point mutation, there is still no significant increase observed, as shown in Table 4. When L1 is introduced instead of L8, some of the *trp*-i fusion strains now show a large increase in β-galactosidase activity when *trp* is derepressed (Reznikoff, Miller, Scaife, and Beckwith, 1969).

These results suggest that there is no barrier to transcription in the *p*, *o*, or *z* region of the *lac* operon. A comparison of W2-L1 with W2-L8, in Table 4, indicates that there is an mRNA stop signal at the end of the *i* gene. Unfortunately, it is not clear from these experiments whether L1 gives an increase in β-galactosidase in these strains because it eliminates a transcriptional stop signal or because it reduces translational polarity. For instance, L1 might change the reading frame whereas L8 might not.

Table 4. Control of β-galactosidase synthesis by the *trp*R gene in fusion strains

Strain	*lac* character	β-galactosidase activities	
		*trp*R⁻	*trp*R⁺
X7700	Wild-type	—	686
X8047-T1ʳ	L1	40	—
W1	Fusion derivative of X8047	445	11
W2-L1		270	42
W3-L1		151	43
W4		445	60
W5-L1		384	64
W6-L1		218	58
W2-L8		62	59
W3-L8		53	51

It is plausible that RNA-polymerase can recognize the end of an operon. It may respond to specific sequences or different configurations of the DNA without the aid of additional factors. Alternatively, protein factors might be required to cause termination of mRNA transcription. Recently Roberts (1969) has purified an *E. coli* protein, the *rho* factor, which behaves as an mRNA stop factor in an in vitro λmRNA synthesizing system (Roberts, unpubl.). In the absence of this factor the RNA product is large and heterogeneous as shown by sucrose gradient centrifugation of RNA which specifically hybridizes with separated strands of λDNA. With *rho* added, one sees a totally different pattern of λmRNA. The large RNA disappears and there appear two new RNA species which probably correspond to the known in vivo messengers.

The existence of an mRNA stop factor immediately suggests the presence of a stop signal on which the factor operates. A feasible model for the *lac* genes would have a region at the end of the *i* gene, and also after the *a* gene which acts as a binding site for the mRNA stop factor. One should then be able to find mutations in this site which result in an increased amount of mRNA read-through.

DELETIONS OF THE PROMOTER

Several deletions (Fig. 5) extending into the *lac* promoter have been isolated (Reznikoff, Miller, Scaife, and Beckwith, 1969). To date none of those isolated recombine with either of the two promoter point mutations. All, however, recombine with both o^c markers tested. These deletions severely lower the levels of the *lac* enzymes. It is difficult to assess the residual promoter activity in these strains because most, if not all, of the deletions have brought the *lac* operon partially under the control of another operon. Thus, all of the W series of deletions are fused to *trp* (Reznikoff, Miller, Scaife, and Beckwith, 1969). This can be shown by detecting a significant increase in β-galactosidase after derepression of the *trp* operon. The *lac* operon in X8605 may be under the control of the T1 operon (Ippen, Miller, Scaife, and Beckwith, 1968). Only L1 (the wild-type *i* gene is read at too low a rate to significantly contribute to the residual level of *lac* enzymes in strains with L1) and W1 can thus be properly evaluated. W1 ends in the *trpE* gene (Reznikoff, Miller, Scaife, and Beckwith, 1969).

In strains with W1, when *trp* is derepressed, the level of β-galactosidase increases from 11 to 445 units (Table 4). Practically all of the β-galactosidase level in the $trpR^+$ state is due to the *trp* basal level, since the introduction of a nonsense mutation into the remainder of the E gene reduces the $trpR^+$ β-galactosidase level to 0.6 units (Reznikoff, unpubl.). Even this low level could be accounted for by a residual read-through past the nonsense block. Two o^c mutations recombine with W1. In addition, the *trpR⁻* level of β-galactosidase is repressed several fold by an *i* gene introduced into the cell on an episome, indicating that the operator is at least partly functional (Reznikoff, Miller, Scaife, and Beckwith, 1969). It should be noted that read-through of the type displayed by W1 (*trpR⁻*) is never repressed more than several fold in the presence of an intact *i* gene.

DISTINCTNESS OF THE OPERATOR AND PROMOTER

In the presence of a wild-type repressor, L1 strains are 100-fold repressible (Miller, Ippen, Scaife, and Beckwith, 1968). Thus, in an extensive deletion of the promoter, the operator is normal or very close to normal. The W1 deletion has less than 0.2% of the normal promoter activity. Yet this deletion still retains an appreciable part of the operator region and some operator function. These two results are incompatible with a model which has the operator and promoter identical.

In addition, three *o-z* deletions (Fig. 5) have been characterized (Eron, Beckwith, and Jacob, this volume). These deletions all end late in the *z* gene and have 40–50% constitutive levels of transacetylase. As can be seen from Table 5, the maximal levels of transacetylase are not greatly reduced in two of the strains. Yet the deletions do not recombine with any of the operator constitutive mutations tested. The near maximal level of *S145* is further evidence that part of the promoter is distinct from part of the operator in the *lac* operon.

It is difficult to prove that two elements are completely distinct. It remains possible that part of the promoter region overlaps with some of the operator. If there were significant overlap between the operator and promoter, one would expect some operator mutants to have maximal levels of the *lac* enzymes which were lower than wild type. Recently, Sadler (pers. commun.) has isolated a large number of operator constitutive mutations. Almost all of these strains have normal induced levels of β-galactosidase. A small percentage have a 50% reduction in the maximal level. Since these are hydroxyl-amine induced and are revertable, they appear to be point

Table 5. Thiogalactoside transacetylase activities of *o-z* deletion strains

	− inducer	+ inducer
S20	5	12
S145	43	88
S146	31	54
Wild-type	0.2	100

Values are presented as percentage of the fully induced wild-type control.

mutations. Among the revertants of the reduced-level mutants are a class of strains with partially restored o+ levels. The maximal level of these revertants is now 25% of the normal level. One interpretation of this finding is that there is a small region of overlap between these two elements and that these mutations are in that region. Then, the pseudo-revertant would actually be a third base substitution, different from the wild type and the mutant.

All of the promoter mutants have a lower inducibility ratio (Scaife and Beckwith, 1966; Miller, Ippen, Scaife, and Beckwith, 1968). Instead of being 1000-fold inducible, L8 and L29 are about 200–250-fold inducible. One interpretation of this result is that this inducibility ratio is merely that of a 0.5% operator constitutive and that there is a slight degree of overlap between the operator and promoter.

Both of the above results are difficult to interpret however. If the operator is transcribed, it is conceivable that some alteration in the operator could reduce the level of β-galactosidase, perhaps by altering the secondary structure of the message and thus affecting the ribosomal binding site.

The basal level result is harder to interpret. It can be argued that only part of the *lac* basal level is due to transcription initiation at the *lac* promoter, and part reflects some other process, for instance read-through of the *i* gene message. If this is true, then a mutation in the *lac* promoter would not lower the basal level by the same ratio as it would the induced level.

Other evidence for the distinctness of the promoter and operator should come from revertant studies of promoter mutants. If one studied 2-aminopurine induced revertants of L1, and analyzed those which mapped in the *lac* promoter, one could ask whether any have an altered operator. An analogous study can be extracted from the data of Table 3 (Arditti, Scaife, and Beckwith, 1968). Although the promoter mutant L37 has an induction ratio of 300 (compared with 1000 for wild type), it can be seen that some of the second site revertants, U82, U63 and NG11, have the same 250–300-fold induction ratio. This might argue that either the original or the second site mutation has a slight loss of operator activity. These effects are small and subject to several objections. For instance, the relevant question is really whether the wild type promoter overlaps with the operator, and not whether a reconstructed promoter does.

One should distinguish here between genetic overlap, and functional overlap. If the same region of the DNA interacts both with RNA polymerase and the repressor, then genetic overlap exists. If these two regions do not overlap, but are very close together, the binding of the repressor to the operator could still interfere with the binding of RNA polymerase to the promoter. This would be a functional overlap. Perhaps the crucial experiments can only be done in vitro. The best way to prove that there is a functional overlap between the operator and promoter is to demonstrate competitive binding between the repressor and RNA-polymerase.

UP-PROMOTER MUTATIONS

It should be possible to change a low level promoter by mutation into one which now functions at a higher rate. By screening revertants of a TSS mutant in the *i* gene, Müller-Hill found two mutations (induced by nitrosoguanidine) which resulted in a 10-fold higher level of *lac* repressor (Müller-Hill, Crapo, and Gilbert, 1968). One of these mutations, termed Q, has been mapped, and is at the left end of the *i* gene (Miller, Beckwith, and Müller-Hill, 1968), Fig. 3. This fact, plus other data, makes it likely that Q is a mutation in the *i*-promoter resulting in an increase in the *i* gene message (Müller-Hill, Crapo, and Gilbert, 1968).

Recently, I have selected additional mutations in the *i*-promoter, starting out with the double mutant *i*^{Q}, L1. Some of the β-galactosidase in this strain is due to a contribution from the *i*-promoter, since L1 has fused the *lac* genes to the *i* gene. By selecting for higher levels of permease, and screening for strains which synthesize more repressor, SQ (super Q) was isolated. When combined with Q, this mutation allows a fifty-fold overproduction of the *lac* repressor (Miller and Platt, in prep.). This leads one to ask whether a natural promoter can be raised by mutation from a low level one to a high level one by a series of mutations. Actually, one could also consider the second site revertants of L8 and L1 as up-promoter mutants (Scaife and Miller, unpubl.; Arditti, Scaife, and Beckwith, 1968). If only three or four base changes separate the highest level promoters from the lowest level ones, one could make the conversion with base analog mutagens.

Alternatively, it might be possible to isolate mutants which are the result of an insertion of genetic material into the *i* promoter. It has recently been shown that insertions of varying amounts of DNA occur spontaneously within a gene (Jordan, Saedler, and Starlinger, 1968; Shapiro, 1969). If some of the foreign material contains an efficient promoter, and it is inserted in the correct place, Q-like mutations would result.

If there is a space containing no mRNA stop signals preceeding the *i* gene, then a mutation increasing the level of transcription of the gene or genes preceeding *i* would also increase the level of repressor. In fact, high level promoters might actually have evolved in this manner, with a further deletion of the material in between occurring at later times (suggested to me by Gilbert and Müller-Hill).

STUDIES ON mRNA IN VIVO AND IN VITRO

By measuring the pulse labeled RNA from IPTG induced cells, and then hybridizing to denatured DNA from ϕ80d*lac* phage, Gros and coworkers have been able to detect specific *lac* mRNA (Contesse, Naono, and Gros, 1966; Attardi, Naono, Rouviere, Jacob, and Gros, 1963). Much of this work is discussed by Gros (this volume). These workers have shown that there is little message specific to *lac* which is detectable in extracts of strains with the promoter point mutant L8, and none in strains with very early polar mutations. However, chloramphenicol significantly increases the proportion of large, *lac* specific message in nonsense mutants, while it has no effect on the promoter mutant (Contesse and Gros, 1968; Contesse, Crepin, and Gros, 1969). Since it is thought that chloramphenicol prevents accelerated message breakdown in polar mutants, these authors conclude that the promoter mutant has an effect at the transcription level.

While suggestive, these results are not conclusive. What is really needed is an in vitro mRNA synthesizing system, using ϕ80d*lac* DNA or even pure *lac* DNA, which synthesizes specific *lac* messenger. When this is achieved, one can attempt to demonstrate a different amount of *lac* messenger between wild-type and the promoter mutants. One example of such a system, and its use in the study of promoter mutants comes from the work of Roberts. He uses λDNA as a template for RNA polymerase, and measures RNA which hybridizes with the appropriate purified single strand of λDNA. He recently has been able to demonstrate that λ*sex*, a presumed promoter mutant in λ, synthesizes less RNA hybridizable to the *1* strand (Roberts, unpubl.). In addition, he has looked at λC17. In vivo evidence indicates that this mutation is an up-promoter mutation for at least the *o* and *p* genes of λ (Pereira da Silva and Jacob, 1968; Packman and Sly, 1968). In vitro, he finds that λC17 synthesizes more RNA from the *o-p* region of the *r* strand than wild type.

SUMMARY

The initiation of transcription of the *lac* operon occurs at the promoter site. The location of this region is such that the order of genetic elements is: promoter, operator, structural genes. Both point mutations and deletions in the *lac* promoter region have been isolated. These result in lowered maximal levels of expression of the *lac* enzymes. Mutations which raise the level of the *i*-promoter have also been isolated. These result in elevated levels of repressor.

The properties of deletions cutting into the promoter, and of *o-z* deletions prove that the promoter and operator sites do not completely overlap.

By deleting the controlling elements of *lac*, fusions of the *lac* operon to other operons have been isolated. Studies of the properties of *trp-lac* fusions indicate the existence of a messenger stop signal at the end of the *i* gene.

REFERENCES

ARDITTI, R. R., J. G. SCAIFE, and J. R. BECKWITH. 1968. The nature of mutants in the *lac* promoter region. J. Mol. Biol. *38:* 421.

ATTARDI, G., S. NAONO, J. ROUVIERE, F. JACOB, and F. GROS. 1963. Production of mRNA and regulation of protein synthesis. Cold Spring Harbor Symp. Quant. Biol. *28:* 363.

BECKWITH, J. R. 1964. A deletion analysis of the *lac* operator region in *E. coli.* J. Mol. Biol. *8:* 427.

BECKWITH, J. R., and E. R. SIGNER. 1966. Transposition of the *lac* region of *E. coli.* I. Inversion of the *lac* operon and transduction of the *lac* by φ80. J. Mol. Biol. *19:* 254.

BECKWITH, J. R., and E. R. SIGNER, and W. EPSTEIN. 1966. Transposition of the *lac* region of *E. coli.* Cold Spring Harbor Symp. Quant. Biol. *31:* 393.

BRENNER, S., and J. R. BECKWITH. 1965. *Ochre* mutants, a new class of suppressible nonsense mutants. J. Mol. Biol. *13:* 629.

CONTESSE, G., M. CREPIN, and F. GROS. 1969. Transcription de l'operon lactose chez des mutants promoteurs de *E. coli.* Compt. Rend. Acad. Sci. *268:* 2301.

CONTESSE, G., and F. GROS. 1968. Action du chloramphenicol sur la transcription de l'operon lactose chez des mutants polaires d'*Escherichia coli.* Compt. Rend. Acad. Sci. *266:* 262.

CONTESSE, G., S. NAONO, and F. GROS. 1966. Effet des mutations polaires sur la transcription de l'operon lactose chez *E. coli.* Compt. Rend. Acad. Sci. *263:* 1007.

DAVIES, J., and F. JACOB. 1968. Genetic mapping of the regulator and operator genes of the *lac* operon. J. Mol. Biol., *36:* 413.

FRANKLIN, N. C., W. F. DOVE, and C. YANOFSKY. 1965. The linear insertion of a prophage into the chromosome of *E. coli* shown by deletion mapping. Biochem. Biophys. Res. Commun. *18:* 910.

GILBERT, W., and B. MÜLLER-HILL. 1966. Isolation of the *lac* repressor. Proc. Nat. Acad. Sci. *56:* 1891.

IPPEN, K., J. H. MILLER, J. G. SCAIFE, and J. R. BECKWITH. 1968. New controlling element in the *lac* operon of *E. coli.* Nature *217:* 825.

JACOB, F., and J. MONOD. 1961. On the regulation of gene activity. Cold Spring Harbor Symp. Quant. Biol. *26:* 196.

JACOB, F., A. ULLMAN, and J. MONOD. 1964. Le promoteur, élément génétique necessaire a l'expression d'un opéron. Compt. Rend. Acad. Sci. *258:* 3125.

JACOB, F., A. ULLMAN, and J. MONOD. 1965. Deletions fusionnant l'opéron lactose et un opéron *purine* chez *Escherichia coli.* J. Mol. Biol. *13:* 704.

JORDAN, E., H. SAEDLER, and P. STARLINGER. 1968. o° and strong polar mutations in the *gal* operon are insertions. Mol. Gen. Genet. *102:* 353.

MILLER, J. H., J. R. BECKWITH, and B. MÜLLER-HILL. 1968. Direction of transcription of a regulatory gene in *E. coli.* Nature *220:* 1287.

MILLER, J. H., K. IPPEN, J. G. SCAIFE, and J. R. BECKWITH. 1968. The promoter-operator region of the *lac* operon of *E. coli.* J. Mol. Biol. *38:* 413.

MORSE, D. E., and C. YANOFSKY. 1969. Amber mutants of the *trp*R regulatory gene. J. Mol. Biol. *44:* 185.

MÜLLER-HILL, B., L. CRAPO, and W. GILBERT. 1968. Mutants that make more *lac* repressor. Proc. Nat. Acad. Sci. *59:* 1259.

PACKMAN, S., and W. S. SLY. 1968. Constitutive λDNA replication by λC17, a regulatory mutation related to virulence. Virology *34:* 778.

PARDEE, A. B., and J. R. BECKWITH. 1962. Control of constitutive enzyme synthesis. p. 255. Symposium on Informational Macromolecules. Academic Press, New York.

PEREIRA DA SILVA, L. H., and F. JACOB. 1968. Étude génétique d'une mutation modifiant la sensibilité a l'immunité chez le bacteriophage λ. Ann. Inst. Pasteur *115:* 145.

REZNIKOFF, W. S., J. H. MILLER, J. G. SCAIFE, and J. R. BECKWITH. 1969. A mechanism for repressor action. J. Mol. Biol. *43:* 201.

ROBERTS, J. 1969. Promoter mutation in vitro. Nature *223:* 480.

SCAIFE, J. G., and J. R. BECKWITH. 1966. Mutational Alteration of the maximal level of *lac* operon expression. Cold Spring Harbor Symp. Quant. Biol. *31:* 403.

SCHAEFLER, S. 1967. Isolation of constitutive β-galactosidase permease mutants in *E. coli.* by selection for raffinose fermentation. Bact. Proc. p. *54.*

SHAPIRO, J. A. 1969. Mutations caused by the insertion of genetic material into the galactose operon of *E. coli.* J. Mol. Biol. *40:* 93.

ZABIN, I. 1963. Proteins of the *lac* system. Cold Spring Harbor Symp. Quant. Biol. *28:* 431.

Chapter IX

Glucose Effects:
Inducer Exclusion and Repression

BORIS MAGASANIK

Department of Biology
Massachusetts Institute of Technology
Cambridge, Massachusetts

INTRODUCTION

The inhibitory effect of glucose on the formation of β-galactosidase by *E. coli* was recognized at an early date by Monod (1947). He observed diauxic growth of the organism in a medium containing a mixture of glucose and lactose as sources of carbon. The phenomenon is illustrated in Fig. 1, from a later paper by Epstein, Naono, and Gros (1966). It can be seen that the synthesis of the enzyme is almost completely inhibited during the first phase of rapid growth on glucose. The differential rate of enzyme synthesis is highest during the period of very slow growth that follows the exhaustion of glucose. Enzyme synthesis continues at a somewhat lower differential rate when rapid growth resumes on lactose.

β-galactosidase is not the only enzyme whose rate of synthesis is reduced by the presence of glucose in the medium. It has been found that glucose interferes generally with the synthesis of catabolic enzymes other than those involved in the degradation of glucose by enteric bacteria, bacilli, yeasts, and other microorganisms (Magasanik, 1961).

I shall attempt to show in this chapter that glucose interferes with the synthesis of β-galactosidase in inducible strains of *E. coli* in three ways. It excludes the inducer from cells that do not contain a high level of the *lac y* gene controlled permease; it represses β-galactosidase strongly, but transiently, when added to cells growing on another source of carbon (transient repression); it represses the enzyme weakly but permanently during balanced growth (catabolite repression). Both repressive effects can be overcome by the addition of cyclic AMP. The repressive effects have as their target the promoter site of the *lac* system and interfere with the initiation of transcription of the *lac* operon.

189

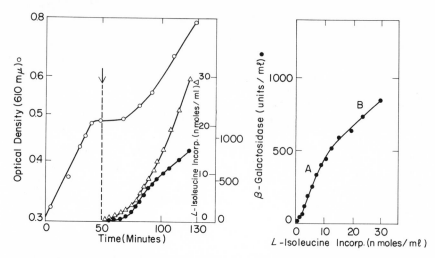

FIGURE 1. Diauxic growth and the differential rate of β-galactosidase synthesis. The cells (*E. coli* 200 PS/F'*lac*, inducible for β-galactosidase) are growing in a medium containing 0.4 mg/ml of glucose and 2 mg/ml of lactose. Radioactive isoleucine was added at the arrow. From Epstein, Naono and Gros (1966).

INDUCER EXCLUSION

Cohn and Horibata (1959a) reported that glucose at a concentration of 10^{-3} M completely prevented synthesis of β-galactosidase and of β-galactoside permease when added together with 5×10^{-4} M TMG to uninduced cells of *E. coli*, growing on succinate. When glucose was added to a culture that had been in contact with inducer for 15 min, this strong inhibition of enzyme synthesis was not observed; rather, enzyme was produced at approximately one-half the differential rate of a control culture without glucose. These effects of glucose are shown in Fig. 2. The experiments illustrated in Fig. 2 also reveal that the inhibition can be overcome by increasing the concentration of TMG. The fact that preinduction can partly overcome the effect of glucose suggested, in line with the analysis of the preinduction phenomenon by Monod (1956), that the acquisition of the β-galactoside permease makes it possible for the cells to become induced in the presence of glucose. The correctness of this view was demonstrated by Cohn and Horibata (1959a) who found that preinduction does not overcome the inhibitory effect of glucose in a mutant lacking the β-galactoside permease. On the other hand, β-galactosidase itself is not required for the acquisition by the *lac* system of resistance to glucose: a β-galactosidase-less mutant is able to form β-galactoside permease in the presence of glucose after preinduction.

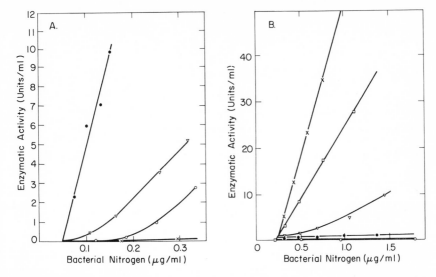

FIGURE 2. Effect of glucose on the synthesis of β-galactosidase induced by methyl β-D-thiogalactoside (TMG). In A, glucose and TMG were added simultaneously to the cells (*E. coli* ML30, normal *lac* system) growing on succinate. ●————●, 0.5 mM TMG; ∇————∇, 20 mM TMG and mM glucose; ○————○, 3 mM TMG and mM glucose; x————x, 0.5 mM TMG and 1 mM glucose. In B, 1 mM glucose was added to the cells (*E. coli* ML30) growing on succinate at various times after the start of induction by 0.1 mM TMG. x————x, No glucose added; ○————○, zero min; ●————●, 5 min; ∇————∇, 10 min; □————□, 15 min. From Cohn and Horibata (1959a).

These facts indicate that the acquisition of the permease during induction in the absence of glucose enables the cells to form subsequently β-galactosidase and β-galactoside permease in the presence of glucose. Cohn and Horibata (1959b) suggested that the high internal concentration of TMG in the preinduced cells counteracts the inhibitory effects of glucose. According to this idea, a competitive relationship between glucose and inducer would be expected. This competition can be best observed in cells lacking the β-galactoside permease, whose internal level of inducer is proportional to the concentration of inducer in the medium. Clark and Marr (1964) therefore exposed a permease-less mutant of *E. coli* to different concentrations of IPTG in media containing 0.04 M glycerol or 0.02 M glucose as major source of carbon and measured the differential rates of enzyme synthesis. Their results, illustrated in Fig. 3, show that at concentrations of IPTG insufficient to give maximal rates of enzyme synthesis on glycerol, glucose exerts a stronger inhibitory effect than at higher concentrations of IPTG. Nevertheless, it is impossible to overcome the inhibitory effect of glucose completely by raising the concentration

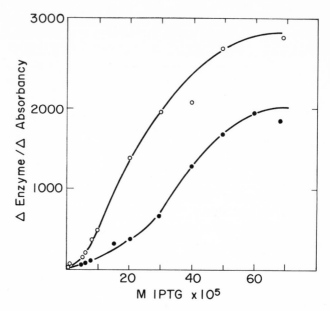

FIGURE 3. The effect of isopropyl-β-D-thiogalactoside (IPTG) concentration on the differential rate of β-galactosidase synthesis during growth on glucose or glycerol. *E. coli* strain ML3, which lacks β-galactoside permease grows on 40 mM glycerol (open circles) or on 20 mM glucose (closed circles). From Clark and Marr (1964).

of IPTG. In fully induced cultures, the differential rate of enzyme synthesis on glucose is approximately two thirds that on glycerol. Similar observations have been made in many other strains; generally, the maximal differential rate on glucose is one half that on glycerol.

The results obtained by Clark and Marr are in good agreement with the observation of Cohn and Horibata (1959a, b) (see Fig. 2) that preinduction does not completely protect against glucose. Glucose appears therefore to have two effects: one that can be overcome by inducer and one insensitive to inducer. This conclusion receives additional support by the finding of Cohn and Horibata (1959b) that in a constitutive mutant β-galactosidase synthesis is less sensitive to glucose than in the inducible parent. The constitutive mutant produces the enzyme in the presence of glucose at approximately the same rate as the parent strain when induced before glucose addition.

Clark and Marr (1964) interpreted their observation of an inducer-specific glucose effect as evidence that glucose could increase the level or activity of the *i* gene controlled repressor. However, there is no independent experimental evidence for this view. As a matter of fact, the results of Cohn and Horibata and of Clark and Marr can be equally well accounted for by assuming that glucose interferes with the entry of inducer into cells whose β-galactoside permease level is low. In this case, too, inhibition of enzyme synthesis by glucose would be overcome by increasing the level of inducer or by increasing the specific permease through induction in the absence of glucose. There is good experimental evidence for this hypothesis. Cohn and Horibata (1959a) have shown that glucose has very little effect on TMG uptake mediated by the y gene controlled permease, and Kepes (1960) has shown that glucose has a strong inhibitory effect on TMG uptake not mediated by this permease. It is quite likely that in uninduced cells the phosphotransferase system (Kundig, Ghosh, and Roseman, 1964) facilitates the entry of inducers of the *lac* system. Recent observations suggest that glucose-1-phosphate or glucose-6-phosphate may regulate the entry of sugars by this system (Kaback, 1969; Pastan and Perlman, 1969).

If we return to a consideration of the glucose-lactose diauxie (Fig. 1) we can explain the failure of the culture to form enzyme in the presence of glucose by the ability of glucose to exclude lactose from the cell. This is corroborated by two observations: cells preinduced in the absence of glucose can be induced by lactose in the presence of glucose and an increase in the lactose level of the culture prevents diauxic growth (Loomis and Magasanik, 1967).

In addition to glucose, there are other compounds that interfere with the formation of β-galactosidase by preventing the entry of inducer. Of particular interest is D-galactose, a compound that is in addition a weak inducer of the *lac* operon. In contrast to glucose, galactose interferes with the transport of inducers by the *lac* y gene-controlled permease. The effect of galactose is most marked in galactokinase-less mutants, apparently because their inability to metabolize galactose results in a higher intracellular level of the sugar (Loomis and Magasanik, 1966).

PHYSIOLOGIC BASIS OF REPRESSION

TRANSIENT REPRESSION

I shall now consider the effects of glucose on the *lac* system that cannot be attributed to the exclusion of inducer. These effects can only be investigated in cells exposed to IPTG at a concentration not less than 0.5 mM (see Fig. 3); even in such cells, the possibility must be kept in mind that the particular experimental condition may have enhanced the ability of glucose to prevent the entry of inducer.

Following an observation of Boezi and Cowie (1961), Moses and Prevost (1966) reported that the addition of 10 mM glucose to cells of a number of strains of *E. coli* growing on glycerol and exposed to 0.5 mM IPTG brought about a strong, but temporary inhibition of β-galactosidase formation. During the period of this strong inhibition, which lasted, depending on the strain, between 0.1 and 0.5 of a generation, the growth rate was slightly increased; in other words, the effect of glucose was not to arrest the overall synthesis of protein but to prevent specifically formation of the enzyme. After the period of strong repression, enzyme synthesis in the culture that had received glucose continued at approximately one-half the differential rate of a glycerol culture. This weak repression is generally seen when glycerol and glucose cultures are compared (see Figs. 2 and 3).

At the same time, Paigen (1966a) reported on a similar transient repression of β-galactosidase by glucose. However, his effect could only be seen in a particular strain of *E. coli* K12. This sensitivity to glucose arose in a gal^- (K^-T^-) mutant, strain W12, but is apparently not related to the defects in galactose metabolism. Paigen's experimental procedure differed slightly from that of Moses and Prevost: he grew the cells on glycerol, harvested the cells and then suspended them in a medium containing glucose as only source of carbon. Thus, in the experiments of Moses and Prevost the cells were exposed to both glucose and glycerol and in Paigen's experiment, only to glucose. This difference in procedure accounts for the difference in the observations: most strains of *E. coli* experience transient repression when they are freshly exposed to glucose during growth on glycerol, but only certain mutant strains experience it when shifted from a glycerol to a glucose medium. These observations are illustrated in Fig. 4a from a paper by Tyler, Loomis, and Magasanik (1967). It can be seen that in *E. coli* strain 3000, cells grown in a glycerol medium and then shifted to a glucose medium produce β-galactosidase at approximately one half the rate of those cells that remained in the glycerol medium; the glycerol-grown cells exposed to glucose in the presence of glycerol produce the enzyme initially at a very low differential rate and gradually approach the differential rate characteristic of the glucose culture.

The analysis of the transient effect is made difficult by the permanent but weaker repression of β-galactosidase synthesis by glucose. The susceptibility of different strains to the two effects of glucose differs somewhat and it is apparent that a relatively weak transient effect could be missed when followed by a relatively strong permanent effect. It is, therefore, advantageous to study the transient effect of glucose in an organism resistant to the permanent effect of glucose. Such an organism is available in a mutant of strain 3000, strain LA12, isolated by Loomis and Magasanik (1965), which has a mutation in the *cat* gene, which abolishes sensitivity to catabolite repression of catabolite-sensitive enzymes (Tyler et al., 1969). Fig. 4b shows that this organism continues to make β-galactosidase at

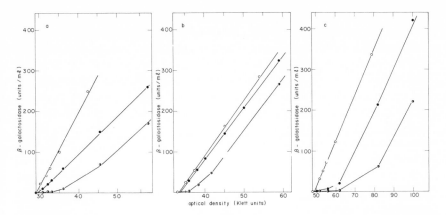

FIGURE 4. Transient repression of induced β-galactosidase synthesis by glucose. The strains of *E. coli* used had a normal *lac* system. (a) Strain 3000, normal sensitivity to catabolite repression; (b) strain LA12, insensitive to catabolite repression and slow growth on glucose; (c) strain LA12G, insensitive to catabolite repression and rapid growth on glucose. The cells were grown in a medium containing 0.4% glycerol as the only source of carbon. They were transferred to media containing 1 mM isopropyl-β-D-thiogalactoside and 0.4% glycerol (0), or 0.4% glucose (●), or a mixture of glucose and glycerol (◑) as source of carbon. From Tyler, Loomis, and Magasanik (1967).

the same differential rate whether it continues to grow on glycerol or is shifted to glucose; when glucose is added to the glycerol culture, the transient repression occurs, but after recovery the rate of enzyme synthesis is the same as in the culture that has not received glucose.

Strain LA12 grows slower on glucose than its parent strain 3000. A mutant of LA12, selected for its ability to grow rapidly on glucose, strain LA12G (Loomis and Magasanik, 1965), has retained the ability of strain LA12 to form β-galactosidase at the same differential rate on glucose as on glycerol; this organism experiences a transient strong repression of β-galactosidase synthesis when shifted from the glycerol medium to the glucose medium (Fig. 4c). Apparently, the mutation which enables strain LA12G to grow on glucose more rapidly than strain LA12, has also made it possible for glucose to exert the transient effect in the absence of another carbon source. It seems likely that the strain described by Paigen (1966a) resembles strain LA12G, and differs from the other strain of *E. coli* by increased ability to take up glucose.

The possibility that the cause of transient repression is exclusion of the inducer by glucose can be definitely ruled out. Cells forming β-galactosidase constitutively because of a mutation in the *lac i* gene or the *lac o* site are sensitive to transient repression by glucose. This is illustrated in Fig. 5a and b from the paper by Tyler, Loomis, and Magasanik (1967).

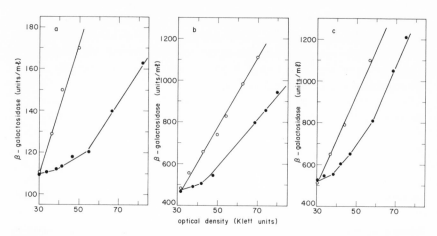

FIGURE 5. Transient repression of constitutive β-galactosidase synthesis by glucose. The cells were grown on 0.4% glycerol as sole source of carbon. The cultures were divided and glucose was added to one portion. (0), Culture containing only glycerol; (●) culture containing glucose and glycerol. (a) Strain 2000, *lac* o^c; (b) strain 3300, *lac* i$^-$; (c) strain t-5, *lac* i$^-$ and resistant to catabolite repression. From Tyler, Loomis, and Magasanik (1967).

After the escape from transient repression these constitutive cells, just as fully-induced cells of the wild type, produce the enzyme at a differential rate one-half that of the cells growing on glycerol. Strain T-5 (Fig. 5c), a *lac* i$^-$ mutant to the *cat*$^-$ strain LA12G experiences transient repression but subsequently produces β-galactosidase at the same rate as in the medium containing only glycerol.

An investigation of the conditions necessary and sufficient for transient repression revealed that many compounds other than glucose exert this effect when added to cells growing on a variety of carbon sources. The cells must possess a permease permitting rapid entry of the added compound, but the compound need not be metabolized and the degree and duration of the transient repression are not related to the intracellular level of the compound.

A good example of these conclusions is the observation that TMG, which cannot be metabolized, exerts transient repression on β-galactosidase in *lac* i$^-$y$^+$z$^+$ cells, but not in cells that are either *lac* i$^+$ or *lac* y$^-$. β-galactosidase itself is not involved in the repression, since another susceptible enzyme, tryptophanase, is transiently repressed by TMG in *lac* i$^-$z$^-$y$^+$ cells (Tyler and Magasanik, 1970).

Another example is the observation that glycerol and α-glycerolphosphate cause transient repression only in strains that form the elements of the *glp*- system, glycerolkinase, glycerolphosphate dehydrogenase and glycerolphosphate permease, constitutively. Of these three elements only glycerolkinase is required for repression by glycerol, and only glycerol-phosphate permease for repression by α-glycerolphosphate. No relation between the intracellular level of glycerolphosphate and the intensity of transient repression was found in the experiments with the *glp-* constitutive strains (Tyler and Magasanik, 1970).

Finally, glucose analogs, such as 2-deoxyglucose and α-methylglucoside, repress transiently β-galactosidase in the wild strain (Tyler, Loomis, and Magasanik, 1967) and glucose transiently represses the enzyme in a mutant lacking glucose-6-phosphate dehydrogenase, as well as hexose-phosphate isomerase (Tyler and Magasanik, 1970). In these instances, the cell possesses the constitutive glucose permease system that involves phosphorylation of glucose or glucose analogs but cannot metabolize the phosphorylated compounds. Again, there is no relation between the intracellular level of glucose-6-phosphate and the intensity of transient repression.

The weak permanent repression characteristic of glucose depends on the metabolism of glucose beyond glucose-6-phosphate. No permanent repression is exerted by glucose on the mutant that cannot metabolize it beyond glucose-6-phosphate, nor by TMG, glycerol, α-glycerolphosphate, or the glucose analogs (Tyler et al., 1969; Tyler and Magasanik, 1970; Tyler, Loomis, and Magasanik, 1967). This observation, together with the fact that strain LA12G is insensitive to permanent repression by glucose but highly sensitive to transient repression, suggests that the effector or effectors of transient repression and of the weaker permanent repression are formed by different pathways.

Prevost and Moses (1967) suggested that a phosphorylated metabolite of glucose may be the effector of transient repression. They found that the pools of glucose-6-phosphate, fructose-1, 6-diphosphate, 6-phosphogluconic acid and NADPH increase during the transient repression exerted by glucose. It is, however, unlikely that the addition of nonmetabolizable compounds, which as we discussed earlier, are capable of exerting transient repression, would affect the pools of these phosphorylated metabolites. Moreover, Tyler and Magasanik (1970) observed transient repression by succinate in a mutant strain incapable of generating glucose-6-P or 6-phosphogluconic acid under the conditions of the experiment and in another strain unable to generate fructose-1, 6-diphosphate under the conditions of the experiment. There is, therefore, no evidence that an increase on the intracellular level of phosphorylated metabolites is the cause of transient repression.

There is also no evidence that transient repression is related to a change in RNA metabolism. The rate of RNA synthesis does not change significantly after addition of glucose and the sedimentation pattern of the newly-made RNA is indistinguishable from that made in the absence of glucose (Tyler, Loomis, and Magasanik, 1967).

There is good evidence that the phosphotransferase system described by Kundig, Ghosh, and Roseman (1964) plays an important role in transient repression. This system consists of an enzyme (EI), which catalyzes the transfer of phosphate from phosphoenolpyruvate to a small protein, HPr; and of a set of enzymes (EII), which catalyze the transfer of phosphate from phospho-HPr to different carbohydrates. The system is essential for the entry of the carbohydrates into the cell (Tanaka, Fraenkel, and Lin, 1967). Mutants in EI or HPr are unable to grow on a variety of carbohydrates including glucose. Mutants in individual EII enzymes lose the ability to grow on a particular carbohydrate, for example glucose. Pastan and Perlman (1969) report that the β-galactosidase of mutants deficient in EI or HPr is more sensitive to transient repression by glucose or α-methylglucoside than the β-galactosidase of the wild strain. The β-galactosidase of a mutant lacking the specific EII for glucose is insensitive to repression by glucose and galactose.

Different behavior was observed in another EI deficient mutant. This mutant also lacks glucokinase and is, therefore, completely incapable of glucose metabolism (Tanaka, Fraenkel, and Lin, 1967). Because of a mutation in the *lac i* gene, this EI deficient strain produces β-galactosidase constitutively. Tyler and Magasanik (1970) found that in this EI-deficient strain β-galactosidase is insensitive to transient repression by glucose and by TMG; this insensitivity is apparently a consequence of the defect in EI, since in a revertant whose EI is normally functional, β-galactosidase is sensitive to repression by glucose and by TMG. The loss of sensitivity to TMG is not a consequence of diminished entry of TMG; wild strain, EI-deficient mutant, and revertant concentrate TMG equally well.

Similar results were obtained with a mutant of the EI-deficient strain whose glycerol degrading system (*glp*) is constitutive: glycerol failed to exert transient repression of β-galactosidase. As expected, a replacement of the defective EI system by a functional one through transduction restored the sensitivity of β-galactosidase to repression by glycerol (Tyler and Magasanik, 1970).

It is therefore clear that mutational alterations in the phosphotransferase system may affect the sensitivity of the cell to transient repression. There is, however, no obvious relation between the known functions of the components of the phosphotransferase system in carbohydrate transport and their role in transient repression. Nevertheless, because of the association of the phosphotransferase system with the cell membrane, the results suggest that transient repression is triggered by an interaction of the exogenously-added compound with the phosphotransferase system during its passage through the cell membrane.

This idea is in good accord with the observation by Tyler and Magasanik (1970) that β-galactosidase is transiently repressed by glucose in cells of a *lac i⁻* strain growing on lactose. This organism produces glucose from lactose and consequently, the addition of glucose does not alter the endogenous, but only the exogenous composition of the culture. The newly-added compound may interact during passage through the membrane with the phosphotransferase system and produce an effector of transient repression.

The most intriguing aspect of the phenomenon of transient repression is the escape. Very little is known about the change that occurs after approximately one third or one half a generation time restoring the cells' ability to make the susceptible enzyme at a rapid rate. It has been shown that all the cells of the population are subject to the repression and that all escape at approximately the same time (Tyler and Magasanik, 1969). It is also known that, after escape from transient repression exerted by one compound, the cells are still sensitive to transient repression by another compound (Tyler and Magasanik, 1970). Finally, cells kept in a medium lacking a source of nitrogen do not escape from transient repression; after restoration of the nitrogen source, the usual period elapses before the escape takes place (Paigen, 1966a; Tyler, Loomis, and Magasanik, 1967).

The class of enzymes showing susceptibility to transient repression has not been exhaustively defined. In addition to β-galactosidase, the other elements of the *lac* system, the permease and the transacetylase are transiently repressed by glucose (Tyler, Loomis, and Magasanik, 1967). The severe transient repression by glucose of tryptophanase, D-serine deaminase and galactokinase has been reported (Paigen, 1966a; Moses and Prevost, 1966). On the other hand, alkaline phosphatase is not repressed by glucose (Tyler and Magasanik, 1970). The enzymes sensitive to transient repression are inducible and have catabolic functions; they are also subject to varying degrees to the less severe permanent repression exerted by glucose.

CATABOLITE REPRESSION

The basic observation has already been described in the preceding sections. The differential rate of β-galactosidase synthesis in fully-induced cells growing exponentially on glucose is approximately one half that in cells growing exponentially on glycerol or succinate (see Figs. 2, 3 and 4). This effect of glucose is not a reflection of interference with inducer uptake since constitutive β-galactosidase synthesis is similarly repressed by glucose (see Fig. 5).

The repressive effect is not only exerted by glucose. Gluconic acid has a similar effect and glucose-6-phosphate a considerably stronger effect;

it may reduce the differential rate to approximately one tenth of that observed in the glycerol medium (Hsie and Rickenberg, 1967). In a medium containing succinic acid, lactic acid or fructose as a major source of carbon, the enzyme is formed at approximately the same differential rate as in one containing glycerol (Mandelstam, 1962). The compounds exerting repression are better carbon sources than those which fail to exert repression: the growth rate on glucose or glucose-6-phosphate is approximately 30–40% greater than the growth rate on glycerol, but no quantitative correlation between the rate of growth and the degree of repression can be made.

Many other enzymes in a variety of microorganisms are similarly repressed by the presence of glucose in the growth medium. In many instances the repression is much more severe than that observed in the case of β-galactosidase. An investigation of the repression of histidase in *Aerobacter aerogenes* led Neidhardt and Magasanik (1956) to the hypothesis implied in the name later coined for the phenomenon, catabolite repression (Magasanik, 1961). According to this hypothesis enzymes responsible for the catabolism of carbon compounds are sensitive to repression by their ultimate products or by an effector compound whose intracellular concentration depends on the level of these products. The ultimate products of catabolism, the catabolites, are compounds such as ATP, phosphoenolpyruvate, α-ketoglutarate, ribose-5-phosphate, etc., the building blocks and energy donors for the biosynthetic reactions. Repression of catabolic enzymes by these catabolites is analogous to repression of biosynthetic enzymes by their ultimate products, with the interesting difference that each biosynthetic pathway leads to a different product, while catabolic pathways lead to the same mixture of products. We may therefore expect that the metabolism of one carbon compound may produce catabolites capable of causing repression of the enzymes responsible for the degradation of another carbon compound.

According to this view, catabolite repression will occur when a compound is metabolized so rapidly that the level of catabolites is greater than required for the biosynthetic reactions. Glucose is metabolized more rapidly than other carbon compounds; it may be expected that its degradation will increase the catabolite pools sufficiently to cause repression of the enzymes responsible for the catabolism of other compounds. The view that the catabolism of glucose, rather than the glucose molecule itself, is responsible for the repressive effect, is substantiated by the finding that glucose fails to exert the characteristic permanent repression of β-galactosidase in a mutant lacking glucose-6-phosphate dehydrogenase and hexosephosphate isomerase (Tyler et al., 1969). As mentioned earlier, glucose does transiently repress β-galactosidase in this strain (Tyler and Magasanik, 1970).

According to the catabolite repression hypothesis, the synthesis of a sensitive enzyme should be inhibited when the intracellular level of catabolites exceeds the demands of biosynthesis, whatever be the source of catabolites. A convenient way of creating such an unbalanced condition is to deprive the cells of the source of nitrogen or, in the case of auxotrophic mutants, of the required amino acid, purine or pyrimidine (Magasanik, 1957). The slow rate of protein synthesis in such cells can be readily measured by assaying the rate of incorporation of a labeled amino acid.

In the review published in 1957, I postulated that in such starved cells the metabolism of any carbon source should prevent the synthesis of enzymes sensitive to catabolite repression; in cells starved for the required nitrogen source or nutrilite and also for the carbon source, synthesis of the sensitive enzymes should proceed at a rate corresponding to the overall rate of protein synthesis. I was able to point out that this phenomenon had actually been observed in the case of β-galactosidase. Pardee (1955) had reported that glycerol-grown cells of a uracil-requiring mutant of *E. coli* fail to produce β-galactosidase when induced in a medium lacking uracil but containing glycerol; they produce the enzyme induced in a medium containing neither uracil nor a source of energy. A careful study by Mandelstam (1957, 1961) extended these results. It showed that nitrogen-, pyrimidine- or amino acid-starved cells produce β-galactosidase at the same differential rate as unstarved cells when induced in a medium free of any utilizable carbon source; addition of such a carbon source (glycerol in the case of glycerol-grown cells, succinate in the case of succinate-grown cells) prevents synthesis of any measurable amount of enzyme. The extreme imbalance of catabolism and anabolism in the starved cells has lead to a much more severe repression of β-galactosidase than that produced by glucose in normally growing cells.

In general, any condition that leads to a severe decrease in the rate of protein synthesis without concomitant reduction in the rate of catabolism results in repression of β-galactosidase. Such conditions are, in addition to starvation for an amino acid, purine or pyrimidine, starvation for thymine or phosphate (McFall and Magasanik, 1960, 1962), and damage of the cells by ultraviolet radiation (Bowne and Rogers, 1962; Pardee and Prestidge, 1963) or by the decay of incorporated radiophosphorous (McFall, 1961).

The effects of starvation on the constitutive synthesis of β-galactosidase were also explored by Mandelstam (1962). In a series of elegant experiments he determined the rate of β-galactosidase synthesis in *E. coli* ML308, a constitutive mutant growing in nitrogen-limited chemostats with glucose or glycerol as the source of carbon. The results of these experiments are illustrated in Fig. 6. It can be seen that decreasing the growth rate by restriction of the rate of supply of ammonia leads to a marked

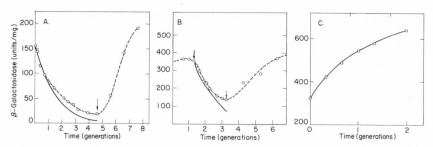

FIGURE 6. Effect of nitrogen-starvation and of energy-starvation on the constitutive synthesis of β-galactosidase. The cells (*E. coli* ML308, constitutive for β-galactosidase) were grown in flask culture and transferred to a continuous-culture apparatus. (A) Glucose as carbon source and nitrogen-limited medium; the initial doubling time was 165 min. At the arrow, the flow rate was changed to give a doubling time of 51 min. The continuous curve is the theoretical curve for total repression of enzyme synthesis. (B) Glycerol as carbon source and nitrogen-limited medium. The initial doubling time was 165 min. After 1.3 generations (left hand arrow), this was changed to 300 min. At the right hand arrow, the flow rate was changed to give a doubling time of 70 min. The continuous curve is the theoretical curve for total repression. (C) Glucose as carbon source and limiting. The doubling time was 173 min (Mandelstam, 1962).

fall in the enzyme level in cells growing on glucose or on glycerol. In another experiment, it was shown that decreasing the growth rate by restriction of the rate of supply of glucose results in an increased level of β-galactosidase. Thus, it is quite clear that under the condition of nitrogen starvation constitutive synthesis of β-galactosidase is repressed whether glucose or glycerol is the source of carbon. However, the degree of repression does not only depend on the rate of nitrogen-limited growth, but also on the nature of the carbon source. When the growth rate is limited by nitrogen to approximately one third of the unlimited rate on glucose, glucose reduces the rate of β-galactosidase formation to less than one tenth of the maximal rate, but glycerol has no effect. Apparently, the effector of catabolite repression can be produced from both glucose or glycerol, but is more readily produced from glucose.

This hypothetical effector has not yet been identified. Galactose has been proposed (McFall and Mandelstam, 1963) but was later shown not to play a specific role in catabolite repression (Beggs and Rogers, 1966; Loomis and Magasanik, 1966; Paigen, 1966b; Llanes and McFall, 1969). It has also been shown by the use of appropriately blocked mutants that neither a phosphate ester easily derived from glucose, such as glucose-6-phosphate, glucose-1-phosphate, UDP-glucose, UDP-galactose, galactose-1-phosphate, and 6-phosphogluconate nor a compound of the citric acid cycle, is specifically required for catabolite repression (Loomis and Magasanik, 1966). The observation that N-acetyl-glucosamine can cause repression in a mutant that cannot metabolize this compound because it lacks N-acetylglucosamine-6-phosphate deacetylase has led Dobrogosz (1969) to the hypothesis that N-acetylglucosamine-6-phosphate is the effector of catabolite repression for β-galactosidase. This interpretation is, however, questionable since N-acetylglucosamine represses β-galactosidase only transiently, unless it is used at a concentration sufficiently high to inhibit growth.

It is not known whether a specific effector of catabolite repression for the *lac* system exists. A mutation in a site unlinked to the *lac* operon, *cat⁻*, which was thought to cause specifically the release of the *lac* operon from catabolite repression (Loomis and Magasanik, 1965), has now been shown to release other susceptible systems as well (Rickenberg, Hsie, and Janeček, 1968). For a detailed discussion of the *cat⁻* mutation, see Tyler et al., 1969.

MOLECULAR BASIS OF REPRESSION

Recent observations have suggested the interesting possibility that cyclic 3', 5' AMP plays a key role in transient repression and catabolite repression. The presence of cyclic 3', 5' AMP in *E. coli* was discovered by Makman and Sutherland (1965). These investigators found the nucleotide at a level of approximately 0.007 mM in acetate-grown cells of the Crooke's strain and at a level of approximately 0.002 mM in glucose-grown cells of this strain. Suspension of the cells in phosphate buffer devoid of a source of energy led to a marked increase in the level of cyclic AMP: its concentration rose to 0.1 mM in the course of 20 min. Addition of glucose to these starved cells brought about a very rapid loss of cyclic AMP.

These observations suggested to Perlman and Pastan (1968a) that cyclic AMP may play a role in the repression exerted by glucose on β-galactosidase. They treated glycerol-grown cells of the Crooke's strain with EDTA according to the method of Leive (1965) to make them permeable to nucleotides. They returned these cells to the glycerol medium, and induced them with IPTG in the presence or absence of glucose and of cyclic AMP; they followed β-galactosidase synthesis for a period of 20 min. Under these conditions the major effect of glucose is transient repression; this repression was fully overcome by the addition of 0.3 mM cyclic AMP.

Ullmann and Monod (1968) showed that the addition of cyclic AMP could overcome catabolite repression. The nucleotide was found to have no effect on the differential rate of β-galactosidase synthesis when added at a level of 5 mM to untreated cells of *E. coli* strain 3000 growing on succinate in the presence of IPTG; it increased the differential rate of enzyme synthesis of similar cells growing on glucose almost to that observed in the cells growing on succinate.

Later investigations by Perlman, de Crombrugghe, and Pastan (1969) show that, in untreated cells, cyclic AMP can overcome transient repression by glucose when supplied at 1 mM concentration and catabolite repression by glucose when supplied at 5 mM concentration.

The effect of cyclic AMP is not restricted to β-galactosidase. Addition of the nucleotide accelerates the synthesis of many other catabolite-sensitive enzymes by enteric organisms growing in a glucose-containing medium; it has no effect on the synthesis of catabolite-insensitive enzymes, such as alkaline phosphatase and tryptophan synthetase (Perlman and Pastan, 1968a; Pastan and Perlman, 1969; deCrombrugghe et al., 1969).

Although these observations leave no doubt that repression by glucose can be overcome by exogenously added cyclic AMP, they do not prove that endogenous cyclic AMP plays a role in the synthesis of catabolite-sensitive enzymes. Important evidence for this view would be the demonstration that the endogenous level of cyclic AMP is lower in glucose-6-phosphate- or glucose-grown cells than in glycerol-grown cells (condition of catabolite repression) and that the level is drastically reduced when cells growing on glycerol are exposed to glucose (condition of transient repression). So far such changes in the intracellular level of cyclic AMP have not been reported.

Indirect evidence for a reduction of the level of cyclic AMP under conditions of catabolite repression was provided by an observation of Monard, Janeček, and Rickenberg (1969). They found that cells of E. coli contain an enzyme capable of converting cyclic 3′, 5′ AMP to AMP, presumably a phosphodiesterase. The level of this enzyme was higher in glucose-grown cells of the wild strain than in glucose-grown cells of a mutant insensitive to repression by glucose, though sensitive to repression by glucose-6-phosphate. They suggest that in the wild strain glucose activates the enzyme and thus reduces the intracellular level of cyclic AMP. However, no evidence has been presented that the enzyme of the wild strain is *less* active in glycerol-grown cells than in glucose-grown cells, nor that the enzyme of the mutant is *more* active in glucose-6-phosphate-grown cells than in glucose-grown cells. Furthermore, it has not been shown that the insensitivity to the repression exerted by glucose and the decreased level of the phosphodiesterase are the results of a single mutation.

An enzyme capable of forming cyclic AMP from ATP was recently discovered in extracts of E. coli (Tao and Lipmann, 1969). A mutant of E. coli unable to grow on lactose or galactose was found to lack this enzyme and could not be induced to form β-galactosidase unless cyclic AMP is added (Perlman and Pastan, 1969). This observation supports the view that cyclic AMP plays an essential role in the synthesis of the enzyme. However, it has not yet been shown that a single mutational event is responsible for the inability of the strain to form the cyclase and for the dependence of β-galactosidase synthesis on exogenously supplied cyclic AMP.

Other evidence for a role of cyclic AMP in the synthesis of β-galactosidase has recently been published by Chambers and Zubay (1969). They found that the synthesis of β-galactosidase in a cell-free system from *E. coli* is stimulated 8-30-fold by approximately 5×10^{-4} M cyclic 3', 5' AMP. However, this observation does not prove that the nucleotide is directly involved in the formation of the enzyme. The system used by the investigators contains all the soluble components of the cell; among them might be the effector of transient repression or of catabolite repression and cyclic AMP may exert its effect by causing the inactivation of the effector.

It is clearly important to discover the step in enzyme synthesis that is sensitive to transient repression or to catabolite repression; only then will it be possible to understand the role of cyclic AMP in counteracting one or both of these repressive effects. This step appears to be the initiation of transcription of the *lac*-specific DNA. The evidence for this view comes from kinetic studies of β-galactosidase synthesis. The accumulation of β-galactosidase begins approximately 3 min after addition of the inducer. When the inducer is removed at this time, enzyme synthesis continues in the inducer-free medium for approximately 8 min (Pardee and Prestidge, 1961). Nakada and Magasanik (1962) produced strong catabolite repression by starving an *E. coli* auxotroph of threonine in the presence of glycerol (Fig. 7). They found that cells exposed to the inducer in such a medium for 4 min failed to produce any enzyme when threonine was restored after removal of the inducer. On the other hand, cells exposed to inducer for 4 min in a medium containing neither threonine nor glycerol, produced enzyme when glycerol was added after removal of the inducer. The amount of enzyme produced by these cells induced in the absence of both glycerol and threonine was approximately proportional to the rate of protein synthesis in the medium after removal of inducer: the cells that received glycerol produced more enzyme than those that did not. These findings show that the repression prevents the acquisition of the capacity to produce β-galactosidase, but does not prevent the expression of the acquired capacity. Similar experiments in which glucose was used as the agent of catabolite repression or transient repression lead to the same conclusion (Kepes, 1963; Nakada and Magasanik, 1964).

E. coli begins to acquire the capacity for the rapid synthesis of β-galactosidase immediately upon contact with inducer, though the actual accumulation of the enzyme only begins approximately 3 min later (Kepes, 1963). When inducer is removed at different time intervals after its addition and the cells are permitted to make in the absence of inducer all

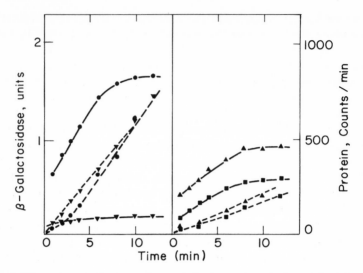

FIGURE 7. Effect of catabolite repression on induction and production of β-galactosidase. The cells (*E. coli* strain 200P, lacks β-galactoside-permease and requires threonine, leucine and thiamine), were grown in a medium containing 0.2% glycerol as source of carbon and the required supplements. They were suspended in media lacking glycerol or threonine and incubated at 30°C for 5 min. Then 0.5 mm IPTG was added and the incubation was continued for 4 min. The cells were collected by filtration and incubated in media without IPTG and containing radioactive leucine. The solid lines represent β-galactosidase formed and the broken lines leucine incorporated into protein in the absence of inducer. ●———●, induced without glycerol and threonine, incubated in complete medium; ▼———▼, induced in medium containing glycerol but no threonine, incubated in complete medium; ▲———△, induced without glycerol and threonine, incubated in medium with glycerol but without threonine, ■———■, induced without glycerol and threonine, and incubated in medium lacking both glycerol and threonine. From Nakada and Magasanik (1962).

the β-galactosidase they are capable of making, the resulting enzyme yields are proportional to the time during which the cells have been in contact with inducer. The delay between addition of inducer and the actual appearance of the enzyme is in part due to the time required for the completion of the transcription of the DNA segment that contains the structural gene for β-galactosidase. This is shown by the fact that addition of actinomycin D, an inhibitor of RNA synthesis, completely prevents the formation of the enzyme when added as late as 2 min after the inducer (Leive, 1965).

When actinomycin D is added to cells that are already accumulating the enzyme, an immediate decline in the rate of this accumulation is observed (Leive and Kollin, 1967). This is the expected result of an arrest of messenger RNA synthesis. When inducer is taken away from cells that are already accumulating the enzyme, the decline in the rate of accumulation is delayed for approximately 2 min (Kepes, 1963; Kaempfer and

Magasanik, 1967). This is the expected result of an arrest of initiation of transcription of the β-galactosidase specific messenger RNA: already initiated, but not yet completed RNA chains continue to be made and enhance initially the rate of enzyme accumulation.

The imposition of transient repression has exactly the same result as removal of inducer. This is shown in Fig. 8 from a paper by Tyler and Magasanik (1969). Cells growing on glycerol were induced; three min later, inducer was withdrawn or glucose was added. In both cases enzyme accumulation declined after an initial delay with exactly the same kinetics.

This experiment excludes the possibility that transient repression acts on translation or on transcription. In both instances, less enzyme should have accumulated in the culture subjected to transient repression than in the culture deprived of inducer. It is in excellent agreement with the view that both the repressor controlled by the *lac i* gene and the effector generated from glucose arrest initiation of transcription of the *lac* operon. The finding that β-galactosidase, permease, and transacetylase respond coordinately to transient repression is in agreement with this view (Tyler, Loomis, and Magasanik, 1967).

A careful study by Jacquet and Kepes (1969), in which the effect of glucose was compared with the effects of o-nitrophenyl galactoside—a competitive antagonist of the inducer, of actinomycin D—an inhibitor of transcription, and of rifampicin—an inhibitor of the initiation of tran-

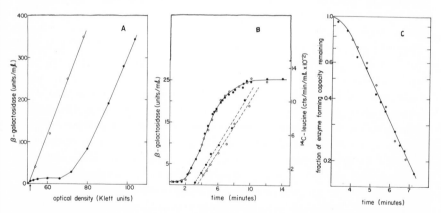

FIGURE 8. Kinetics of transient repression. The cells (*E. coli*, strain LA12G, normal *lac* system and insensitive to catabolite repression) were exposed to 1 mM isopropyl-β-D-thiogalactoside during growth on 0.4% glycerol at zero-time. (A) (0) Control culture; (●) at 3 min culture received 0.4% glucose and radioactive leucine. (B,C) (●) Culture which received .4% glucose and radioactive leucine at 3 min; (0) culture which was filtered and resuspended in inducer-free glycerol medium containing glycerol and radioactive leucine. From Tyler and Magasanik (1969).

scription, confirms that transient repression affects exclusively the initiation of transcription.

As expected, cyclic AMP overcomes catabolite repression and transient repression when added at the time of the initiation of transcription. It does not stimulate the progress of transcription or translation (Perlman and Pastan, 1968b; Jacquet and Kepes, 1969).

Conflicting observations were recently reported by Yudkin and Moses (1969). These authors claim that glucose inhibits not only the initiation of transcription but also translation. However, the view that the only step sensitive to catabolite repression and transient repression is the initiation of transcription is strongly supported by the results of the studies presented in the next section, which show that the promoter site of the *lac* operon is the target of the repression.

GENETIC BASIS OF REPRESSION

We have seen that the removal of inducer, the imposition of catabolite repression, and the imposition of transient repression all have the same result: arrest of the initiation of transcription of the *lac* operon. Nevertheless, the genetic sites that play a role in the induction process do not appear to be involved in transient repression or catabolite repression.

I have mentioned earlier that at least some *lac* i^- and o^c strains respond normally to transient repression and catabolite repression (Fig. 5 and 6). The initial constitutive synthesis of β-galactosidase in zygotes formed by the mating of an F^- strain whose *lac* genes are deleted with a normal Hfr-strain is subject to catabolite repression (Loomis and Magasanik, 1964); these zygotes should initially contain no *i*-gene product of any sort. According to Palmer and Moses (1967, 1968), certain constitutive mutants are sensitive to catabolite repression but not to transient repression. They obtained these results with strain RV-o_{67}^c, (thought to be a deletion of *lac i* and *lac o*, but now known to carry separate mutations in each of these genes), and with strain A84, which produces an incomplete *i*-gene product due to a nonsense mutation in this gene (Müller-Hill, 1966). However, Perlman and Pastan (1968b) observed transient repression in strain RV-o_{67}^c, and Tyler and Magasanik (1969) observed transient repression in both RV-o_{67}^c and A84. The reason for the contradiction in the results is not clear. As pointed out by Tyler and Magasanik (1969), it is not always easy to observe transient repression in cells that contain, as those of constitutive mutants do, a high level of enzyme at the time of the addition of glucose.

Additional evidence against any involvement of the *i*-gene product in transient repression has been obtained by Silverstone and Magasanik (unpubl. exp.). They found that in a strain in which *lac i,* but not the *lac* operon has been fused by deletion to the *trp* operon (Reznikoff et al., 1969) β-galactosidase is sensitive to transient repression by glucose.

A recent study has identified the *lac p* region, the promoter, as the catabolite-sensitive site of the *lac* operon (Silverstone et al., 1969). The order of the *lac* genes is *i p o z y a* (Ippen et al., 1968; Miller et al., 1968). The promoter, *p,* has been characterized as a site essential for the formation of the products of the structural genes *z, y* and *a*. Mutations in *p, lac p⁻*, cause a great reduction of the rate of formation of the products of the structural genes in *cis* position; these mutations do not alter the response of the *lac* operon to the *lac i*-gene repressor (Scaife and Beckwith, 1966). It has been possible to transpose the *lac* genes to a region of the chromosome near the *trp* genes; these groups of genes can then be fused by deletions (Beckwith, Signer, and Epstein, 1966). In the strains used in the experiments shown in Table 1 (Silverstone et al., 1969; and Silverstone and Magasanik, unpubl. observ.), the deletion extends from *trp B*

Table 1. Effect of glucose-6-phosphate on β-galactosidase synthesis in strains with fused *trp-lac*

Strain[a]	*lac i*	*lac P*	*trp R*	IPTG 10^{-3}M	Rate of β-galactosidase synthesis[b] on glycerol	Rate of β-galactosidase synthesis[b] on glucose-6-phosphate
1	del	+	+	−	20.	1.12
2	+	+	+	+	17	0.68
3	del	del	+	−	0.33	0.27
				+	0.18	0.22
4	+	del	+	−	0.09	0.07
				+	0.16	0.12
5	del	del	−	−	1.6	1.7
				+	1.5	1.4
6	+	del	−	−	0.59	0.54
				+	2.10	1.90

[a] In strain 1 the operons are fused by a deletion from *trp B* to *lac i*; strain 2 is identical with strain 1, except that it contains the F'*lac i⁺z⁻* episome; in strains 3–6, the operons are fused by a deletion from *trp B* to *lac p*; strain 4 carries the F'*lac i⁺z⁻* episome; strain 5 has the mutation making the *trp* operon insensitive to repression by tryptophan, *trp R⁻*; strain 6 has the *trp R⁻* mutation and carries the F'*lac i⁺z⁻* episome.

[b] The rate of enzyme synthesis is given as the increase in enzyme units in one ml of culture per increase in bacterial density expressed in Klett units. Enzyme units are given as mμmoles of substrate converted or product formed per minute. A Klett unit corresponds to approximately 4.2×10^6 bacteria.

to *lac i* (strains 1 and 2) or from *trp B* to *lac p* (strains 3–6). In the second type of deletion, the rate of β-galactosidase synthesis is controlled by tryptophan; this is shown by the fact that mutation to insensitivity of the *trp* operon to repression (*trp R⁻*) greatly increases the rate of β-galactosidase synthesis (compare strains 3 and 5). When *lac p* is intact (strains 1 and 2), β-galactosidase shows the usual great sensitivity to the catabolite repression exerted by glucose-6-phosphate. When *lac p* is deleted and synthesis of the enzyme depends on the promoter of the catabolite-insensitive *trp* operon, β-galactosidase is completely insensitive to repression by glucose-6-phosphate. It can also be seen that the product of the *lac i*-gene is not involved in catabolite repression. Introduction of an episome carrying *lac i⁺* produces strains in which the chromosomal *lac* operon is repressed unless the inducer IPTG is added, but the susceptibility of the operon to repression by glucose-6-phosphate is not re-established.

Examination of the *trp r⁻* strain with the *trp b⁻ lac p* fusion showed that the deletion of *lac p* has made β-galactosidase also insensitive to transient repression by glucose (Silverstone and Magasanik, unpubl. observ.).

The validity of the conclusion that *lac p* is the catabolite-sensitive site of the *lac* operon can be tested by examining another strain in which elements of the *lac* operon are fused to another chromosomal site by a deletion covering *lac p*. Such a strain was described by Jacob, Ullman, and Monod (1965). In this organism, a deletion extends from *pur e* to *lac z;* the β-galactoside permease and the transacetylase are subject to repression by adenine. Unfortunately, we were unable to obtain this strain until very recently, after a paper by Moses and Yudkin (1968) had been published, in which they claimed that in this organism the transacetylase is subject to catabolite repression exerted by glucose. Our findings (Silverstone and Magasanik, unpubl. exp.) disagree with this conclusion.

We used a strain whose pertinent genetic character was as follows:

$$\frac{lac\ i^+p^+o^+z^+[ya]^{\text{del}}}{F'[pur\ e\text{-}lac\ z]^{\text{del}}\ lac\ y^+a^+}$$

This organism, by virtue of its chromosomal genes produces β-galactosidase, but no transacetylase, upon induction with IPTG; by virtue of its episomal genes, it produces the transacetylase at high rate in purine-free medium and at a low rate in a medium containing adenine (Table 2). We found β-galactosidase, but not transacetylase, to be repressed by glucose or glucose-6-phosphate (Table 2). Apparently the fusion of the *lac* genes to *pur e* has eliminated the target of catabolite repression.

In addition to the strains in which large deletions have removed the *lac p* site and fused the remaining *lac* genes to other operons, there

Table 2. Effect of glucose and of glucose-6-phosphate on the synthesis of β-galactosidase and of thiogalactoside transacetylase in a strain with the genetic composition

$$lac\ i^+p^+o^+z^+\ [ya]\ ^{del}/F'[pur\ e\text{-}lac\ z]\ ^{del}lac\ y^+a^+$$

Carbon source $+10^{-3}$ M IPTG	Units[a] per mg of protein	
	β-Galactosidase	Thiogalactoside transacetylase
Glycerol	18,000	44.6
Glycerol and adenine	16,400	1.5
Glucose	6,880	51.1
Glucose-6-phosphate	2,860	66.6

[a]Enzyme units are given as mμmoles of substrate converted per minute.

exist also strains with point mutations in *lac p* (Scaife and Beckwith, 1966; Ippen et al., 1968). These organisms can be induced with IPTG to produce β-galactosidase at approximately 5% of the rate characteristic of their *lac p⁺* parent. In these strains β-galactosidase is subject to transient repression and catabolite repression; these effects can be overcome by the addition of cyclic AMP (Pastan and Perlman, 1968; Perlman, deCrombrugghe, and Pastan, 1969).

The *lac p⁻* mutants can revert (Arditti, Scaife and Beckwith, 1968); the revertants produce β-galactosidase at high rate upon induction. We have found that in 10 to 20% of these revertants the formation of the enzyme is insensitive to catabolite repression.

One strain of this type, UV-5, was studied in detail (Silverstone, Arditti and Magasanik, unpubl.). As shown in Table 3, the rate of β-galactosidase production by strain UV-5 in a glycerol medium is approximately one half that of *E. coli* strain CA 8000 from which its *lac p⁻* parent, strain L-8 was derived. In contrast to strains CA 8000 and L-8, it produces β-galactosidase and transacetylase at the same differential rate on glycerol, glucose and glucose-6-phosphate. On the other hand, tryptophanase is fully sensitive to repression by glucose and glucose-6-phosphate.

In other experiments, it was found that nitrogen-starved cells of strain UV-5 produce β-galactosidase at the same differential rate in the presence or absence of a utilizable carbon source. As mentioned in an earlier section, strains sensitive to catabolite repression fail to produce the enzyme when supplied with such a carbon source in the absence of a source of nitrogen. Finally, glucose does not transiently repress β-galactosidase when added to cells of strain UV-5 growing on glycerol.

The mutation to catabolite insensitivity is *cis* dominant. This could be shown by introducing into the mutant cells an episomal normal *lac* system.

Table 3. Enzyme synthesis in strains with altered *lac* promoter

Strain	Derived from	Carbon source	Rate of enzyme synthesis[a]		
			β-Galactosidase	Thiogalactoside transacetylase	Tryptophanase
CA8,000	—	glycerol	47	0.80	0.182
		glucose	24	0.29	0.021
		glucose-6-P	8	0.13	0.004
L-8	CA8,000	glycerol	2.2	0.04	0.162
		glucose	0.9	0.02	0.019
		glucose-6-P	0.4	0.01	0.002
UV-5	L-8	glycerol	26	0.42	0.177
		glucose	24	0.39	0.023
		glucose-6-P	25	0.38	0.002

[a] The rate of enzyme synthesis is given as the increase in enzyme units in one ml of culture per increase in bacterial density expressed in Klett units. Enzyme units are given as mμmoles of substrate converted or product formed per min. A Klett unit corresponds to approximately 4.2×10^6 bacteria.

Only the β-galactosidase produced by the chromosomal *lac z* gene is insensitive to catabolite repression.

The mutation responsible for the restoration of promoter function and resistance to catabolite repression is very closely linked to the original *lac p⁻* mutation. When a phage *p1* lysate of the catabolite-insensitive strain was used to transduce a strain defective in the 25% linked *lac z* and *pro c* sites, all of 50 *lac⁺*, *pro⁺* transductants were found to possess a catabolite-insensitive β-galactosidase; when a special selection method for *lac p⁻* recombinants was applied to the analysis of a transduction by this phage lysate of a *pro C⁻*, *lac⁺* strain, it was found that two out of 40,000 Pro⁺ transductants had obtained only the original *lac p⁻* mutation site and not the mutation site responsible for normal promoter function and catabolite insensitivity.

In at least one other system, the promoter site also appears to be the target of catabolite repression. The synthesis of the histidine degrading enzymes in *Bacillus subtilis* (Chasin and Magasanik, 1968) or in *Salmonella typhimurium* (Brill and Magasanik, 1969) can be prevented or rendered insensitive to catabolite repression by mutations in a site closely linked to the structural genes of these enzymes. It could be shown that in *S. typhimurium* the character of this genetic site affects only the structural genes in *cis* position (Smith and Magasanik, unpubl. observ.). Just as in the case of the *lac* system, the histidine degrading enzymes of some of the revertants obtained from the pleiotropically negative mutants are insensitive to catabolite repression (Chasin and Magasanik, 1968; Brill and Magasanik, 1969).

Thus, catabolite-sensitive promoters can by mutation become catabolite-insensitive. The reverse has been observed by Friedman and Margolin (1968). They studied a mutant unable to form any of the enzymes specific for leucine biosynthesis because of a defect in a site at one end of the *leu* operon; a revertant isolated from this mutant could form these enzymes in the absence, but not in the presence, of glucose. Apparently, an alteration in the *leu* promoter rendered the normally catabolite-insensitive enzymes of the *leu* operon sensitive to catabolite repression.

HYPOTHETICAL MECHANISM OF REPRESSION

A considerable amount of crucial information concerning the repression is now available and has been presented in the preceding sections. However, more facts need to be elucidated to allow the formulation of the overall mechanism of the effect. Nevertheless, it is useful to consider at this time a hypothesis which accounts for the observed facts and suggests new experimental approaches. It is based on the observations described in the preceding sections and on new observations on the action of RNA polymerase, which show that the template specificity of the enzyme is determined by proteins that have been called σ factors (Burgess et al., 1969; Travers and Burgess, 1969; Losick and Sonenshein, 1969). These factors are apparently required for the attachment of the polymerase core to the sites on the DNA where transcription is normally initiated. The hypothesis is expressed by four statements. (1) There are two classes of operons: one with catabolite-insensitive promoters, the other with catabolite-sensitive promoters. This statement is supported by the observation that mutations in the promoter site may convert catabolite-sensitive operons to catabolite-insensitive operons and vice versa. (2) Different protein factors must associate with the RNA polymerase core for the initiation of transcription of the two classes of operons. This statement is supported by the observation that the repression specifically prevents initiation of transcription. There is, however, no evidence that the two postulated protein factors actually exist. (3) Initiation of transcription by the catabolite-sensitive factor requires 3′,5′ cyclic AMP. This statement is supported by the evidence that formation of β-galactosidase in a cell-free system requires cyclic AMP and that a mutant deficient in the enzyme catalyzing the conversion of ATP to cyclic AMP can form catabolite-sensitive enzymes only in the presence of cyclic AMP. The cyclic AMP might enhance the binding of the factor to the polymerase core or of the polymerase complex to the promoter. (4) Under conditions of catabolite repression and of transient repression a metabolite is produced which activates a system capable of destroying cyclic AMP or of causing its release from the cell (Monard, Janeček, and Rickenberg, 1969; deCrombrugghe et al., 1969). This statement is supported by evidence that enzymes for the synthesis and degradation of cyclic AMP are present in the cell and that exogenously added cyclic AMP overcomes the repression. However, the metabolite has not been identified and it has not yet been shown conclusively that the intracellular level of cyclic AMP is reduced under conditions of repression.

According to this hypothesis for the mechanism of the repression, the operon specificity of the system is determined exclusively by the promoter. All the other components are involved in the control of all catabolite sensitive enzymes. There is, however, reason to believe that the system of repression has greater specificity and complexity. In *Aerobacter aerogenes* both β-galactosidase and histidase are subject to repression by glucose and in both instances, the repression can be overcome by the addition of cyclic AMP; the repression of histidase, but not that of β-galactosidase, can also be overcome by depriving the cell of a source of glutamate other than histidine (Neidhardt and Magasanik, 1957; Prival and Magasanik, unpubl.). It is apparent that a scheme in which control is exerted exclusively by changing the level of cyclic AMP cannot account for these findings.

The greater specificity could be achieved by several catabolite-sensitive protein factors with specificity for different promoters. In this scheme, the binding of these factors to the RNA polymerase core is specifically inhibited by different effectors whose intracellular level depends on the composition of the growth medium. Cyclic AMP counteracts the effectors by preventing their interaction with the protein factors or by activating an enzyme that destroys them. Finally, the level of cyclic AMP depends, as in the simpler scheme, on a metabolite produced under conditions of catabolite repression.

REFERENCES

ARDITTI, R. R., J. G. SCAIFE, and J. R. BECKWITH. 1968. The nature of mutants in the *lac* promoter region. J. Mol. Biol. *38:* 421.

BECKWITH, J. R., E. R. SIGNER, and W. EPSTEIN. 1966. Transposition of the *lac* region of *E. coli.* Cold Spring Harbor Symp. Quant. Biol. *31:* 393.

BEGGS, W. H. and P. ROGERS. 1966. Galactose repression of β-galactosidase induction in *Escherichia coli.* J. Bacteriol. *91:* 1869.

BOEZI, J. A. and D. B. COWIE. 1961. Kinetic studies of β-galactosidase induction. Biophys. J. *1:* 639.

BOWNE, S. W., Jr. and P. ROGERS. 1962. Ultraviolet light and enzyme synthesis. J. Mol. Biol. *5:* 90.

BRILL, W. J. and B. MAGASANIK. 1969. Genetic and metabolic control of histidase and urocanase in *Salmonella typhimurium,* Strain 15–59. J. Biol. Chem. *244:* 5392.

BURGESS, R. R., A. A. TRAVERS, J. J. DUNN, and E. K. F. BAUTZ. 1969. Factor stimulating transcription by RNA polymerase. Nature *221:* 43.

CHAMBERS, D. A. and G. ZUBAY. 1969. The stimulatory effect of cyclic adenosine 3′,5′-monophosphate on DNA-directed synthesis of β-galactosidase in a cell-free system. Biochem. *63:* 118.

CHASIN, L. A. and B. MAGASANIK. 1968. Induction and repression of the histidine-degrading enzymes of *Bacillus subtilis.* J. Biol. Chem. *243:* 5165.

CLARK, D. J. and A. G. MARR. 1964. Studies on the repression of β-galactosidase in *Escherichia coli.* Biochim. Biophys. Acta *92:* 85.

COHN, M. and K. HORIBATA. 1959a. Inhibition by glucose of the induced synthesis of the β-galactoside-enzyme system of *Escherichia coli.* Analysis of maintenance. J. Bacteriol. *78:* 601.

————, ————. 1959b. Physiology of the inhibition by glucose of the induced synthesis of the β-galactoside-enzyme system of *Escherichia coli.* J. Bacteriol. *78:* 624.

CROMBRUGGHE, B. DE, R. L. PERLMAN, H. E. VARMOS, and I. PASTAN. 1969. Regulation of inducible enzyme synthesis in *Escherichia coli* by cyclic adenosine 3′,5′-monophosphate. J. Biol. Chem. *244:* 5828.

216 *Magasanik*

DOBROGOSZ, W. J. 1969. Corepressor system for catabolite repression of the *lac* operon in *Escherichia coli*. J. Bacteriol. *97:* 1083.

EPSTEIN, W., S. NAONO, and F. GROS. 1966. Synthesis of enzymes of the lactose operon during diauxic growth of *Escherichia coli*. Biochem. Biophys. Res. Commun. *24:* 588.

FRIEDMAN, S. B. and P. MARGOLIN. 1968. Evidence for an altered operator specificity: catabolite repression control of the leucine operon in *Salmonella typhimurium*. J. Bacteriol. *95:* 2263.

HSIE, A. W. and H. V. RICKENBERG. 1967. Catabolite repression in *Escherichia coli*: The role of glucose 6-phosphate. Biochem. Biophys. Res. Commun. *29:* 303.

IPPEN, K., J. H. MILLER, J. SCAIFE, and J. BECKWITH. 1968. New controlling element in the *lac* operon of *E. coli*. Nature *217:* 825.

JACOB, F., A. ULLMANN, and J. MONOD. 1965. Délétions fusionant l'opéron lactose et un opéron purine chez *Escherichia coli*. J. Mol. Biol. *31:* 704.

JACQUET, M. and A. KEPES. 1969. The step sensitive to catabolite repression and its reversal by 3'-5' cyclic AMP during induced synthesis of β-galactosidase in *E. coli*. Biochem. Biophys. Res. Commun. *36:* 84.

KABACK, H. R. 1969. Regulation of sugar transport in isolated bacterial membrane preparations from *Escherichia coli*. Proc. Nat. Acad. Sci. *63:* 724.

KAEMPFER, R. O. R. and B. MAGASANIK. 1967. Mechanism of β-galactosidase induction in *Escherichia coli*. J. Mol. Biol. *27:* 475.

KEPES, A. 1960. Études cinétiques sur la galactoside-permease d'*Escherichia coli*. Biochim. Biophys. Acta *40:* 70.

———. 1963. Kinetics of induced enzyme synthesis. Determination of the mean life of galactosidase-specific messenger RNA. Biochim. Biophys. Acta *76:* 293.

KUNDIG, W., S. GHOSH, and S. ROSEMAN. 1964. Phosphate bound to histidine in a protein as an intermediate in a novel phosphotransferase system. Proc. Nat. Acad. Sci. *52:* 1067.

LEIVE, L. 1965. Some effects of inducer on synthesis and utilization of β-galactosidase messenger RNA in actinomycin-sensitive *Escherichia coli*. Biochem. Biophys. Res. Commun. *20:* 321.

LEIVE, L. and V. KOLLIN. 1967. Synthesis, utilization and degradation of lactose operon mRNA in *Escherichia coli*. J. Mol. Biol. *24:* 247.

LLANES, B. and E. MCFALL. 1969. Effect of galactose on β-galactosidase synthesis in *Escherichia coli* K-12. J. Bacteriol. *97:* 217.

LOOMIS, W. F., Jr. and B. MAGASANIK. 1964. The relation of catabolite repression to the induction system for β-galactosidase in *Escherichia coli*. J. Mol. Biol. *8:* 417.

———, ———. 1965. Genetic control of catabolite repression of the *lac* operon in *Escherichia coli*. Biochem. Biophys. Res. Commun. *20:* 230.

———, ———. 1966. Nature of the effector of catabolite repression of β-galactosidase in *Escherichia coli*. J. Bacteriol. *92:* 170.

———, ———. 1967. Glucose-lactose diauxie in *Escherichia coli*. J. Bacteriol. *93:* 1397.

LOSICK, R. and A. L. SONENSHEIN. 1969. Change in the template specificity of RNA polymerase during sporulation of *Bacillus subtilis*. Nature *224:* 35.

MAGASANIK, B. 1957. Nutrition of bacteria and fungi. Ann. Rev. Microbiol. *11:* 221.

_____. 1961. Catabolite repression. Cold Spring Harbor Symp. Quant. Biol. *26:* 249.

MAKMAN, R. S. and E. W. SUTHERLAND. 1965. Adenosine 3′,5′-phosphate in *Escherichia coli*. J. Biol. Chem. *240:* 1309.

MANDELSTAM, J. 1957. Turnover of protein in starved bacteria and its relationship to the induced synthesis of enzyme. Nature *179:* 1179.

_____. 1961. Induction and repression of β-galactosidase in nongrowing *Escherichia coli*. Biochem. J. *79:* 489.

_____. 1962. The repression of constitutive β-galactosidase in *Escherichia coli* by glucose and other carbon sources. Biochem. J. *82:* 489.

McFALL, E. 1961. Effects of ^{32}P decay on enzyme synthesis. J. Mol. Biol. *3:* 219.

McFALL, E. and B. MAGASANIK. 1960. Thymine starvation and enzyme synthesis. Biochim. Biophys. Acta *45:* 610.

_____, _____. 1962. The effects of thymine and of phosphate deprivation on enzyme synthesis in *Escherichia coli*. Biochim. Biophys. Acta *55:* 900.

McFALL, E. and J. MANDELSTAM. 1963. Specific metabolic repression of three induced enzymes in *Escherichia coli*. Biochem. J. *89:* 391.

MILLER, J. H., K. IPPEN, J. G. SCAIFE, and J. R. BECKWITH. 1968. The promoter-operator region of the *lac* operon of *Escherichia coli*. J. Mol. Biol. *38:* 413.

MONARD, D., J. JANEČEK, and H. V. RICKENBERG. 1969. The enzymic degradation of 3′,5′ cyclic AMP in strains of *E. coli* sensitive and resistant to catabolite repression. Biochem. Biophys. Res. Commun. *35:* 584.

MONOD, J. 1947. The phenomenon of enzymatic adaptation. Growth *11:* 223.

_____. 1956. Remarks on the mechanism of enzyme induction. p. 7. In O. H. Gaebler [ed.] Enzymes: Units of biological structure and function, Academic Press, New York.

MOSES, V. and C. PREVOST. 1966. Catabolite repression of β-galactosidase synthesis in *Escherichia coli*. Biochem. J. *100:* 336.

MOSES, V. and M. D. YUDKIN. 1968. Catabolite repression in *Escherichia coli*. A study of two hypotheses. Biochem. J. *110:* 135.

MÜLLER-HILL, B. 1966. Suppressible regulatory constitutive mutants of the lactose system of *Escherichia coli*. J. Mol. Biol. *15:* 374.

NAKADA, D. and B. MAGASANIK. 1962. Catabolite repression and the induction of β-galactosidase. Biochim. Biophys. Acta *61:* 835.

_____, _____. 1964. The roles of inducer and catabolite repressor in the synthesis of β-galactosidase by *Escherichia coli*. J. Mol. Biol. *8:* 105.

NEIDHARDT, F. C. and B. MAGASANIK. 1956. Inhibitory effect of glucose on enzyme formation. Nature *178:* 801.

_____, _____. 1957. Reversal of the glucose inhibition of histidase biosynthesis in *Aerobacter aerogenes*. J. Bacteriol. *73:* 253.

PAIGEN, K. 1966a. Phenomenon of transient repression in *Escherichia coli*. J. Bacteriol. *91:* 1201.

_____. 1966b. Role of the galactose pathway in the regulation of β-galactosidase. J. Bacteriol. *92:* 1394.

PALMER, J. and V. MOSES. 1967. Involvement of the *lac* regulatory genes in catabolite repression in *Escherichia coli*. Biochem. J. *103:* 358.

———, ———. 1968. The role of the regulator-gene product (repressor) in catabolite repression of β-galactosidase synthesis in *Escherichia coli*. Biochem. J. *106:* 339.

PARDEE, A. B. 1955. Effect of energy supply on enzyme induction by pyrimidine-requiring mutants of *Escherichia coli*. J. Bacteriol. *69:* 233.

PARDEE, A. B. and L. S. PRESTIDGE. 1961. The initial kinetics of enzyme induction. Biochim. Biophys. Acta *49:* 77.

———, ———. 1963. Inactivation of β-galactosidase induction by ultraviolet light. Biochim. Biophys. Acta *76:* 614.

PASTAN, I. and R. L. PERLMAN. 1968. The role of the *lac* promotor locus in the regulation of β-galactosidase synthesis by cyclic 3′,5′-adenosine monophosphate. Proc. Nat. Acad. Sci. *61:* 1336.

———, ———. 1969. Repression of β-galactosidase synthesis by glucose in phosphotransferase mutants of *Escherichia coli*. J. Biol. Chem. *244:* 5836.

PERLMAN, R. L., B. deCROMBRUGGHE, and I. PASTAN. 1969. Cyclic AMP regulates catabolite and transient repression in *E. coli*. Nature *223:* 810.

PERLMAN, R. and I. PASTAN. 1968a. Cyclic 3′,5′-AMP: Stimulation of β-galactosidase and tryptophanase induction in *E. coli*. Biochem. Biophys. Res. Commun. *30:* 656.

———, ———. 1968b. Regulation of β-galactosidase synthesis in *Escherichia coli* by cyclic adenosine 3′,5′-monophosphate. J. Biol. Chem. *243:* 5420.

———, ———. 1969. Pleiotropic deficiency of carbohydrate utilization in an adenyl cyclase deficient mutant of *Escherichia coli*. Biochem. Biophys. Res. Commun. *37:* 151.

PREVOST, C. and V. MOSES. 1967. Pool sizes of metabolic intermediates and their relation to glucose repression of β-galactosidase synthesis in *Escherichia coli*. Biochem. J. *103:* 349.

REZNIKOFF, W. S., J. H. MILLER, J. G. SCAIFE, and J. R. BECKWITH. 1969. A mechanism for repressor action. J. Mol. Biol. *43:* 201.

RICKENBERG, H. V., A. W. HSIE, and J. JANEČEK. 1968. The CR mutation and catabolite repression in *Escherichia coli*. Biochem. Biophys. Res. Commun. *31:* 603.

SCAIFE, J. and J. R. BECKWITH. 1966. Mutational alteration of the maximal level of *lac* operon expression. Cold Spring Harbor Symp. Quant. Biol. *31:* 403.

SILVERSTONE, A. E., B. MAGASANIK, W. S. REZNIKOFF, J. H. MILLER, and J. R. BECKWITH. 1969. Catabolite sensitive site of the *lac* operon. Nature *221:* 1012.

TANAKA, S., D. G. FRAENKEL, and E. C. C. LIN. 1967. The enzymatic lesion of Strain MM6, a pleiotropic carbohydrate-negative mutant of *Escherichia coli*. Biochem. Biophys. Res. Commun. *27:* 63.

TAO, M. and F. LIPMANN. 1969. Isolation of adenylcyclase from *Escherichia coli*. Proc. Nat. Acad. Sci. *63:* 86.

TRAVERS, A. A. and R. R. BURGESS. 1969. Cyclic re-use of the RNA polymerase sigma factor. Nature *222:* 537.

TYLER, B., W. F. LOOMIS, Jr., and B. MAGASANIK. 1967. Transient repression of the *lac* operon. J. Bacteriol. *94:* 2001.

TYLER, B. and B. MAGASANIK. 1969. Molecular basis of transient repression of β-galactosidase in *Escherichia coli*. J. Bacteriol. *97:* 550.

————, ————. 1970. Physiological basis of transient repression of catabolic enzymes in *Escherichia coli*. (In press).

TYLER, B., R. WISHNOW, W. F. LOOMIS, Jr., and B. MAGASANIK. 1969. Catabolite repression gene of *Escherichia coli*. J. Bacteriol. *100:* 809.

ULLMANN, A. and J. MONOD. 1968. Cyclic AMP as an antagonist of catabolite repression in *Escherichia coli*. Fed. Europ. Biol. Soc. Letters *2:* 57.

YUDKIN, M. D. and V. MOSES. 1969. Catabolite repression of the *lac* operon. Repression of translation. Biochem. J. *113:* 423.

Chapter X

Polarity and Translational Punctuation

DAVID ZIPSER

Cold Spring Harbor Laboratory
Cold Spring Harbor, New York

INTRODUCTION

The three structural proteins of the *lac* operon are produced in different molar ratios. While the mechanism which gives rise to this natural polarity is still unknown, the complex phenomena of mutational polarity, with its relationship to polypeptide initiation and termination, seems to be the most likely direction from which an understanding of natural polarity will come.

In this chapter the current status of work on the mechanism of polypeptide initiation and termination will be reviewed briefly. Then I will discuss in detail the phenomena of mutational polarity in the *lac* operon and its relationship to polypeptide initiation and termination.

INITIATION

Each separate polypeptide chain synthesized by an operon has an initiation code sequence. A complex mechanism is required to recognize this sequence and initiate polypeptide synthesis at the correct site and rate and in the right reading frame. The nature of the code sequence and the mechanism of initiation is under very active study using a variety of techniques. The current status of this work is summarized in the scheme shown in Fig. 1 (see Kolakofsky, Dewey, and Thach, 1969 for more detailed review and bibliography). A 30 S ribosomal subunit, an F-met charged $tRNA_f$, and a messenger RNA react in the presence of GTP and 3 protein factors f 1, f 2 and f 3. The GTP is split in the reaction and the product is a multi-molecular complex containing 30 S ribosome-F-met-$tRNA_f$-mRNA-f 1. In the second step of the initiation reaction a 50 S ribosomal subunit is added to this complex to form a 70 S ribosome and the f 1 factor

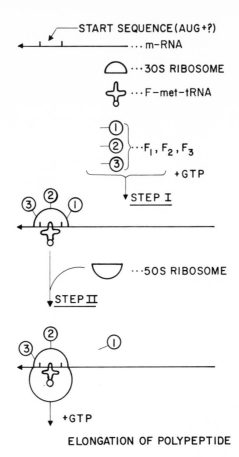

FIGURE I. This is a summary of what we now know about the mechanism of polypeptide initiation. Note that factor 3 is not needed for artificial messengers.

is released. Before polypeptide chain elongation can take place another reaction involving GTP takes place. After this, the complex is ready to read the messenger and elongate the polypeptide chain. These reactions are generally observed in in vitro systems. In such systems either artificial or natural mRNA can be used. When artificial mRNA is used the only apparent coding requirement for initiation is the AUG or GUG codon (Ghosh, Söll and Khorana, 1967). The factor f_3 is not required. When natural messenger is used f_3 is required but the exact code cannot be determined in this type of experiment.

So far the only kind of experiments aimed directly at the problem of the initiation code sequence other than the AUG codon have been attempts at sequencing of RNA phage. These studies have confirmed that AUG is the initial codon in several phage proteins (Steitz, 1969, and Hindley and

		f- met	ala	ser	asn	phe
COAT, R17	GGGGUUUGAAGC	AUG	GCU	UCU	AAC	UUU

		f- met	ala	lys	leu	glu
COAT, Qβ	???AAUUUGAUC	AUG	GCA	AAA	UUA	GAG

		f- met	ser	lys	thr	thr
SYNTHETASE, R17	UGAGGAUUACCC	AUG	UCG	AAG	ACA	ACA

		f- met	arg	ala	phe	ser
A PROTEIN, R17	GAGGUUUGACCU	AUG	CGA	GCU	UUU	AGU

FIGURE 2. This is the current status of the initiation code obtained by sequencing the ribosome binding sites of R17 (Steitz, 1969) or Qβ (Hindley and Staples, 1969) RNA phages.

Staples, 1969). Two general possibilities are suggested by sequence work (see Fig. 2). One is that some form of secondary structure using base pairing but relatively insensitive to exact sequence is responsible for making a good start at a particular AUG codon. The second line of thought hypothesizes that a code involving a specific base sequence delineates an AUG as a start. The current status of the sequence work, shown in Fig. 2, does not permit a distinction between these models to be made yet.

TERMINATION

Of the 64 triplet codons 3, UAG, UGA and UAA code for chain termination. This is an active process involving the ribosomes and at least 2 specific protein factors but *no* tRNA. The protein factor R1 is required to terminate at UAG or UAA while the protein factor R2 is required for UAA or UGA termination (Scolnick, et al., 1968). When any one of the three terminator codons is introduced into a structural gene, by mutation, polypeptide synthesis terminates releasing a polypeptide fragment which contains the amino acid sequence from the N-terminus to the site of the terminator codon. These mutations are called nonsense mutations. Fragments of β-galactosidase produced by nonsense mutations have been isolated and studied. This work is discussed in Zabin's chapter. While there is little doubt that the nonsense codons are involved in normal chain terminations, the nature of the termination code actually used for a structural gene has not yet been determined.

POLARITY

Polar mutations are genetic alterations in one gene which decrease the amount of product synthesized by all the distal genes of an operon. Polarity was first discovered in the *lac* operon (Francklin and Luria, 1961; Jacob

Table 1(a)

Mutant No.	% Wild permease	Z CRM
$z_8^- y^+$	4–8	−
$z_4^- y^+$	90	+
$z_{4'}^- y^+$	9	−
$z_1^- y^+$	95	+

Table I(a): These are data taken from Francklin and Luria (1961). The permease is measured by the uptake of C^{14}-labeled TMG. CRM stands for cross reacting material. Note the correspondance of CRM$^-$ to high polarity (i.e., low permease). This almost certainly reflects the nonsense nature of polar mutations.

Table 1(b)

Mutant No.	% Wild β-galactosidase	% Wild permease	% Wild acetylase
$z_2^- y^+$	<.1	<1	<1
$z_1^- y^+$	<.1	100	100
$z_{250}^- y^+$	<.1	50	46
$z_{73}^- y^+$	<.1	19	14
$z_8^- y^+$	<.1	5	5
$z^+ y_X^-$	100	<1	100
$z^+ y_U^-$	100	<1	5

Table I(b): These data come from Jacob and Monod (1961). Two points are clear; first the coordinate nature of polarity, shown in mutant 250, 73, 211 and S; second is the possibility of polar mutant in the y gene (i.e., y_U^-).

and Monod, 1961) and the type of data obtained is illustrated in Table I. Even from this early data it is clear that mutants in one structural gene can govern the amounts of product made by other genes.

The only base substitution mutations that have been shown to be polar are those which create one of the three nonsense codons (Newton, et al., 1965). The kind of data used to establish this result are given in Table 2. Here the polarity was measured for a group of mutants that mapped under a small deletion (Fig. 3). It is clear that all the nonsense mutants are strongly polar and none of the missense is significantly polar. This type of analysis has now been extended to several hundred mutants isolated with different base substitution mutagenes and no nonsuppressible, base substitution, polar mutant has been found. This, however, is negative evidence and the possibility that rare kinds of non-nonsense base substitutions can be polar has not been ruled out. The argument that no such mutant exists is strengthened by the fact that we have also shown that over $300 z^+ y^-$ mutants all map in y. If a base change in z not leading

Table 2

	Mutant No.		% Wild acetylase
Missense	32		86.5
	126		99.1
	270		94.0
	290		72.6
	823		72.8
		Average	85.0
UAG	125		4.9
	422		6.6
	503		1.7
	779		1.9
	608		11.0
		Average	5.2
UGA	268		12.4
	498		3.7
	521		3.5
	590		1.0
	721		6.1
	827		12.0
		Average	6.5

Table 2: (Zipser, 1967) The 16 mutants shown here are all those which mapped under deletion r9 (Fig. 3) from a set of about 100 independent NG mutants. The two kinds of nonsense were all polar but varied between 1 and 12% acetylase. The average acetylase for the two types of nonsense (no UAA were found in this region) was about the same and much less than the acetylase produced by the missense mutants.

to a complete z^- phenotype could be very polar, it would have shown up as a z^+y^- mutant mapping in z.

Knowing that nonsense mutants are polar, it is logical to ask how polar they are. This simple question has a very complex answer. First of all, as can be seen from the data already given in Tables 1 and 2, different nonsense mutations differ in their degree of polarity. Since there are three different nonsense codons the first question to be answered is, could the difference lie here? Again Table 2 already gives part of the answer. UAG mutants differ among themselves as do UGA mutants. A more critical test is to ask what about the three nonsense mutations at the same site. That is, when UAG, UGA and UAA alleles are generated at the same codon (in

Figure 3. Map of the *lac* operon showing deletion r9 approximately to scale.

different strains, of course) what is their polarity? The answer is that in most cases different allelic nonsense codons have exactly the same degree of polarity (Zipser, 1967). However, in some very recently discovered cases, not yet thoroughly studied, allelic nonsense codons have very different polarities (Norkin, unpubl.).

For the vast majority of nonsense mutations in *z*, the main factor in determining the degree of polarity is related to map position. The first indications of this came from observations that nonsense mutations near the operator end of *z* were very polar, often making less than 1% of M & A, while mutations at the other end were hardly polar at all, making from 50% to 100% of the wild type levels of M & A (Newton, et al., 1965). Mutants in between had a range of polarity in between these extremes. This led to an early notion that there was a continuous gradient of polarity along the *z* gene. Work on other operons, notably histidine, cast doubt on this continuous gradient hypothesis and recent extensive studies in the *lac* operon, to which I will return, have shown that the gradient is quite complex (Martin, et al., 1966). However, the idea of a continuous gradient led to a series of important experiments. Since nonsense mutants near the *z-y* boundary were not very polar, it was suggested that the distance from a nonsense mutant to the next polypeptide initiation sequence was an important factor in determining polarity. Two kinds of tests of this hypothesis have been carried out.

In the first (shown in Fig. 4) a highly polar nonsense mutant near the operator end of *z* was "moved" closer to the *z-y* boundary by combining it with a large *z* deletion (Zipser and Newton, 1967). When this was done, the polarity of the mutant sharply decreased. This result is, of course,

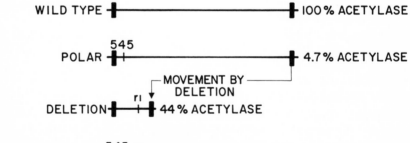

FIGURE 4. (From Zipser and Newton, 1967). The effect of moving a nonsense mutation, 545, closer to the *z-y* boundary is demonstrated. The deletion r1 is slightly polar itself but the double 545-r1 is six times *less* polar than 545 alone.

consistent with the theory that the distance between termination and reinitiation is an important factor in how much reinitiation there will be.

The second test of this hypothesis is much more significant for the question of punctuation. It was argued that if a polypeptide reinitiation site was introduced near a nonsense codon, the nonsense would become much less polar. The strategy used to put a reinitiation site near a highly polar nonsense mutation was as follows: Strongly polar z^- mutants do not grow on the sugar Melibiose at 40°C because at that temperature melibiose requires the *lac* operon permease. Melibiose positive revertants of polar mutants can be isolated. If reinitiation sites could occur as mutations near the original polar mutations, they would be melibioses positive if they lowered the polarity of nearby nonsense mutations. Thus, one class of Mel$^+$ revertants should be polypeptide reinitiations sites near the polar mutants. This expectation has proven correct (Grodzicker and Zipser, 1968) and several such new polypeptide initiation sites generated by mutations have been isolated. There are two important consequences of this result. First of all, it confirms the hypothesis that the distance from a nonsense to a new start is an important factor in determining the degree to which nonsense mutant is polar. Secondly, it gives us a way to obtain for study initiation mutants contained within structural genes.

When the nonsense mutation used to select a polypeptide reinitiation mutation is separated, by genetic techniques, from the initiation site mutation, a new kind of z gene is available that has an additional reinitiation site in it. The obvious question to ask is, what does this z gene produce? The answer is that it is almost indistinguishable from wild-type. The β-galactosidase made is not distinguishable from wild-type β-galactoside and could differ from it by at most a single amino acid change. This is not surprising but does raise the possibility that within the wild-type z gene there are reinitiation sites that occur naturally. This is in fact the case and these internal, naturally-occurring reinitiation sites can be mapped by two independent methods. The first is based on the observation of Yanofsky and Ito, (1966) who found that when two nonsense mutations were put in the same cistron of the tryp operon, the polarity of this double mutant was the same as that of the most operator proximal of the pair. However, when two nonsense mutations are put in different cistrons, the polarity of the double is greater than either member of the pair. The interpretation here is that when a reinitiation sequence at the cistron boundary is between two nonsense mutations, the polarity of the second mutation can be expressed. By constructing many double nonsense mutants within the z gene, this method was used to test for and map any initiation sites occurring within the z-structural gene (Michels and Zipser, 1969; Newton, 1969). Figure 5 shows such an experiment. Two

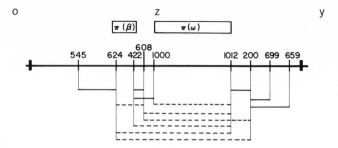

FIGURE 5. (From Michels and Zipser, 1969). The map of the *z* gene shows the position of 9 *z*⁻ nonsense mutants. Horizontal lines below the map show the double mutants constructed. The solid lines (———) mean that the double had about the same polarity as the first (i.e., most operator proximal) mutant of the pair. The dashed (- - - - -) lines mean that the double was much more polar than either mutant. $\pi(\beta)$ and $\pi(\omega)$ are the restart containing regions defined as those crossed *only* by dashed lines.

regions of the *z* gene are shown to have reinitiation sequences within them by the double mutant criterion. The second method of mapping the naturally-occurring restarts within the *z* gene is based on the fact that the closer a nonsense mutation is to an initiation sequence the less polar it is. Thus, each internal restart should be reflected by a peak in the gradient of polarity. The current status of this gradient can be seen in Fig. 6 (Zipser, et al., 1970). There are three clear peaks all in the two regions shown to have reinitiation sequences by the double mutant method. These internal restarts also explain the complexity of the gradient shown in Fig. 6.

The above discussion shows clearly how fruitful the study of polarity has been toward an understanding of translational level punctuation. We can generalize these results in the following way. The distance from a termination mutation to a reinitiation code sequence helps to determine the efficiency of polypeptide initiation at the start code. It is obvious to propose that this mechanism is used to determine the natural polarity of the *lac* operon. Whether this is true still remains a completely open question. We do not yet know if other factors besides terminator-initiator distance play a role in determining the efficiency of starting. In particular, we would like to know if there are a series of different start sequences each with its own inherent initiation efficiency.

An obvious and fruitful question has been to ask what happens to the messenger RNA (mRNA) of operons with polar mutations using DNA-RNA hybridization as a probe for mRNA (Contesse, Naono, and Gros, 1966; Imamoto and Yanofsky, 1967). These experiments have shown that polar mutants lower the total amount of operon specific mRNA. They do not, however, decrease the number of messengers made. What

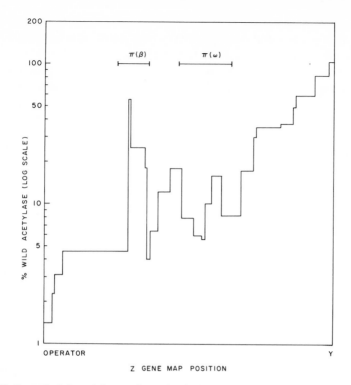

FIGURE 6. Current status of the gradient of polarity. The length of each horizontal line is proportional to the genetic size of the segment. The height of the horizontal line is proportional to the average amount of acetylase made by mutants in the segment. The vertical scale is logarithmic.

happens is that polar mutants contain two classes of messenger: normal length mRNAs which are present in a reduced amount, and short messengers which have apparently terminated at or near the site of the nonsense mutation.

SUMMARY AND CONCLUSIONS

While considerable information is now available on the mechanism of initiation and termination of polypeptide synthesis, the full code for these processes is not yet known. It seems certain that AUG, coding for F-Met, is widely if not exclusively used as the first codon of proteins. There must, however, be more to the start sequence and little is yet known about what this may be. No normal terminator is yet known but it is hard to imagine that one or more of the nonsense codons do not play a role in termination.

The isolation of new start mutations for polypeptide synthesis within the structural gene for β-galactosidase may subsequently lead to more information about the nature of the start code.

The question of determining the relative levels of enzyme produced within an operon is still in its infancy. The phenomena of polarity supplies us with a model of how this governor, internal to the operon, might work. If, for example, there is some untranslated space between the end of z and the beginning of y and between the end of y and the beginning of a, then "polar" effects would be expected by analogy with nonsense mutants and restarts within structural genes. However, so far no experiments to demonstrate these intercistron spaces have given either positive or negative answers.

What models have been proposed to account for bacterial polarity? Unfortunately, to devise such models it is necessary to know details of operon function which are not yet clearly understood. For this reason, most speculation on the mechanism of polarity has either been general or else has forced the speculator to make guesses about how the operon works. These speculations have centered about several important issues. For example, to explain the directional nature of polarity, it is necessary to evoke a process that begins at one end of the operon and proceeds to the other. One proposal is the so-called "threading" hypothesis (Martin, Silbert, Smith and Whitfield, 1966) which states that ribosomes can only attach to mRNA near its 5' end. They then proceed along, translating the sequential structural genes into protein. A fraction of the ribosomes would then fall off the messenger in the untranslated region, giving rise to polarity. Critical tests of the "threading" hypothesis are in progress. If there is no "threading" and ribosomes can enter messenger anywhere, then the basis of the directional phenomena must be found elsewhere. Other possibilities have been suggested. One proposal is to couple polypeptide synthesis, which would start as soon as a 5' mRNA end was synthesized, with the further elongation of the messenger (Stent, 1964). The ribosomes translating the mRNA are envisaged as pushing the DNA-dependent RNA polymerase along. Nonsense mutants would stop the progress of the ribosomes and thus inhibit the progress of mRNA synthesis. This, in turn, would lead to promiscuous mRNA termination or perhaps excessive mRNA breakdown.

These general lines of thought, "threading" and "coupling", have dominated the field. They are clearly not mutually exclusive and this has given rise to a variety of mixed theories, but several questions about operon function will have to be answered before polarity is understood in molecular terms.

First, do ribosomes attach to mRNA only at its 5' end, or can they attach at various internal sites? This question really has two phases: is it physically possible for ribosomes to attach and initiate polypeptide synthesis at internal mRNA sites, and, if so, what conditions must be met by the mRNA to actually allow significant ribosome attachment under in vivo conditions? By "conditions," I mean such factors as mRNA-DNA attachment, mRNA-RNA polymerase interaction and self-interaction of mRNA, which is generally referred to as secondary structure.

Second, is the absence of the operator distal ends of mRNA in cells with polar mutants due to messenger termination, breakdown or perhaps to something else? Here the data favor termination, but no critical test has been made.

Third, are the small number of full-size mRNA molecules made by polar mutant strains polar themselves during translation, or does each full-size mRNA make wild-type levels of the various enzymes? Ideally, this question needs to be answered independently of question 2, because it is particularly important in view of the work with the RNA bacteriophage.

Fourth, what is the "normal" mechanism of messenger termination?

The *lac* operon system has played only a modest role in work on punctuation at the translational level so far. However, many of the more subtle questions in this field will undoubtedly benefit, in the future, from studies with *lac* because of the very high state of the genetic and biochemical art of this operon.

ACKNOWLEDGMENTS

Recipient of a National Science Foundation Grant (#GB7127) and a National Institutes of Health Grant (#GM14676).

REFERENCES

CONTESSE, G., S. NAONO, and F. GROS. 1966. Effet des mutations polaires sur la transcription de l'opéron lactose chez *E. coli*. Compt. Rend. Acad. Sci. *263* Series D: 1007.

FRANCKLIN, N. C. and S. E. LURIA. 1961. Transduction by bacteriophage p1 and the properties of the *lac* genetic region in *E. coli* and *S. dysenteriae*. Virology *15*: 299.

GHOSH, H. P., D. SOLL, and H. G. KHORANA. 1967. Initiation of protein synthesis in vitro as studied by using ribopolynucleotides with repeating nucleotide sequences as messengers. J. Mol. Biol. *25*: 275.

GRODZICKER, T. and D. ZIPSER. 1968. A mutation which creates a new site for the re-initiation of polypeptide synthesis in the z gene of the *lac* operon of *E. coli*. J. Mol. Biol. *38*: 305.

HINDLEY, J., and D. H. STAPLES. 1969. Sequence of a ribosome binding site in bacteriophage Qβ-RNA. Nature *224*: 964.

IMAMOTO, F., and C. YANOFSKY. 1967. Transcription of the trypotophan operon in polarity mutants of *E. coli*. J. Mol. Biol. *28:* 25.

JACOB, F., and J. MONOD. 1961. On the regulation of gene activity. Cold Spring Harbor Symp. Quant. Biol. *26:* 193.

KOLAKOFSKY, D., K. DEWEY, and R. E. THACH. 1969. Purification and properties of initiation factor f_2. Nature *223:* 694.

MARTIN, R. G., D. F. SILBERT, D. W. E. SMITH, and H. J. WHITFIELD, Jr. 1966. Polarity in the histidine operon. J. Mol. Biol. *21:* 357.

MARTIN, R. G., H. J. WHITFIELD, D. B. BERKOWITZ, and M. J. VOLL. A molecular model of the phenomenon of polarity. Cold Spring Harbor Symp. Quant. Biol. *31:* 215.

MICHELS, C. A. and D. ZIPSER. 1969. Mapping of polypeptide reinitiation sites within the β-galactosidase gene. J. Mol. Biol. *41:* 341.

NEWTON, A. 1969. Re-initiation of polypeptide synthesis and polarity in the *lac* operon of *E. coli*. J. Mol. Biol. *41-3:* 329.

NEWTON, A. W., J. R. BECKWITH, D. ZIPSER, and S. BRENNER. 1965. Nonsense mutations and polarity in the *lac* operon of *Escherichia coli*. J. Mol. Biol. *14:* 290.

SCOLNICK, E., R. TOMPKINS, T. CASKEY, and M. NIRENBERG. 1968. Release factors differing in specificity for termination codons. Proc. Nat. Acad. Sci. *61:* 768.

STEITZ, J. A. 1969. Polypeptide chain initiation: nucleotide binding sequences of the ribosomal binding sites in bacteriophage R17 RNA. Nature *224:* 957.

STENT, G. 1964. The operon: on its third anniversary. Science *144:* 816.

YANOFSKY, C. and J. ITO. 1966. Nonsense codons and polarity in the tryptophan operon. J. Mol. Biol. *21:* 313.

ZIPSER, D. 1967. UGA: A third class of suppressible polar mutants. J. Mol. Biol. *29:* 441.

ZIPSER, D., and A. NEWTON. 1967. The influence of deletions on polarity. J. Mol. Biol. *25:* 567.

ZIPSER, D., S. ZABELL, J. ROTHMAN, T. GRODZICKER, M. WENK, and M. NOVITSKI. The fine structure of the gradient of polarity in the *z* gene of the *lac* operon of *E. coli*. J. Mol. Biol. (in press).

Isolation of β-Thiogalactoside Binding Proteins of *Escherichia coli* by Specific Adsorbents

SHIRO TOMINO and KENNETH PAIGEN

Department of Experimental Biology
Roswell Park Memorial Institute
Buffalo, New York

The isolation of some proteins is frustrated by their presence in very small quantities, or by the lack of a practicable assay method. Unfortunately, many proteins of biological importance fall into this group. Included are genetic repressors, permeases, and hormone and neural receptors. One way of obviating these difficulties is through the use of an adsorbent which specifically retains the protein of interest. This can be achieved by choosing a low-molecular ligand which binds to the active site of the protein and then coupling this ligand to an inert matrix. Proteins whose active sites recognize ligand will then adsorb to the matrix provided that the ligand has been coupled through a portion of its molecule which is not required for binding. Several laboratories have applied this and related techniques to the isolation of antibody proteins (Onoue, et al., 1965; Campbell and Weliky, 1967; Robbins, et al., 1967; Avrameas and Ternynck, 1967; Hoyer, et al., 1968), binding proteins (McCormick, 1965; Agrawal and Goldstein, 1965; Cuatrecasas and Wilchek, 1968) and certain enzymes (Lerman, 1953; Arsenis and McCormick, 1964; Arsenis and McCormick, 1966; Pogell, 1966; Cuatrecasas, et al., 1968; Alberts, 1968). The significance of this approach is that the physical isolation of the protein derives from the properties of its active site and in principle does not require the availability of an in vitro assay. In some cases the final identification can be confirmed by the comparison of extracts from physiologically or genetically altered cells.

Such a procedure of affinity chromatography offers considerable promise

233

for the isolation of repressor proteins. Toward this purpose we have constructed adsorbents with β-thiogalactoside ligands attached to insoluble protein polymers, and studied their utility in the isolation of the set of *E. coli* proteins whose active sites recognize a β-thiogalactoside configuration. This set should include the repressor proteins of the *lac* and *gal* operon, both of which bind β-thiogalactosides either as inducers or co-repressors (Monod *et al.*, 1951; Müller-Hill *et al.*, 1964; Buttin, 1963).

METHODS

Preparation of BGG polymer: Bovine-gamma-globulin (BGG*, Pentex Inc.) was polymerized according to the method of Onoue, *et al.* (1965) which consists of mercaptosuccinylation followed by crosslinking of the sulfhydryl groups with the tri-functional reagent, tris-[1-(2-methyl) aziri-dinyl]phosphine oxide. The resulting water insoluble polymer of BGG (polyBGG) was suspended in 0.5M NaCl and stored in the cold over a few drops of CHCl$_3$. The protein concentration of polymer suspensions was determined by the Biuret method (Layne, 1957) after solution of the polymer in hot 2N NaOH.

BGG polymer prepared in this way contains a high concentration of free carboxyl groups since the original carboxyl groups of the protein remain intact and each of the original amino groups is now replaced by an additional free carboxyl. The reactive carboxyls provide convenient sites for the attachment of specific ligand groups.

Coupling of p-aminophenyl-thiogalactoside (PAPTG): The coupling of β-thiogalactosides to polyBGG was performed by the carbodiimide-activated formation of peptide bonds (Sheehan and Hess, 1955; Goodfriend *et al.*, 1964) between amino-substituted thiogalactosides and the carboxyl group of the protein polymer. Most such reactions were carried out using 1-ethyl-3-(3-dimethyl-aminopropyl)carbodiimide hydrochloride (Otto Chemical Co.). Occasionally 1-cyclohexyl-3-[2-morpholinyl-(4)-ethyl]carbodiimide *metho-p*-toluenesulfonate (Aldrich Chemicals Co.) was used with essentially identical results. In practice, 2% carbodiimide and varying concentrations of PAPTG (Cyclo Chemical Co.) were added to a 20mg/ml suspension of polyBGG in 0.5M NaCl. The mixture was stirred at room temperature for 2 hours and the pH maintained at 4.75 (Hoare and Koshland Jr., 1967) by adding 1N HCl. Stirring was continued unattended overnight at room

---

* Abbreviations used: BGG, Bovine-gamma-globulin. PAPTG, p-Aminophenyl-thiogalacto-side. ABTG, Aminobutyl-thiogalactoside. IPTG, Isopropyl-thiogalactoside. ONPG, o-Nitro-phenyl-galactoside. ONPTG, o-Nitrophenyl-thiogalactoside. PNPTG, p-Nitrophenyl-thiogalac-toside. TMG, Thiomethylgalactoside.

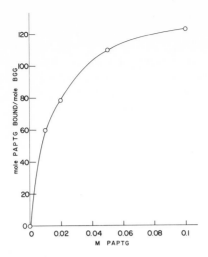

FIGURE 1. *Coupling of PAPTG with polyBGG:* The coupling reaction was carried out as described under METHODS in a final volume of 10 ml. The ratio of PAPTG to BGG was calculated by assuming a molecular weight of 150,000 for BGG.

temperature. The product (polyBGG-galactoside) was washed extensively with 0.5M NaCl to remove unreacted carbodiimide and PAPTG.

The thiogalactoside content of the product was determined by the phenol-sulfuric acid method (Ashwell, 1966) after digesting the product with hot 2N NaOH. Figure 1 shows the relationship between the number of galactoside residue introduced into the polymer and the concentration of PAPTG in the coupling reaction mixture. This relationship provides a simple means for controlling the galactoside content of the product. At 0.1M PAPTG, almost all of the available free carboxyl groups of polyBGG were substituted by the thiogalactoside. This is approximately 110 moles thiogalactoside per mole of BGG or 1 thiogalactoside per 12 amino acid residues. The polyBGG-galactoside was stored frozen in 0.5M NaCl until use as it slowly lost adsorbing capacity at 4°C. Homogenization was necessary to disperse to the polymer after thawing.

Coupling of aminobutyl-thiogalactoside (ABTG): No conditions could be found for the coupling of ABTG to polyBGG in aqueous reaction mixtures; however, the reaction could proceed in organic solvents such as tetrahydrofuran or dimethylsulfoxide. PolyBGG was washed with tetrahydrofuran and suspended at a concentration of 20 mg/ml in tetrahydrofuran-water (4:1 v/v) containing 2% carbodiimide reagent and 0.1M ABTG (Cyclo Chemicals Co.). The mixture was stirred at room temperature with the pH maintained at 6.0 for 2 hours. After stirring overnight unattended, the resulting conjugate was washed in the same way as polyBGG-PAPTG. Under these conditions, 56 moles of ABTG were coupled per mole BGG.

Preparation of cell-free extract of E. coli: Strain Q91 (*lac i^Q.**) was grown at 30°C to saturation in K-medium (Weigle *et al.*, 1959) without heat induction of the prophage. All other strains were grown in the same medium at 37°C. Cells were harvested and washed with 0.02M tris-HCl buffer pH 7.5 containing 0.01M $MgSO_4$. After adding the same buffer (4 ml/g packed cells), cells were disrupted by passing through a French press. Extracts were incubated for 5 minutes in the cold with 2 μg/ml of pancreatic DNase (Worthington Biochemical Co.). Unbroken cells and cell debris were then removed by centrifugation by a Spinco model L centrifuge at 78,000 X g for 90 minutes. The resulting supernatant was used as the source of *E. coli* protein.

For the study of IPTG binding, the crude extract from the *lac i^Q* strain (Q91) was precipitated by ammonium sulfate at 33% saturation (Gilbert and Müller-Hill, 1966; Riggs and Bourgeois, 1968). The precipitate was dissolved in 0.02M potassium-phosphate buffer pH 6.8 and the remaining ammonium sulfate was removed by passing the solution through a column of Sephadex G-50 equilibrated with the same buffer.

Adsorption and elution of β-galactosidase: A fixed amount of crude extract from a *lac* constitutive strain (W 1317) was mixed with varying amounts of polyBGG-galactoside in 1 ml of 0.1M tris-HCl buffer pH 7.5 containing 0.01M $MgSO_4$, 0.014M mercaptoethanol and 0.4M NaCl. The mixtures were shaken at 30°C for 20 minutes. PolyBGG-galactoside and bound enzyme were then sedimented and the supernatant fraction assayed for β-galactosidase activity and for absorption at 280mμ. The adsorbent was washed twice with the same buffer and the β-galactosidase finally eluted with 1 ml of the same buffer containing 0.1M isopropylthiogalactoside (IPTG) or other sugars at the concentration indicated. The elution was performed by shaking the mixtures at 30°C for 20 minutes followed by centrifugation. In several experiments, tris buffer was replaced by sodium phosphate buffer pH 7.0.

Assay of β-galactosidase: β-galactosidase activity was determined by the hydrolysis of O-nitrophenyl-galactoside (ONPG) as described previously (Paigen, 1963) with the omission of the lysozyme step.

Equilibrium dialysis: A 0.5 ml aliquot of sample solution was dialysed against 10 ml of 0.02M tris-maleate buffer pH 7.0 containing 0.01M $MgSO_4$, 0.014M mercaptoethanol, 0.2M KCl, 5% sucrose and 5×10^{-7} M C^{14}-IPTG (sp. act., 6μc/μmole). Dialysis was carried out in the cold with gentle shaking overnight. The radioactivity of the dialysed samples and

---

*Kindly supplied by Dr. J. H. Miller. The strain has the following genotype: $F^-(\Delta lac\ pro)_{XIII}Str^s\ \phi80dlac\ i^Qz^-C_{i857}t_s\ 696/F'\ lac\ pro\ i^{QA-2}z^+$

the solution outside the bag were determined in a liquid scintillation counter. IPTG binding activity was expressed as the excess of radioactivity inside the bag.

Electrophoresis: Dilute protein solutions were concentrated for electrophoresis by ultra filtration using a pressure filtration apparatus (S&S Co., model MD-50). Samples for electrophoresis were prepared in 5% sucrose. Polyacrylamide gel electrophoresis was performed as described by Clarke (1964) except that the gelling buffer was changed to contain 29g glycine and 12g tris per liter. Electrophoresis was carried out at room temperature applying a current of 3mA/tube. Protein was stained with naphthol blue black.

RESULTS

β-Galactosidase as a model protein: We have used the binding of β-galactosidase to polyBGG-galactoside as a model system for studying the interaction between galactoside adsorbents and proteins whose active sites recognize these ligands. This is possible since β-thiogalactosides act as competitive inhibitors of β-galactosidase activity (Monod, et al., 1951; Rickenberg, 1960). As a preliminary experiment, polyBGG-PAPTG preparations with different numbers of galactoside residues were incubated with crude *E. coli* extract at various salt concentrations. After incubation, polyBGG-galactoside was removed by centrifugation and the amount of enzyme adsorbed was estimated by difference from that remaining in the supernatant (Fig. 2). It is apparent that polyBGG-galactoside can adsorb β-galactosidase from a crude extract of *E. coli*. The extent of adsorption was dependent on both the galactoside content of the polymer and the ionic environment. At sufficiently low-salt concentrations even a polyBGG which is devoid of galactoside residues adsorbs β-galactosidase. However, this non-specific adsorption is overcome by raising the NaCl concentration. At high-salt concentration where non-specific adsorption is negligible, the ability of polyBGG-PAPTG to adsorb β-galactosidase is a function of the galactoside content of the polymer.

To determine the optimum conditions for β-galactosidase recovery we have examined the adsorption of this enzyme and its elution by IPTG as a function of pH and ionic strength. These results can be summarized by the statement that a low-pH and low-salt concentration favor adsorption and a high-pH and a high-salt concentration favor elution. For preparative purposes, the most useful buffer has been 0.1M tris-HCl, pH 7.5 containing 0.4M NaCl, 0.01M MgSO$_4$, and 0.014M mercaptoethanol. A series of experiments on the interaction between β-galactosidase and polyBGG-galactosides was therefore carried out in this medium.

The adsorption capacity of polyBGG-PAPTG for β-galactosidase was

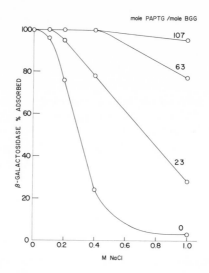

FIGURE 2. *Effect of NaCl concentration on β-galactosidase adsorption:* One mg of *E. coli* (W 1317) protein was incubated at different NaCl concentrations with 1 mg of polyBGG-PAPTG in 0.1M phosphate buffer pH 7.0. After centrifugation, an aliquot from each supernatant was assayed for β-galactosidase.

determined. Increasing amounts of an adsorbent preparation (105 moles PAPTG/mole BGG) were added to a series of tubes containing fixed amounts of *E. coli* extract in tris-salt buffer. The β-galactosidase remaining in the supernatant after centrifugation progressively decreased with increasing amounts of adsorbent, whereas little OD 280mμ adsorbing material was removed (Fig. 3A). In this experiment the polymer was able to adsorb all of the β-galactosidase from an approximately equal weight of crude extract protein. Washing the adsorbent with 0.1M IPTG eluted about 60% of the adsorbed β-galactosidase, and only a very small amount of protein.

The same experiment was performed with a polyBGG containing 56 moles ABTG per mole of BGG (Fig. 3B). Essentially the same curves were obtained as with PAPTG adsorbent. However, polyBGG containing ABTG residue is more active than one containing PAPTG in binding β-galactosidase. Although the polyBGG-ABTG contained half as much galactoside as the polyBGG-PAPTG used, it adsorbed approximately twice as much β-galactosidase per unit weight under same conditions. The recovery of β-galactosidase was essentially the same. This difference in capacity probably reflects the relative affinities of galactosides with different aglycones for the active sites of β-galactosidase. Unfortunately, although the polyBGG-ABTG has a higher capacity, its preparation is not easily reproduced and polyBGG-PAPTG has proved more useful for routine work.

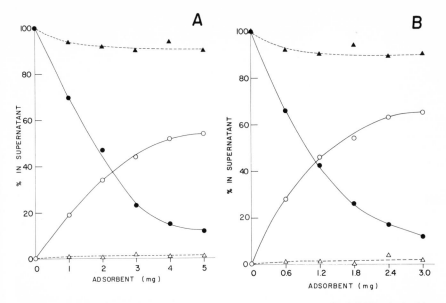

FIGURE 3. *Adsorption and elution of β-galactosidase:* Varying amounts of polyBGG-galactoside were incubated with 2.8 mg of *E. coli* (W 1317) protein. Adsorption and elution of β-galactosidase were performed in tris-salt buffer as described under METHODS. Results are expressed as a percentage of the total amount originally present.

A   PolyBGG-PAPTG (105 moles PAPTG/mole BGG)
B   PolyBGG-ABTG (56 moles ABTG/mole BGG)

●—●   β-galactosidase remaining unadsorbed
○—○   β-galactosidase eluted by 0.1M IPTG
▲--▲   O.D. 280mμ remaining unadsorbed
△--△   O.D. 280mμ eluted

The adsorption of β-galactosidase is interfered with only slightly by the presence of excess non-galactosidase protein. To show this, a fixed amount of extract from a *lac* constitutive strain (W 1317) was mixed with increasing amounts of extract from a *lac* deletion strain (W 4132) and incubated with adsorbent (Fig. 4). Increasing the amount of *lac* deletion protein inhibited the adsorption of β-galactosidase somewhat, but even when the amount of non-β-galactosidase protein was increased by 10-fold, adsorption was only reduced by 30%.

The ability of low molecular weight compounds to elute adsorbed β-galactosidase is quite specific. Only small molecules which are known to react with the active site of the enzyme are able to do so. This was demonstrated by measuring the ability of various sugars to inhibit the adsorption of β-galactosidase to polyBGG-galactoside under conditions where 80% of the enzyme was adsorbed in the absence of any competing ligand (Table 1). IPTG, which is a competitive inhibitor of the enzyme, was

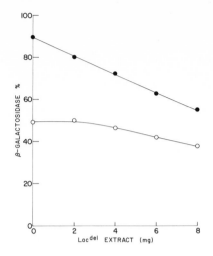

FIGURE 4. *Interference with β-galactosidase adsorption: E. coli* extract (W 1317, 0.8 mg protein) was incubated with 1 mg of polyBGG-PAPTG (105 moles PAPTG/mole BGG) in the presence of increasing amounts of extract from a *lac* deletion strain (W 4132) in tris-salt buffer. Adsorption and elution were carried out as described under METHODS.

●——● β-galactosidase remaining unadsorbed
○——○ β-galactosidase eluted by 0.1M IPTG.

Table 1

Sugars	Concentration (M)	% Inhibition of adsorption
none	—	0
PNPTG	2.5×10^{-3}	9
ONPTG	$.5 \times 10^{-3}$	34
TMG	$.5 \times 10^{-2}$	50
IPTG	$.5 \times 10^{-3}$	57
PAPTG	$.5 \times 10^{-3}$	15
Glucose	$.5 \times 10^{-2}$	5
Fucose	$.5 \times 10^{-2}$	2
Galactose	$.5 \times 10^{-2}$	13
Lactose	$.5 \times 10^{-2}$	51

Table 1. Inhibition of β-galactosidase adsorption: 1.2 mg of *E. coli* (W 1317) protein was incubated with 1 mg of adsorbent (108 moles PAPTG/mole BGG) in the presence of various sugar derivatives at the concentration indicated. After centrifugation, an aliquot from each supernatant was assayed for β-galactosidase.

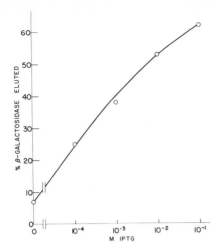

FIGURE 5. *Effect of IPTG concentration on β-galactosidase elution:* 2 mg of *E. coli* (W 1317) protein was incubated with 1.5 mg of polyBGG-PAPTG (105 moles PAPTG/mole BGG) in tris-salt buffer in each of a series of tubes. The adsorbent was centrifuged, washed with buffer and eluted with IPTG at the concentration indicated in the figure.

the most potent inhibitor of β-galactosidase adsorption. Thiomethylgalactoside (TMG) and o-nitrophenyl-thiogalactoside (ONPTG), which are also enzyme inhibitors, and the substrate lactose also prevent adsorption. No inhibitory effect was seen with free galactose, glucose or fucose.

The concentration dependency of IPTG elution of β-galactosidase was studied (Fig. 5) by first adsorbing the enzyme to polyBGG-PAPTG and then eluting with various concentrations of IPTG. As expected, more enzyme is eluted at higher IPTG concentrations. However, the range of concentrations over which elution occurs is very large and can be readily accounted for only by assuming a wide range of dissociation constants for the binding of individual β-galactosidase molecules. Adsorption must be quite strong for an appreciable percentage of enzyme molecules since even 0.1M IPTG is not sufficient to completely elute the enzyme. (That this is a very high concentration of IPTG is indicated by our measured value of 2.7×10^{-3}M for the ionization constant of this compound.)

The nature of the interaction between β-galactosidase and polyBGG-galactoside suggested that the polymer could be used for the single-step purification of enzyme by column chromatography. For this purpose a column was prepared from the polyBGG-ABTG adsorbent mixed with cellulose powder to improve the flow characteristics. After equilibration with buffer, a crude extract of a *lac* constitutive strain was continuously passed through the column. At first all of the β-galactosidase but only a

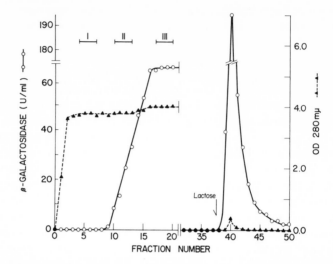

FIGURE 6. *Column chromatography of E. coli extract on polyBGG-ABTG:* PolyBGG-ABTG (75 mg, 56 moles ABTG/mole BGG) was mixed with 1 g of cellulose powder in 1.5 cm diameter column. After washing the column with tris-salt buffer, *E. coli* extracts (W 1317) prepared in the same buffer (protein conc. 1.4 mg/ml) was pumped through at a flow rate of 12 ml per hour. 5 ml fractions were collected and aliquots were assayed for β-galactosidase and for OD 280 mμ. After the column was saturated with β-galactosidase, it was washed with buffer until no β-galactosidase activity was detectable in the effluent. β-Galactosidase was finally eluted with 0.2M lactose in the same buffer.

o——o β-Galactosidase
▲——▲ O.D. 280mμ

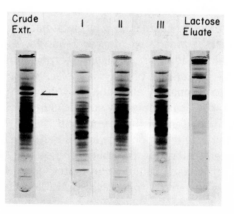

FIGURE 7. *Electrophoresis of column fractions:* Samples from the experiment shown in Fig. 6 were analysed by polyacrylamide electrophoresis as described under METHODS. The arrow in the figure indicates the position of β-galactosidase.

small percentage of the total protein were retained by the column. Finally, the column became saturated and β-galactosidase began to flow through (Fig. 6). The flow of crude extract was then stopped, and the column washed with buffer until the effluent was free of β-galactosidase and UV absorbing material. β-Galactosidase was then eluted with 0.2M lactose dissolved in the same buffer. The column fractions indicated in the figure were pooled, concentrated by ultrafiltration and subjected to disc electrophoresis on polyacrylamide gel (Fig. 7). The band of β-galactosidase, which can be seen in the crude extract, was missing from the early column discharge when β-galactosidase activity was completely adsorbed. It reappeared again after the column became saturated with enzyme. The fraction eluted by lactose contained a β-galactosidase band together with several minor bands but was free of most *E. coli* proteins. To prove that the proteins eluted by lactose are indeed coded for by the *lac* operon, we have compared extracts of a *lac⁺* inducible strain grown in the presence and absence of an inducer. Identical quantities of extract from each culture were prepared and chromatographed on polyBGG-galactoside columns using the procedure just described. The column fractions were then analysed by electrophoresis (Fig. 8). β-Galactosidase is easily recognized

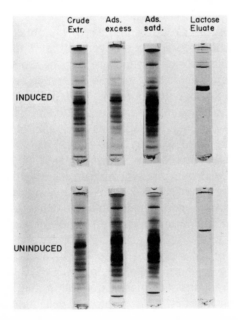

FIGURE 8. *Electrophoresis of column fractions:* The *E. coli lac⁺* inducible strain (W 3350) was grown in the presence (5 × 10⁻⁴M IPTG) or absence of inducer. A cell-free extract from each culture (total protein, 70 mg) was chromatographed on polyBGG-ABTG (75 mg) as described under Fig. 6. Column fractions were analysed by electrophoresis as described.

in the crude extract obtained from induced, but not from uninduced cells. This band disappears from the effluent as long as enzyme is completely adsorbed by the column. The lactose eluates from both columns show the β-galactosidase band. Additional bands of low mobility are obvious in the eluate from induced cells, but are barely discernible in that from uninduced cells, suggesting that these materials are also coded by the *lac* operon. They may represent aggregates of β-galactosidase (Appel *et al.*, 1965). It is worth noting that in this experiment the polyBGG-galactoside adsorbent was capable of isolating β-galactosidase even from an extract of uninduced cells, which are supposed to contain 1000 times less β-galactosidase than induced cells.

Lac Repressor Protein: PolyBGG-galactoside can also be applied to the isolation of other galactoside binding proteins. Our initial efforts have been concentrated on the *lac* repressor protein. Crude extracts from a wild-type strain were mixed with various buffers at different pH's and ionic strengths. These were passed through polyBGG-galactoside columns, and adsorbed protein eluted with solutions of IPTG in the original buffer. The eluates were concentrated and analysed by electrophoresis. The buffer finally selected for chromatography was the one which yielded the largest number of protein bands after electrophoresis of the IPTG eluate. Extracts of wild-type uninduced cells yielded six major bands, one of which was β-galactosidase (Fig. 9). An additional band was obtained from induced wild type and probably represents an aggregate of β-galactosidase, since both it and the β-galactosidase band are missing from induced cells of a *lac z⁻* strain. There was no recognizable difference between the protein patterns obtained from induced *lac y⁺* and induced *lac y⁻* cultures, indicating that *lac* permease was not present in the eluates. This is not surprising since the *y* protein probably was not solubilized by the extraction procedure used (Fox and Kennedy, 1965; Fox, *et al.*, 1967; Kundig, *et al.*, 1966). Extracts of the *lac i*^{Q} strain, which contain high concentrations of *lac* repressor, showed two marked differences which are indicated by arrows in the figure. The slower band in *lac i*^{Q} is not seen in *lac i⁺* and the faster band is greatly increased in intensity. When run simultaneously, the slower band had the same mobility as a sample of purified *lac* repressor protein which was kindly sent by Dr. S. Bourgeois.

The adsorption of *lac* repressor to polyBGG-galactoside columns was confirmed by using equilibrium dialysis to assay IPTG-binding activity in chromatographic fractions. For these experiments the repressor present in the *lac i*^{Q} extract was first concentrated by collecting a 0-33% ammonium sulfate precipitate and then dissolving this in 0.02M phosphate buffer at pH 6.8. This buffer was chosen as permitting maximum IPTG-binding during equilibrium dialysis. The repressor solution was passed through a

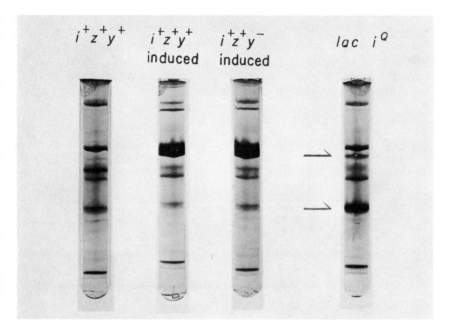

FIGURE 9. *Electrophoresis of IPTG eluates:* E. coli W 3110 ($I^+Z^+Y^+$), W 2241 ($I^+Z^+Y^-$) and Q 91 (*lac* i^Q) were grown in the presence (5 × 10^{-4}M IPTG) or absence of inducer. Extract prepared from approximately 10^{12} cells of each culture was chromatographed on 50 mg of polyBGG-PAPTG. Adsorption was done in 0.1M tris-HCl buffer pH 7.5 containing 0.01M MgSO$_4$, 0.014M mercaptoethanol and 0.2M NaCl. After washing each column with buffer, 0.1M IPTG in the same buffer was passed through the column. The IPTG eluates were analyzed by electrophoresis as described. Arrows indicate the positions of bands which are increased in the *lac* i^Q strain.

polyBGG-galactoside column; the column was then eluted with buffer of increasing ionic strength and the eluate fractions analysed for IPTG-binding activity by equilibrium dialysis (Fig. 10). IPTG-binding activity present in the repressor solution was completely adsorbed to the column, although the majority of protein was not retained and came off the column at the solvent front. IPTG-binding activity, together with a small amount of protein, was eluted at a KCl concentration of 0.2M in the buffer. The combined peak fractions contained 23% of the original IPTG-binding activity and 0.7% of the original UV-absorbing material. Acrylamide gel electrophoresis of the combined peak showed one major band with the same mobility as purified *lac* repressor plus several additional faint bands. Although the recovery of IPTG-binding activity was low in this experiment, it appears that polyBGG-galactoside adsorbents have promise as a means for isolating *lac* repressor protein.

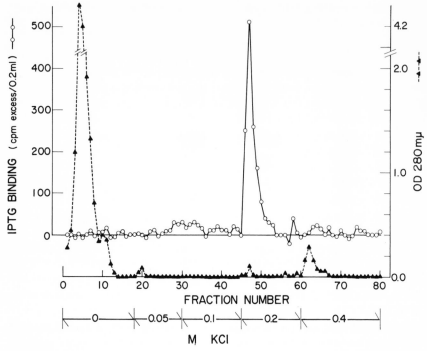

FIGURE 10. *Chromatography of lac i^Q extract:* The 0-33% ammonium sulfate precipitate of *lac i^Q* extract (total protein, 100 mg) was chromatographed on 110 mg of polyBGG-PAPTG (96 moles PAPTG/mole BGG) in 0.02M phosphate buffer pH 6.8 containing 0.01M MgSO$_4$ and 0.014M mercaptoethanol. Stepwise elution was performed by increasing the concentration of KCl in the same buffer as indicated in the figure. Column fractions were collected every 8 ml and IPTG binding activity was assayed by equilibrium dialysis as described under METHODS.

o—o   IPTG binding
△---△   O.D. 280mμ

DISCUSSION

The present work demonstrates that polyBGG-galactoside adsorbents are useful in the isolation of both β-galactosidase and *lac* repressor protein from crude *E. coli* extracts. The model experiments with β-galactosidase show that both the number of ligand groups per unit weight of adsorbent and the structure of the aglycone moiety of the ligand are significant in determining the adsorptive capacity of polyBGG-galactosides. Under optimum conditions this adsorptive capacity of adsorbents is rather high. Also, specific elution is provided only by free ligands able to react with the active site of adsorbed protein. These facts suggest that adsorption primarily results from an interaction between ligand groups on the adsorbent and active sites on the protein.

The number and character of ligand groups on the polymer may influence the affinity, as well as the capacity, of adsorbent for proteins. The number of ligand groups may be an especially significant factor for proteins possessing more than one active site per molecule where the possibility of cooperative binding exists. The nature of the elution curve of β-galactosidase obtained with IPTG suggests that some adsorbed molecules are held much tighter than others and that a detailed physical description of the interaction between protein active sites and polymer ligand groups will be difficult.

Adsorption also is influenced by surface interaction between the polymers and adsorbed proteins. The importance of such interactions is suggested by the considerable non-specific binding of protein which occurs at low-salt concentrations. Other properties of the polymer that may be significant are its surface area per unit weight and its relative porosity for different proteins. The importance of such "non-specific factors" is suggested by our experience with other matrix ligand combinations. We have synthesized adsorbents consisting of PAPTG ligand coupled with CM-cellulose (Hoyer, et al., 1968), bromoacetyl-cellulose (Robbins, et al., 1967) and Sepharose (Cuatrecases, et al., 1968). All of these ligand matrix conjugates were found to be inactive in binding β-galactosidase, except for Sepharose-PAPTG which showed some retardation of β-galactosidase in columns.

It seems probable that polyBGG-galactoside adsorbents will also be effective in the isolation of other proteins whose active sites recognize β-thiogalactosides, such as *lac* permease and *gal* repressor protein. By extension, we anticipate that analogous adsorbents containing different ligand groups will prove useful as specific adsorbents for other proteins. Our experience in the *lac* system suggests that a systematic study of adsorption and elution at various pH's and ionic strengths will be a necessary prerequisite to the sensible use of ligand-coupled adsorbents in the isolation of a new protein. If adsorption does occur, elution of bound protein can be achieved by changing pH or ionic strength, or more specifically, by the addition of low molecular weight compounds that compete for the active site of the protein.

Acknowledgments

We wish to express our gratitude to Dr. Y. Yagi of this Institute for his valuable suggestions during the course of preparation of adsorbents, to Dr. J. Beckwith for supplying the *E. coli lac i*^{Q} strain through Dr. J. H. Miller, and to Dr. S. Bourgeois for sending us purified *lac i*^{Q} repressor.

Supported in part by grants from The National Science Foundation (GB-12290) and The American Cancer Society (P-508).

REFERENCES

ALBERTS, B. M. 1968. Chromatography of DNA-specific proteins on a DNA-cellulose matrix. Federation Proc. *27:* 645.

AGRAWAL, B. B. L., and I. J. GOLDSTEIN. 1965. Specific binding of concanavalin A to cross-linked dextran gels. Biochem. J. *96:* 23c.

APPEL, D., D. H. ALPERS, and G. M. TOMKINS. 1965. Multiple molecular forms of β-galactosidase. J. Mol. Biol. *11:* 12.

ARSENIS, C., and D. B. MCCORMICK. 1964. Purification of liver flavokinase by column chromatography on flavin-cellulose compounds. J. Biol. Chem. *239:* 3093.

ARSENIS, C., and D. B. MCCORMICK. 1966. Purification of flavin mono-nucleotide-dependent enzymes by column chromatography on flavin phosphate cellulose compounds. J. Biol. Chem. *241:* 330.

ASHWELL, G. 1966. New colorimetric methods of sugar analysis. Methods Enzymol. *8:* 85.

AVRAMEAS, S., and T. TERNYNCK. 1967. Biologically active water-insoluble protein polymer. J. Biol. Chem. *242:* 1651.

BUTTIN, G. 1963. Mécanismes régulateurs dans la biosynthèse des enzymes du métabolisme du galactose chez *Escherichia coli* K12. I. La biosynthèse induite de la galactokinase et l'induction simultanée de la séquence enzymatique. J. Mol. Biol. *7:* 164.

CAMPBELL, D. H. and N. WELIKY. 1967. Immunoadsorbents: preparation and use of cellulose derivatives, p. 365. *In* C. A. Williams and M. W. Chase [ed.] Methods in Immunology and Immunochemistry. *1.* Academic Press, New York.

CLARKE, J. T. 1964. Simplified "disc" (polyacrylamide gel) electrophoresis. Annals N.Y. Acad. Sci. *121:* 428.

CUATRECASES, P., M. WILCHEK, and C. ANFINSEN. 1968. Selective enzyme purification by affinity chromatography. Proc. Nat. Acad. Sci. *61:* 636.

FOX, C. F., and E. P. KENNEDY. 1965. Specific labelling and partial purification of the M protein, a component of the β-galactoside transport system of *E. coli*. Proc. Nat. Acad. Sci. *54:* 891.

FOX, C. F., J. R. CARTER, and E. P. KENNEDY. 1967. Genetic control of the membrane protein component of the lactose transport system of *Escherichia coli*. Proc. Nat. Acad. Sci. *57:* 698.

GILBERT, W., and B. MÜLLER-HILL. 1966. Isolation of the *lac* repressor. Proc. Nat. Acad. Sci. *56:* 1891.

GOODFRIEND, T., L. LEVINE, and G. D. FASMAN. 1964. Antibodies to bradykinin and angiotensin: A use of carbodiimide in immunology. Science *144:* 1344.

HOARE, D. G., and D. E. KOSHLAND JR. 1967. A method for the quantitative modification and estimation of carboxylic acid groups in proteins. J. Biol. Chem. *242:* 2447.

HOYER, L. W., W. E. VANNIER, and L. RENFER. 1968. Antibody elution from hapten-cellulose immunoadsorbents: The effect of hapten structure, pH and salt concentration. Immunochemistry 5: 277.
KUNDIG, W., F. D. KUNDIG, B. ANDERSON, and S. ROSEMAN. 1966. Restoration of active transport of glycosides in *Escherichia coli* by a component of a phosphotransferase system. J. Biol. Chem. *241:* 3243.
LAYNE, E. 1957. Spectrophotometric and turbidimetric methods for measuring proteins. Methods Enzymol. *3:* 447.
LERMAN, L. S. 1953. A biochemically specific method for enzyme isolation. Proc. Nat. Acad. Sci. *39:* 232.
McCORMICK, D. E. 1965. Specific purification of avidin by column chromatography on biotin-cellulose. Anal. Biochem. *13:* 194.
MONOD, J., G. COHEN-BAZIRE, and M. COHN. 1951. Sur la biosynthèse de la β-galactosidase (lactase) chez *Escherichia coli.* La specificité de l'induction. Biochim. Biophys. Acta *7:* 585.
MÜLLER-HILL, B., H. V. RICKENBERG, and K. WALLENFELS. 1969. Specificity of the induction of enzymes of the *lac* operon of *E. coli.* J. Mol. Biol. *10:* 303.
ONOUE, K., Y. YAGI, and D. PRESSMAN. 1965. Immunoadsorbents with high capacity. Immunochemistry *2:* 181.
PAIGEN, K. 1963. Changes in the inducibility of galactokinase and β-galactosidase during inhibition of growth in *E. coli.* Biochim. Biophys. Acta *77:* 318.
POGELL, B. M. 1966. Enzyme purification by specific elution procedures with substrate. Methods. Enzymol. *9:* 9.
RICKENBERG, H. V. 1960. Role of the inducer in induced synthesis of β-galactosidase in *Escherichia coli.* Nature *185:* 240.
RIGGS, A. D., and S. BOURGEOIS. 1968. On the assay, isolation and characterization of the *lac* repressor. J. Mol. Biol. *34:* 361.
ROBBINS, J. B., J. HAIMOVICH and M. SELA. 1967. Purification of antibodies with immunoadsorbents prepared using bromoacetyl cellulose. Immunochemistry *4:* 11.
SHEEHAN, J. C., and G. P. HESS. 1955. A new method of forming peptide bonds. J. Am. Chem. Soc. *77:* 1067.
WEIGLE, J., M. MESELSON, and K. PAIGEN. 1959. Density alterations associated with transducing ability in the bacteriophage lambda. J. Mol. Biol. *1:* 379.

Isoenzymes of Bacterial β-galactosidase: Renaturation of Heavier Isoenzymes from Dissociated *E. coli* β-galactosidase

ROBERT P. ERICKSON and EDWARD STEERS, Jr.

Laboratory of Chemical Biology
National Institute of Arthritis and Metabolic Diseases
National Institutes of Health
Bethesda, Maryland

INTRODUCTION

The β-galactosidase of *Escherichia coli* has been shown to exist in multiple molecular forms. These forms consist of increasing mol wt aggregates (having sedimentation coefficients from 23 S to 45 S and designated "heavy" isoenzymes) of a basic monomer beginning with the predominant tetrameric form (16 S). These monomers were not detectably different from the monomers of the common tetrameric species by several criteria (Marchesi et al., 1969). Studies on the β-galactosidases of various species established that the ability to form the heavier isoenzymes (23 S–45 S) was determined by the structural gene for β-galactosidase and was correlated with the relative stability of the tetramer (Erickson and Steers, 1970a). This was corroborated by studies of the non-isoenzyme forming β-galactosidase from *Aerobacter cloacae* (Erickson and Steers, 1970b). The basis for the formation of heavier isoenzymes has been clarified as the process has now been carried out in vitro.

METHODS

PREPARATION OF β-GALACTOSIDASE

β-galactosidase was purified from a constitutive strain, 3300, of *E. coli* K12 as previously described (Marchesi et al., 1969). Briefly, a 20–30% ammonium sulfate fraction of the crude extract was gel filtered on Sepharose 4B followed by Sephadex G-200 and then chromatographed on DEAE-cellulose. Preparations containing heavier isoenzymes were obtained if the Sepharose 4B gel filtration step was eliminated. Purified heavier isoenzymes could be obtained from Sepharose 4B gel filtration of the 0–20% ammonium sulfate fraction (Marchesi et al., 1969).

ENZYME ASSAY

The activity of β-galactosidase was measured with the substrate O-nitrophenyl-β-D-galactopyranoside (ONPG) in buffer B (0.05 M Tris-HCl, pH 7.4, 0.1 M NaCl, 0.01 M MgCl$_2$, 0.05 M β-mercaptoethanol) as previously described (Craven et al., 1965).

DISC GEL ELECTROPHORESIS

Polyacrylamide gel electrophoresis was carried out on pH 8.1, 5% gels as previously described (Erickson and Steers, 1970a). The gels were stained using the BNG (6-bromo-2-napthyl-β-D-galactopyranoside) histochemical procedure for β-galactosidase. For practical purposes, 15 units of enzyme activity gives a detectable band with a ten min incubation using this substrate.

DENATURATION AND RENATURATION OF β-GALACTOSIDASE

β-galactosidase was diluted to the indicated concentrations in 8 M urea in TVNS buffer (0.02 M Tris-HCl, pH 7.2, 0.01 M EDTA, 0.01 M NaCl, 0.01 M β-mercaptoethanol) and dialyzed against the 8 M urea-TVNS for several hours at 25°C. The dialysis bag was then transferred to a volume of TVNS several hundred-fold greater than in the bag and dialyzed for 18 hr at 4°C. D$_2$O solutions contained greater than 99% D$_2$O in place of water while the alcoholic solutions involved a dilution of TVNS to the indicated percentage of alcohol.

UREA AND THERMAL DENATURATIONS

Inactivations of β-galactosidase by heat or increasing concentrations of urea were performed as previously described (Erickson and Steers, 1970a).

ELECTRON MICROSCOPY

Enzyme preparations were negatively stained with 2% phosphotungstic acid neutralized to pH 7.0 with KOH. Samples were mounted on carbon-coated grids and examined in a Phillips EM-200 electron microscope.

ANALYTICAL ULTRACENTRIFUGATION

Sedimentation velocities were determined using Schlieren optics in the Spinco Model E analytical ultracentrifuge as previously described (Erickson and Steers, 1970b).

HYDROGEN EXCHANGE

Denaturation of 5 mg of β-galactosidase was performed as above in a 0.5 ml volume. The dialysis bag was then opened and 0.1 mc/ml of tritiated water was added. The dialysis bag was reclosed and dialyzed against 25 ml of D_2O-TVNS containing 0.1 mc/ml of tritiated water for 18 hr at 4°C. The renatured isoenzymes were observed on polyacrylamide disc gels and separated from tetramers on a 0.9 × 48 cm Sepharose 4B column eluted with buffer B at 6 ml/hr (1 ml fractions). Protein was determined by measuring the optical density at 280 mμ or by the ninhydrin reaction following alkaline hydrolysis (Hirs, 1967). Radioactivity was counted in a scintillation counter using Bray's solution. Efficiency was determined by counting an aliquot of the original solution.

CHEMICALS

The reagents for polyacrylamide gel electrophoresis were obtained from the Canal Industrial Corp. (Bethesda, Md.). Diazo-blue B, BNG (6-bromo-2–napthyl-β-D-galactopyranoside), and Tris (Trizma base) were purchased from the Sigma Chemical Co. (St. Louis, Mo.). 2-mercaptoethanol purchased from Eastman Organic Chemicals (Rochester, N.Y.). ONPG (o-nitrophenyl-β-D-galactopyranoside) was purchased from Calbiochem (Los Angeles, Calif.). D_2O was purchased from K & K Laboratories (Plainview, N.J.) and tritiated water, 100 mc/g, was purchased from New England Nuclear (Boston, Mass.). EDTA was purchased from Fisher Scientific Co. (Fairlawn, N.J.). Urea, reagent grade, was purchased from Baker Chemical Co. (Phillipsburg, N.J.) and was recrystallized once from absolute ethanol.

RESULTS

RENATURATION OF β-GALACTOSIDASE IN MG^{++}-FREE MEDIA

When β-galactosidase is renatured with removal of 8 M urea by dialysis against buffer B, only the tetramer is formed. Our recovery is generally less than 50% while Ullmann et al. (1968) have reported recoveries of 100% utilizing a Mg^{++}-free buffer (TVNS). When we utilize the Mg^{++}-free buffer and 1 mg/ml concentrations of β-galactosidase (higher concentrations are inhibitory when renaturing against buffer B), heavier isoenzymes are detectable (Table 1). Much higher concentrations of β-galactosidase may be used when renaturation is performed in the TVNS buffer, as opposed to buffer B, resulting in a slight increase in the relative yield of heavier isoenzymes. The ability to use higher concentrations of β-galactosidase is important as larger quantities of heavier isoenzymes can be renatured in the small volume (up to 75 λ) usually applied to the disc gel.

TABLE 1. Renaturation of β-galactosidase from 8 M urea: effects of changes in buffer and of β-galactosidase concentration

Concentration	Buffer	% Recovery of activity	Heavier isoenzyme formation % of total activity
1 mg/ml	BB	18.6	0
1 mg/ml	TVNS	103	1–2
2 mg/ml	TVNS	89	1–2
4 mg/ml	TVNS	106	2–3
8 mg/ml	TVNS	78	4–5
16 mg/ml	TVNS	60	4–5

The failure to see isoenzymes in the preparations renatured against buffer B is not merely due to a lower overall yield as similar amounts of units of enzyme were placed on the disc gels in each case. The result was the same whether the starting material contained isoenzymes or only contained tetramer.

STIMULATORY EFFECTS OF D_2O ON HEAVIER ISOENZYME RENATURATION

Replacing the water of the TVNS buffer with D_2O markedly increases the quantities of isoenzymes formed (Table 2, Fig. 1). Again, this result occurs with isoenzyme-free preparations of tetramer. It was possible that the effect is on ionizable groups as the pD of a D_2O solution is about 0.4 units higher than the value obtained on a pH meter (Zerner and Scheraga, 1961). However, as seen in Table 2, an increase in pH in the Mg^{++}-free media is actually slightly inhibitory for isoenzyme formation.

Table 2. Renaturation of β-galactosidase from 8 M urea at 1 mg/ml: effects of D_2O

Buffer	% Recovery of activity	Heavier isoenzyme formation
TVNS, aqueous	59	faint traces*
TVNS, D_2O	93	3 bands*
TVNS, pH 8.0	41	0
TVNS, pH 8.8	31	0

*See Fig. 1.

INHIBITORY EFFECTS OF ALCOHOLS ON HEAVIER ISOENZYME RENATURATION

If the stimulatory effect of D_2O on isoenzyme renaturation was mediated by stabilization of hydrophobic bonds, the addition of a series of alcohols of increasing chain length may be expected to result in inhibition of renaturation (performed at 7 mg/ml in the aqueous TVNS) proportional to the chain length (Schrier and Scheraga, 1962). As seen in Table 3, the

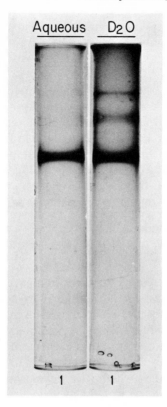

FIGURE 1. BNG-stained polyacrylamide electrophoretograms of β-galactosidase renatured from 8 M urea in TVNS by dialysis against TVNS made up in H_2O or D_2O.

alcohol concentration at which isoenzyme formation is inhibited drops with increasing chain length of the alcohol. With all three alcohols, the total yield of activity, a measure of tetramer renaturation when isoenzymes are not formed, is not affected at the same rate. Thus, in the case of 25%

Table 3. Renaturation of β-galactosidase from 8 M urea at 7 mg/ml: effects of alcohol

Alcohol and its concentration	% of recovery of activity	Heavier isoenzyme formation
10% methanol	56	5–6 bands
20% methanol	34	5–6 bands
25% methanol	17	0
10% ethanol	71	5–6 bands
15% ethanol	62	4–5 bands
19% ethanol	14	0
10% propanol	83	faint traces

methanol, total renaturation is inhibited by 80% at the time that isoenzyme renaturation is being inhibited by >96%.

ENZYMATIC ACTIVITY IN D₂O

Since D_2O had a marked effect on the renaturation of isoenzymes of β-galactosidase, we were interested in determining its effect on other properties of the enzyme. An ammonium sulfate precipitate of purified tetramer was dissolved in buffer B made up in D_2O and dialyzed against it. Its specific activity was then measured with ONPG dissolved in the D_2O-buffer pD 7.4). The specific activity is 49.5% of that of the starting material. This may reflect an isotope effect on the reaction mechanism itself or, alternatively, reflect conformational alterations.

ACCELERATED AGGREGATION IN D₂O

It was noted that solutions of tetramer in D_2O rapidly became opalescent—a phenomenon that does not normally occur in aqueous solutions of β-galactosidase. Turbidometric measurements of tetramer dissolved in D_2O-buffer B as compared to H_2O-buffer B are seen in Fig. 2. The largest difference in turbidity occurs within the first 3 min at which time the first measurement can be made. This suggests a lower solubility of the ammonium-sulfate-precipitated material in D_2O as compared to H_2O together with a continued increase in aggregation.

It was of interest to know whether the heavy isoenzymes could be formed by the association of tetramers. As seen in the disc gels of Fig. 3, the D_2O-promoted the formation of polymers that did not even enter the spacer gel—there is no stainable activity in the running gel. It was possible that

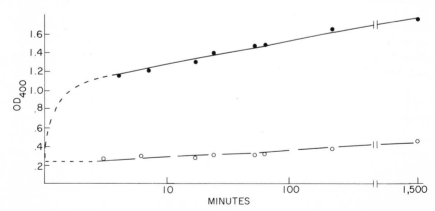

FIGURE 2. Turbidimetric measurements of ammonium sulfate precipitated β-galactosidase dissolved in D_2O-buffer B (—●—) or H_2O-buffer B (—○—) such that the final concentration of ammonium sulfate was less than 5%.

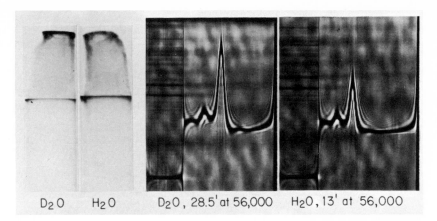

D₂O   H₂O   D₂O, 28.5' at 56,000   H₂O, 13' at 56,000

FIGURE 3. Left: BNG-stained polyacrylamide gels of tetramer in D_2O-buffer B or H_2O-buffer B. Center: Schlieren pattern of 12 mg/ml β-galactosidase in D_2O-buffer B. Right: Schlieren pattern of 5.5 mg/ml β-galactosidase in H_2O-buffer B.

the D_2O induced polymers could have blocked the pores on the top of the spacer gel preventing any isoenzyme that was present from electrophoresing into the gel. Sedimentation velocity analyses, however, show no detectable heavy isoenzymes and reveal that most of the material is in the form of larger polymers which quickly sediment to the bottom of the cell during the initial acceleration to maximum speed (Fig. 3). The sedimentation coefficient of the major peak in the D_2O-buffer B is 10 S which corresponds to the dimer (Marchesi et al., 1969). A small amount of monomer is seen trailing. The control sedimentation velocity pattern, at less than half the concentration, shows a major peak of 16 S, corresponding to tetramer, with some dimer trailing. β-galactosidase, whether in solution or stored under ammonium sulfate, spontaneously dissociates into dimers and monomers, with aging. The batch of β-galactosidase used was two months old at the time of these experiments. These results suggest that D_2O promotes the conversion of most of the tetramer into very rapidly sedimenting species rather than into the heavy isoenzymes of the 23–45 S classes previously described (Marchesi et al., 1969). Thus, for D_2O-mediated aggregation, monomers appear to be obligate intermediates if heavier isoenzymes are to be formed.

Electron-microscopy of negatively-stained preparations of tetramer in D_2O-buffer B show none of the characteristic forms reported by Marchesi et al. (1969) but instead contained only amorphous material.

It seemed possible that D_2O would promote formation of the "sticks" previously seen in heavy isoenzyme preparations (Marchesi et al., 1969) and as reported for purified β-galactosidase by Karlsson et al. (1964).

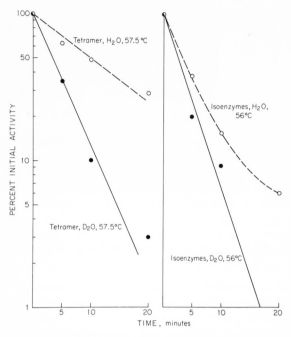

FIGURE 4. Thermal inactivation of purified tetramer (left) or isoenzymes (right) in D_2O-buffer B (—●—) or H_2O-buffer B (—○—).

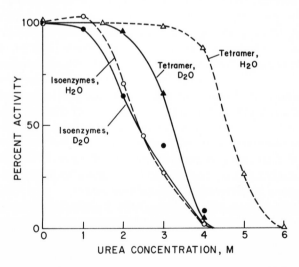

FIGURE 5. Urea inactivation of purified tetramer in D_2O-buffer B (—▲—) or H_2O-buffer B (—△—) and isoenzymes in D_2O-buffer B (—●—) or H_2O-buffer B (—○—).

These "sticks" have dimensions appropriate for laminar stacks of the rosettes that are visible in such preparations. Purified heavy isoenzymes (containing about one-fourth tetramer) were precipitated with ammonium sulfate and dissolved in D_2O-buffer B and H_2O-buffer B at 2 mg/ml. At 4 days, electron microscopy shows large quantities of "sticks" in both preparations with no significant difference between the two.

HEAT AND UREA STABILITIES IN D_2O

Tetramer becomes more sensitive to heat and increasing concentrations of urea when the experiments are performed in D_2O buffer B—a result in accord with the increased spontaneous dissociation to dimers (Fig. 4 and 5). Although the formation of heavier isoenzymes is accelerated by D_2O, preparations of heavier isoenzymes are also more heat and urea labile while in D_2O solutions.

HYDROGEN EXCHANGE OF HEAVIER ISOENZYMES AND TETRAMER

In vitro renaturation of heavier isoenzymes allowed us to study hydrogen out-exchange in isoenzymes as compared to tetramer. Measurements of the number of very slowly out-exchanging hydrogens in a protein has recently been shown to be a valuable tool to detect conformational differences (Schechter et al., 1968). β-galactosidase was dissociated in 8 M urea

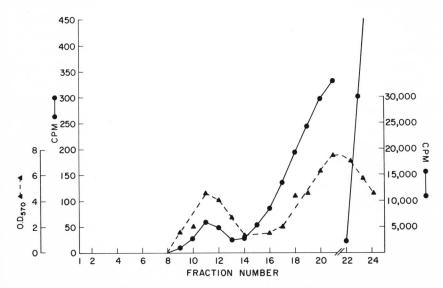

FIGURE 6. Counts per minute (—●—) and ninhydrin readings following alkaline hydrolysis (—▲—) of isoenzymes and tetramer separated on Sepharose 4B following renaturation in ^3H_2O, D_2O-TVNS buffer (see text).

and heavier isoenzymes and tetramer were renatured in ^3H_2O, D_2O-TVNS buffer. The protein was separated from the bulk of the tritiated water and the heavier isoenzymes separated from the tetramer by gel filtration on Sepharose 4B (Fig. 6). The OD_{280} of the isoenzyme peak was aberrantly high with marked turbidity in the peak. Therefore, alkaline hydrolysis followed by ninhydrin determination was used to compare the protein content of the 2 peaks. The OD_{280} of the tetramer peak was used to determine the degree of alkaline hydrolysis which was about 25% complete. The number of very slowly exchangeable hydrogens per monomer was calculated according to Englander (1963). There are 829 slowly exchangeable hydrogens per monomer in the tetramer peak (at about 2 hr). The difference is not due to continued exchange of counts during the gel filtration (with the isoenzyme counts trailing with the tetramer peak) as the counts, as well as the protein, form a clear valley between the 2 peaks.

DISCUSSION

The original description of the isoenzymes of β-galactosidase characterized them as being quite stable by their resistance to pH changes between pH 6 to 10, freezing and thawing, and lyophilization (Appel et al., 1965). Work in this laboratory showed that the isoenzymes were labile in urea but, under conditions in which tetramer renatured with good yields, no heavier isoenzymes were renatured (Marchesi et al., 1969). Utilization of magnesium-free conditions has now allowed us to renature isoenzymes in vitro. The in vitro renaturation studies show that: (1) there is no covalent chemical difference between isoenzymes and tetramers—heavier isoenzymes are renatured even when the starting material does not contain isoenzymes; (2) D_2O-accelerated heavier isoenzyme formation requires monomers as an intermediate; and (3) isoenzymes are conformationally different from tetramer. The first point confirms those results showing that the difference between isoenzyme and non-isoenzyme forming β-galactosidase, the z gene, and is not determined by other cytoplasmic factors (Erickson and Steers, 1970a). The difference in heat and urea stabilities of isoenzymes and tetramer implied a conformational difference between the monomers in the two forms and electron microscopy further suggested it (Marchesi et al., 1969). The difference in number of very slowly out-exchangeable hydrogens between the two forms confirms such a conformational difference. The high number of very slowly exchangeable hydrogens in tetramer (829 out of the 2000 exchangeable expected from the amino acid composition) suggests a "tight" conformation. The considerably smaller number of very slowly exchanging hydrogens in the monomers of isoenzymes suggests a "looser" conformation in which the interior of the monomer is more accessible to the aqueous environment. It seems likely that the requirement for monomers as an intermediate for D_2O-mediated heavier isoenzyme formation is more general, but only the discovery of other modes of stimulating heavier isoenzyme formation will allow the hypothesis to be tested. β-galactosidase is made more stable to urea by lactose (R. E. Huber, pers. commun.) or to heat by a variety of small molecules (Gest and Mandelstam, 1966) but neither fructose nor lactose had any stimulatory effect on the renaturation of heavier isoenzymes (Erickson and Steers, unpubl. observ.).

The requirement for a Mg^{++}-free media is unclear. It does not seem to be related to a different requirement for Mg^{++} in heavier isoenzymes than in tetramer but to the higher yields on renaturation found in the Mg^{++}-free media. We have found, as have Ullmann and Monod (1969), that other divalent cations have an inhibitory effect on the renaturation of β-galactosidase from urea.

Hydrophobic bonding has been implicated in the intermonomeric bonding of the tetramer as β-galactosidase shows more rapid thermal denaturation in alcohol solutions. A lower concentration of alcohol is required for the same effect with increasing length of the alkyl chain (Shifrin and Hunn, 1969). Our data may best be explained if hydrophobic bonding is relatively more important in intermonomeric bonding of isoenzymes as compared to tetramer. D_2O could act by exchanging with the protein hydrogens and increasing the strength of hydrogen bonds in the protein or it could act by increasing hydrophobic bonding in the protein (Nemethy, 1967; Krescheck et al., 1965; Emerson and Holtzer, 1967). Hydrocarbons can weaken hydrophobic bonding by competing with the aliphatic and aromatic side chains of the protein in forming hydrophobic pockets (Schrier and Scheraga, 1962). The inhibition of renaturation inversely proportional to the chain length that we find with added alcohols argues strongly that hydrophobic bonding is important during the *formation* of isoenzymes. Despite this conclusion, there is no simple way to explain all the data relevant to possible hydrophobic interactions. The β-galactosidases which form fewer or no isoenzymes were uniformly more heat and urea sensitive (Erickson and Steers, 1970a). The idea that this indicated decreased hydrophobic bonding between the monomers of these β-galactosidases led to using D_2O during the renaturation process, with a marked stimulation of isoenzyme formation. Isoenzymes themselves are less stable to heat and urea, consistent with this hypothesis. However, both isoenzymes and tetramer are more sensitive to heat and urea when in D_2O. Similarly, complex effects of the substitution of D_2O for H_2O have been observed with tobacco mosaic virus (Paglini and Lauffer, 1968), phycocyanin (Berns,

1963), and poly-L-glutamic acid and poly-L-lysine (Appel and Yang, 1965). Specific aggregation of phycocyanin is promoted by D_2O (Lee and Berns, 1968). Better understanding of the mode of action of D_2O on these proteins, including β-galactosidase, will require simpler techniques for studying the localization of deuterium atoms.

SUMMARY

β-galactosidase (β-D-galactoside galactohydrolase EC 3.2.1.23) renatured from 8 M urea by dialysis against a Mg^{++}-free media (10^{-2} M EDTA) contained trace amounts of heavier isoenzymes. The yield was slightly increased by increasing the concentration of β-galactosidase. Heavier isoenzymes resulted even when tetramer, absolutely free of isoenzymes, was the starting material. At low concentrations of β-galactosidase, D_2O markedly stimulated isoenzyme formation. The inhibitory effect of alcohols on isoenzyme renaturation support the hypothesis that D_2O works by promoting hydrophobic contacts between monomers. D_2O promoted the formation of other aggregates of β-galactosidase but no isoenzymes were formed when denaturation to monomers had not occurred. Isoenzymes and tetramer were renatured from 8 M urea in D_2O with ^3H_2O and separated by chromatography on Sepharose 4B. There was a significant difference between the 2 fractions in very slowly exchangeable hydrogens, further confirming a conformational difference between the tetramer and higher aggregates.

ACKNOWLEDGMENTS

We would like to thank Dr. V. M. Gladhand for performing the electron microscopy and Dr. A. N. Schechter for advice on hydrogen exchange methodology. We are also grateful for the encouragement and support of Dr. C. B. Anfinsen.

REFERENCES

APPEL, P. and J. R. YANG. 1965. Helix-coil transition of poly-L-glutamic acid and poly-L-lysine in D_2O. Biochem. *4:* 1244.

APPEL, S. H., D. H. ALPERS, and G. M. TOMKINS. 1965. Multiple molecular forms of β-galactosidase. J. Mol. Biol. *11:* 12.

BERNS, D. S. 1963. Studies of completely deuteriated proteins. II. Thermal denaturation. Biochem. *2:* 1377.

CRAVEN, G., E. STEERS, Jr., and C. B. ANFINSEN. 1965. Purification, composition and molecular weight of the β-galactosidase of *Escherichia coli* K_{12}. J. Biol. Chem. *240:* 2468.

EMERSON, M. F. and A. HOLTZER. 1967. The hydrophobic bond in micellar systems. Effects of various additions on the stability of micells of sodium dodecyl sulfate and of n-dodecylthrimethylammonium bromide. J. Phys. Chem. *71:* 3320.

ENGLANDER, S. W. 1963. A hydrogen exchange method using tritium and sephadex: its application to ribonuclease. Biochem. *2:* 798.

ERICKSON, R. P. and E. STEERS, Jr. 1970a. A comparative study of isoenzyme formations of bacterial β-galactosidase. J. Bacteriol., *11:* 79.

————, ————. 1970b. Isoenzymes of bacterial β-galactosidases: purification and characterization of a non-isoenzyme forming β-galactosidase of *Aerobacter cloacae*. Arch. Biochem. Biophys., *137:* 399.

GEST, H. and J. MANDESTAM. 1966. Heat denaturation of β-galactosidase, a possible approach to the problem of catabolite repression and its site of action. Nature *211:* 72.

HIRS, C. H. W. 1967. Paper chromatography and electrophoresis; special procedure for peptide maps, p. 335. *In* C. H. W. Hirs [ed.] Methods in enzymology, Vol. XI. Academic Press, New York.

KARLSSON, U., S. KOORAJIAN, I. ZABIN, F. S. SJOSTRAND, and A. MILLER. 1964. High resolution electron microscopy on highly purified β-galactosidase from *Escherichia coli*. J. Ultrastruct. Res. *10:* 457.

KRESCHECK, G. C., H. SCHNEIDER, and H. A. SCHERAGA. 1965. The effect of D_2O on the thermal stability of proteins. Thermodynamic parameters for the transfer of model components from H_2O to D_2O. J. Phys. Chem. *69:* 3132.

LEE, J. J. and D. S. BERNS. 1968. Protein aggregation. The effect of deuterium oxide on large protein aggregates. Biochem. J. *110:* 465.

MARCHESI, S. L., E. STEERS, Jr., and S. SHIFRIN. 1969. Purification and characterization of the multiple forms of β-galactosidase of *Escherichia coli*. Biochim. Biophys. Acta *181:* 20.

NEMETHY, G. 1967. Hydrophobic interactions. Angew. Chem. *6:* 195.

PAGLINI, S. and M. A. LAUFFER. 1968. Polymerization-depolymerization of tobacco mosaic virus protein. XI. Osmotic pressure studies of solutions in water and deuterium. Biochem. *7:* 1827.

SCHECHTER, A. N., L. MORAVEK, and C. B. ANFINSEN. 1968. Suppression of hydrogen exchange in staphylococcal nuclease by ligands. Proc. Nat. Acad. Sci. *61:* 1478.

SCHRIER, E. E. and H. A. SCHERAGA. 1962. The effect of aqueous alcohol solutions on the thermal transition of ribonuclease. Biochim. Biophys. Acta *64:* 406.

SHIFRIN, S. and G. HUNN. 1969. Effect of alcohols on the enzymatic activity and subunit association of β-galactosidase. Arch. Biochem. Biophys. *130:* 530.

ULLMANN, A., F. JACOB, and J. MONOD. 1968. On the subunit structure of wild-type versus complemented β-galactosidase of *Escherichia coli*. J. Mol. Biol. *32:* 1.

ULLMANN, A. and J. MONOD. 1969. On the effect of divalent cations and protein concentrations upon renaturation. Biochem. Biophys. Res. Commun. *35:* 35.

ZERNER, B. and M. L. SCHERAGA. 1961. The kinetics and mechanism of the hydrolysis of o-carboxyphthalimide. J. Amer. Chem. Soc. *83:* 2267.

On the Stoichiometry and Kinetics of ω Complementation of *E. coli* β-galactosidase

AGNÈS ULLMANN and JACQUES MONOD

Institut Pasteur and Collège de France
Paris

We have reported elsewhere on observations which demonstrate that certain complementary fragments of the normally single polypeptide chain which forms the protomer of *E. coli* β-galactosidase, may reassemble both in vivo and in vitro into an enzymatically active structure [For references and map positions of the mutants see Ullmann and Perrin, this volume.] The remarkably high and specific affinity exhibited by these polypeptide fragments, and their capacity to reconstruct a structure presumably close to the native one, albeit via a very different pathway, poses some interesting questions concerning the mechanism of formation of tertiary and quaternary structures. In the present paper we report some, as yet incomplete, experiments aimed at analyzing this mechanism. These experiments concern the kinetics and stoichiometry of the so called "ω complementation". Let us recall that the ω peptide, formed by certain mutants of β-galactosidase corresponds to the last (operator distal) quarter, approximately, of the normal polypeptide. A complementary fragment or "ω acceptor" may be furnished by any mutant (including deletions and nonsense mutations) within the ω segment. Most of the experiments reported here were done using crude extracts of mutants containing respectively, the ω peptide and the ω acceptor peptide. The relative amounts of each of the two peptides, in crude extracts can be estimated by titration against an excess of its complement under standardized conditions.

The ω peptide has been purified and its molecular weight determined as 39,000. The ω acceptor has not, as yet, been purified in a state where it is still active in complementation. However, some information regarding its mol wt and state of aggregation was obtained by sucrose gradient sedimentation and gel filtration of crude extracts. When a low ionic strength buffer is used in a filtration experiment on Sephadex G200, the acceptor peptide is found to elute as a single peak, at the position of the β-galactosidase marker. Using high ionic strength buffer, however, the acceptor is retained on the column, and elutes in a peak very close to lactic dehydrogenase (Fig. 1). In sucrose gradient at low ionic strength, the acceptor assumes a sedimentation constant of 13, while at high ionic strength it exhibits an S value of 6. These observations suggest that, in the latter condition, the acceptor assumes a monomeric state with a molecular weight of about 130,000 while at high ionic strength it presumably aggregates into a tetramer.

Successful complementation between ω and acceptor obtains both at high and low ionic strength. In both cases the active product sediments as a homogeneous peak with an S of 16, equal to that of the native enzyme. It is very likely therefore that the in vitro reformed enzyme is a tetramer, like the native and the in vivo complemented enzyme.

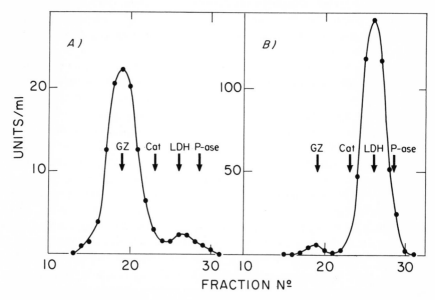

FIGURE 1. Distribution of acceptor activities on a Sephadex column. 1 ml of crude extract of S908 containing 30 mg protein/ml was layered on a Sephadex G200 (1.5 × 60 cm) equilibrated with: A. Tris 2.10^{-2}M $Mg^{++}10^{-2}$M pH 7 B. PO_4-buffer 10^{-1}M $Mg^{++}10^{-2}$M pH 7. The following markers were used: β-galactosidase: GZ; catalase: Cat; lacticodehydrogenase: LDH; and alkaline phosphatase: P-ase. The values are expressed in units/ml β-galactosidase obtained after 60 min of complementation in the presence of an ω donor extract.

We may now turn to the kinetics and stoichiometry of the interaction between ω and acceptor. When two complementary extracts (each at a total concentration of about 5 mg protein ml^{-1}) are mixed, activity begins to appear within a few min and reaches a stable plateau within about 60 min.

When the concentration of one of the components is maintained fixed, and increasing amounts of the other are added, the plateau values vary following more or less complex kinetics as shown in Fig. 2.

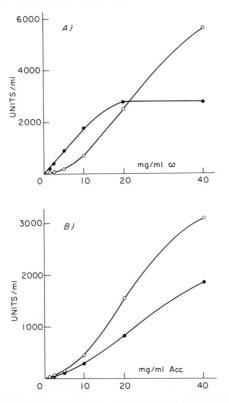

FIGURE 2. Stochiometry of the ω complementation. A. 0.1 ml of an extract of S908 containing 40 mg protein/ml was added to 0.1 ml of an extract of W4680 containing 1–40 mg protein/ml. The values are expressed in units/ml β-galactosidase after 2 hr of complementation. ●———● extract prepared in Tris buffer (Tris 2.10^{-2}M Mg$^{++}10^{-2}$M pH 7). ○———○ extract prepared in PO$_4$-buffer (PO$_4$$10^{-1}$M Mg$^{++}10^{-2}$M pH 7).

B. 0.1 ml of an extract of W4680 containing 40 mg protein/ml was added to 0.1 ml of an extract of S908 containing 1–40 mg protein/ml. The values are expressed in units/ml β-galactosidase after 2 hr of complementation. ●———● extract prepared in Tris buffer (Tris 2.10^{-2}M Mg$^{++}10^{-2}$M pH 7). ○———○ extract prepared in PO$_4$-buffer (PO$_4$$10^{-1}$M Mg$^{++}10^{-2}$M pH 7).

These graphs show that:

1. At low ionic strength (tetrameric acceptor) the plateau value of activity varies linearly with ω and nonlinearly with acceptor concentrations.

2. At high ionic strength (monomeric acceptor) the relation is nonlinear with respect to both.

3. In neither case is saturation observed.

If now the concentration of the mixture is varied, while the total amounts of each component remains constant, the plateau value is found to increase markedly as a function of concentration (Fig. 3). This fact appears

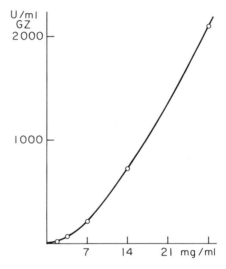

Figure 3. Concentration dependence of complementation. 0.1 ml of an extract of S908 was mixed with 0.1 ml of an extract of W4680 (both prepared in 0.1 M PO_4-buffer containing 10^{-2}M Mg^{++} pH 7). The values in the abscissa represent the final concentration of the mixture expressed in mg protein/ml. β-galactosidase was measured after 3 hr of complementation.

to suggest that one is dealing with an equilibrium reaction, and the experiment shown in Fig. 4 indeed shows that once the plateau has been reached, the mixture still contains *both* ω and acceptor able to further react with an added amount of either type of extract.

If the reaction is one of equilibrium and if, as is likely, only the active product has affinity for galactosides, it should be possible to displace this equilibrium by adding a substrate (or substrate analog) of the enzyme. Figure 5 shows that, at high ionic strength the plateau value may be increased some 10 to 20 times (depending in particular on the initial concentration of acceptor) in the presence of the analog β-phenyl-

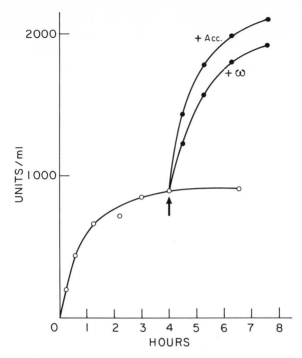

FIGURE 4. 1 ml of an extract of S908 was added to 1 ml of an extract of W4680 (each of them containing 10 mg protein/ml). After 4 hr of complementation, the mixture was divided in three parts and the following additions were performed (to 0.5 ml of mixture): 1. 0.25 ml of buffer 2. +0.25 ml of an extract of W4680 (ω) 3. +0.25 ml of an extract of S908 (Acc.)

ethyl-thio-galactoside (TPEG). The effect of the latter is the same whether it is added at the time of mixing the extracts, or after "completion" of the reaction in its absence (Fig. 6). Moreover, when different concentrations of TPEG are used, the maximal activity varies as a sigmoidal function of the concentration of analog, demonstrating a cooperative effect of the latter (Fig. 7).

By all these criteria, therefore, the reaction of complementation appears to be one of equilibrium between precursors (ω and Ac) and final active product. Yet, it can be shown by other tests that the active complemented enzyme is in fact not in equilibrium with its precursors, and that the role of TPEG is not simply to displace an equilibrium.

As shown by the experiment summarized in Table 1, while concentration of a given mixture *after* attainment of the plateau value does lead to further increase of enzyme activity, dilution of the same extract at the same stage leads to no appreciable loss of activity, even after prolonged

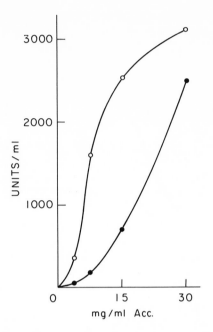

FIGURE 5. Effect of β-phenyl-ethyl-thio-galactoside (TPEG) on complementation. To 0.1 ml of an extract of B9 (containing 30 mg protein/ml), 0.1 ml of an extract of S908 at various protein concentrations (see values in the abscissa) was added. After 6 hr of complementation β-galactosidase activity was measured. ●————● no addition; ○————○ addition at t = 0 of 45.10⁻⁵ᴹ TPEG.

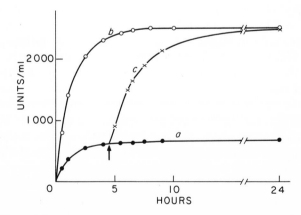

FIGURE 6. Effect of TPEG on complementation. Equal vol of extracts of S908 (5 mg protein/ml) and W4680 (30 mg protein/ml) were mixed at t = 0. a: no addition. b: addition of 5.10⁻⁵ᴹ TPEG at t = 0. c: addition of 5.10⁻⁵ᴹ TPEG at t = 4 hr 30 min.

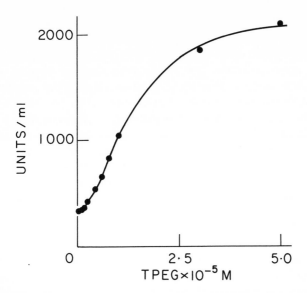

FIGURE 7. Effect of TPEG concentration on complementation. Equal vol of extracts of S908 (4mg protein/ml) and B9 (30 mg protein/ml) were mixed in the absence and presence of TPEG at different concentrations. β-galactosidase was assayed after 4 hr of complementation.

incubation. Dialysis (or dilution) of a mixture, after achievement of the plateau in presence of TPEG, does not lead to any loss of activity. We must conclude that any active product formed at any time under these various conditions is stable, and does not revert to its inactive precursors.

We cannot, at this stage, propose any precise and detailed mechanism

Table 1.

Initial mixture		Concentrated mixture			Diluted mixture		
			U/ml			U/ml	
mg/ml	U/ml	mg/ml	calc.	obt.	mg/ml	calc.	obt.
10	580	18.1	1050	1500	3.9	230	222
21.7	665	52	1600	2500	8.6	262	265
13.6	630	15.8	730	1013	5.5	250	255
7.8	210	14.9	400	1300	0.78	21	21

Equal vol of extracts of S908 and W4680 are mixed at t = 0. Protein concentration of the mixture is shown in the first column. After 4 hr of complementation, each mixture was divided in two parts; one was concentrated (in a dialysis bag against dry Sephadex G100), the other diluted with buffer. The final concentrations achieved are shown in columns 3 and 6. After 3 additional hr of incubation, β-galactosidase was measured. The calculated and actually obtained enzyme values are shown in columns 4, 5 and 7, 8.

to account for these remarkable properties of the complementing system. It is obvious however, that since the final product is stable, both the concentration effect and the effect of TPEG must be interpreted as modifying not an equilibrium, but the relative rates of several competing reactions, only one (or several) of which leads to active, stable enzyme.

The system however appears of great interest for two reasons: (1) The very efficient and highly specific reassociation of the peptide fragments, strongly suggests that both acceptor and ω are able separately to fold into a configuration close to the one which the corresponding segments achieve in the wild-type enzyme. If this can be confirmed, as we hope, it would be necessary to suppose that several partially independent centers of nucleation are responsible for the folding of the long polypeptide chain in the native enzyme.

(2) The TPEG effect shows that, under certain conditions, the presence of a small molecule may specifically influence the pathway of formation of tertiary and quaternary structures of globular proteins. At this point, it is difficult to accept, or to dismiss, the idea that similar interactions might play a biologically significant role in the synthesis of certain proteins.

Structural Studies of ω-complemented β-galactosidase of *Escherichia coli*

MICHEL E. GOLDBERG

Service de Biochimie Cellulaire
Institut Pasteur, Paris, France

In view of the fact that the kinetic parameters of the β-galactosidase reaction exhibited by wild-type and ω-complemented β-galactosidases (Ullmann et al., 1965) are not significantly different, while their structure could hardly be the same, comparative physical studies of these two types of enzymes have been undertaken (Goldberg, 1969; Goldberg et al., 1969). These studies were performed with pure ω-complemented enzyme extracted from the diploid strain MU366/B9 carrying on the chromosome a nonsense mutation within the ω segment and on the episome a z deletion extending to very near the operator proximal boundary of the genetic ω segment. The authors came to the conclusion that, like the wild-type enzyme (Craven et al., 1965), this particular ω-complemented enzyme is a tetramer; its protomer was shown to contain two different polypeptide chains: one of mol wt 110,000 likely to be the acceptor and the other of mol wt 39,000, presumably the ω. These findings led to the conclusions that the region of the gene which lies between the ω barrier (I) and the MU366 mutation is effectively translated into a sequence of amino acids both in the C-terminal part of the acceptor and in the N-terminal part of the ω.

This C-terminal part of the acceptor polypeptide chain can be released from the complemented enzyme by a mild proteolytic treatment without loss of β-galactosidase activity. This suggests that the C-terminal part of the acceptor: (a) is not essential for the enzymatic activity of the complete complemented molecule (b) is presumably located at the surface of the enzyme, well exposed to the solvent.

These conclusions, valid for the ω-complemented β-galactosidase produced by the diploid MU366/B9, cannot be generalized without investi-

273

gating the physical properties of at least another ω-complemented enzyme. The work described in this paper was aimed at verifying that the overall properties of another ω-complemented β-galactosidase (from strain X90/B9) are similar to those of the enzyme produced by the diploid MU366/B9. Strain X90/B9 was chosen because X90 is also a nonsense mutation in the ω region, located however much closer to the operator distal end of the galactosidase structural gene than is MU366. The prediction is that the overlap between the acceptor and ω polypeptide should be larger than in the former case.

PHYSICAL PROPERTIES OF THE ENZYME

ω-complemented β-galactosidase of strain X90/B9 was purified as described for that of strain MU366/B9. The protein obtained after purification appeared homogeneous by high-speed sedimentation and by polyacrilamide gel electrophoresis.

Following dialysis against 0.1 M sodium phosphate at pH 7.0, 0.01 M β-mercaptoethanol and 0.01 M magnesium chloride, the protein was centrifuged to equilibrium in a double sector cell. One sector of the cell contained the dialysis buffer while the other contained the protein solution. The initial protein concentration was 0.117 mg/ml as measured by the optical density of the solution at 280 mμ assuming that the extinction coefficients, on a weight basis, of the wild-type and ω-complemented enzymes are the same. The centrifugation was performed at 10,000 rpm and the protein distribution analyzed by use of the interference optics following the "white and green light" method described by Goldberg and Edelstein (1969).

The results are shown in Fig. 1. The experimental points unambiguously fit a straight line the slope of which provides the molecular weight of the complemented enzyme. Assuming the partial specific volume of the wild-type and complemented enzymes to be identical one obtains a mol wt of 670,000 for the enzyme synthesized by the diploid X90/B9.

ENZYMATIC PROPERTIES

In order to compare the catalytic properties of the β-galactosidases produced by the wild-type E. coli and by the two diploid strains MU366/B9 and X90/B9, the turnover numbers of these three enzymes have been determined. The substrate used was o-nitrophenyl-β-galactopyranoside and the assay was conducted as described by Perrin (1965).

The results are summarized in Table 1. It can be seen from the figures in the last column that the turnover numbers of the three enzymes are the same within experimental errors.

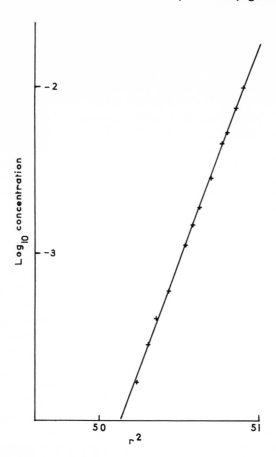

FIGURE 1. Sedimentation equilibrium of X90/B9 complemented galactosidase. The experimental results are plotted as the logarithm of the protein concentration (expressed as fringe displacement) as a function of the square of the distance to the axis of rotation (expressed in cm). See the text for the experimental conditions.

TABLE 1. Catalytic properties of β-galactosidases

Strains	Specific activities in units/mg	Turnover numbers in moles/mol sec
Wild-type	910,000	8,200
MU366/B9	810,000	8,000
X90/B9	745,000	8,300

DISCUSSION

If one assumes that the enzyme produced by strain X90/B9 is a tetramer (like that of the wild-type and of strain MU366/B9) one can compute a protomer mol wt of 167,000 (i.e. 670,000/4). The molecular weight of the ω polypeptide coded for by the B9 episome being approximately 40,000 (Goldberg and Edelstein, 1969) one can then compute the molecular weight of the acceptor polypeptide produced by the X90 mutant. The value obtained is 127,000 and compares very favorably with that found by Zabin and Fowler (this book) after purification of the X90 protein using immunological criteria during the purification. Thus one can safely conclude that the X90 polypeptide chain is shorter by about 6% than the wild-type protomer: as expected for a nonsense mutation the X90 mutation leads to a chain termination.

Table 2 summarizes the physical properties of the wild-type and ω-complemented enzymes so far studied. It can be seen that the molecular weights found for the wild-type protomer and for the two acceptor chains agree fairly well with the values predicted from genetic distances (Zabin and Fowler, this book).

From these results it can be inferred that the schematic structural model proposed for the ω-complemented enzyme of strain MU366/B9 may be valid also for the enzyme of the diploid X90/B9. This model (Goldberg, 1969) is best summarized by the following diagram (Fig. 2).

The type and position of the mutation carried by the acceptor-producing strain defines the length of the extrapeptide which presumably corresponds to the homology region mentioned above. In this model the ω and acceptor globules (Goldberg, 1969) supposedly achieve tertiary and quaternary structures very similar to those of the corresponding globules of the wild-type enzyme, at least once the interactions which lead to the complementation have taken place, and the active site built by the folding and association of the different globules must be very similar. An argument strongly supporting this assumption is the fact that the turnover numbers

TABLE 2. Physical properties of three β-galactosidases

Strains	Molecular weights		
	Native enzyme	Protomer	Acceptor chain
Wild-type	540,000[a]	135,000[b]	—
MU366/B9	595,000[a]	150,000[c]	110,000[a]
X90/B9	670,000[a]	167,000[c]	127,000[c]

[a] measured by sedimentation equilibrium (see text); [b] measured by the Archibald method in a denaturing solvent (Ullmann et al., 1968); [c] calculated (see text).

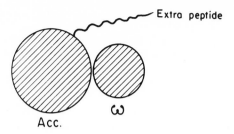

FIGURE 2. Structural model for complemented galactosidase. Acc.—acceptor globule: ω—ω globule. Extra peptide—that part of the acceptor polypeptide chain corresponding to the homology region mentioned in the text.

of the wild-type and of the two complemented enzymes are identical. This finding is quite remarkable: in spite of the enormous structural differences between the wild-type and X90/B9 enzymes (the complemented protomer contains two polypeptide chains and its molecular weight is larger by 32,000 than the molecular weight of the unique polypeptide chain of the wild-type protomer) their active sites are not significantly different and the complemented enzyme remains fully functional.

In conclusion it appears that the overall physical properties of the ω-complemented β-galactosidase of strain X90/B9 confirm the observations made on strain MU366/B9. Thus it seems reasonable to extend the structural model described above to the enzyme of the diploid X90/B9 and generalize it to all ω-complemented galactosidases.

In this respect, it is worth noting that all mutants in the ω segment so far isolated as *lac⁻* are able to complement ω donors. Let us define the acceptor (or ω) association area as those residues of the globule which interact with the ω (or acceptor) globule to provide the association between ω and acceptor. All acceptor proteins possess the proper acceptor association area but an incorrect ω association area. That the acceptor association area is functional can be concluded from the fact that the acceptor protein can associate with a functional ω peptide. On the other hand, if the ω association area were correct, it would interact with the acceptor association area thus preventing complementation with a functional ω peptide. Then, from the observation mentioned above, it appears that all mutations in the ω region which can be picked up as *lac⁻* lead to a protein with an incorrect ω association area. This strong correlation between enzymatic activity and ω association area suggests that all the essential features of the ω globule are carried by its association area. Thus, the ω association area can be considered as the single stereospecific site of the ω globule which in turn can be thought of as an independently folded globular protein.

REFERENCES

CRAVEN, G. R., E. STEERS, and C. B. ANFINSEN. 1965. Purification, composition, and molecular weight of the β-galactosidase of *Escherichia coli* K12. J. Biol. Chem. *240:* 2468.

GOLDBERG, M. E. 1969. Tertiary structure of *Escherichia coli* β-galactosidase. J. Mol. Biol. *46:* 441.

GOLDBERG, M. E. and S. J. EDELSTEIN. 1969. Sedimentation equilibrium of pauci-disperse systems. Subunit structure of complemented β-galactosidase. J. Mol. Biol. *46:* 431.

PERRIN, D. 1965. Ph.D. dissertation. Paris University.

ULLMANN, A., M. E. GOLDBERG, D. PERRIN, and J. MONOD. 1968. On the determination of molecular weight of proteins and protein subunits in the presence of 6 M guanidine hydrochloride. Biochemistry *7:* 261.

ULLMANN, A., D. PERRIN, F. JACOB, and J. MONOD. 1965. Identification par complementation in vitro et purification d'un segment peptidique de la β-galactosidase d'Escherichia coli. J. Mol. Biol. *12:* 918.

Partial Loss of Activity of Individual Molecules of Aged β-galactosidase

M. BORIS ROTMAN

Division of Biological and Medical Sciences
Brown University
Providence, Rhode Island

INTRODUCTION

Previous studies of bacterial β-galactosidase at the single molecule level have shown that thermal denaturation of the enzyme resulted in an all-or-none inactivation (Rotman, 1961). In contrast to this observation, it is shown here that enzyme inactivation caused by prolonged storage results in a population of molecules with intermediate levels of activity ranging from less than five to one hundred percent of that present in the native β-galactosidase molecule.

The significance of these findings is discussed in terms of the free energy of newly synthesized versus aged enzyme.

MATERIALS AND METHODS

Buffers, chemicals, and growth medium. Buffer B contained 10 mM tris (hydroxymethylaminomethane), 10 mM $MgCl_2$, 100 mM NaCl and 50 mM 2-mercaptoethanol. The latter was added to the buffer prior to its use. The pH of the buffer was adjusted to 7.5 (23°C) with acetic acid. Buffer P was prepared by adjusting a 20 mM solution of Na_2HPO_4 to pH 7.2 (23°C) with a 20 mM solution of NaH_2PO_4. Solutions with urea (ultra pure grade, Mann Research Lab., Inc.) were prepared with buffer B.

5-Bromo-4-chloro-3-indolyl-β-D-galactopyranoside was obtained from Cyclo Corp. Fluorescein-di-(β-D-galactopyranoside) and o-nitrophenyl-β-D-galactopyranoside (ONPG) were purchased from Mann Research Laboratories, Inc. The former was purified by descending chromatography on

S & S orange paper using 1-pentanol:1-propanol:water = 40:11:15 as solvent (Rotman, Zderic, and Edelstein, 1963).

Bacterial cultures were grown in minimal medium (Davis, 1949) containing 0.4% sodium lactate (Fisher Co.).

Purification of β-galactosidase (β-D-galactoside galactohydrolase 3.2.1.23). The procedure described by Craven, Steers, and Anfinsen (1965) was used to purify the β-galactosidase extracted from a 500 *l* culture of *Escherichia coli* 3.300. Our enzyme preparation gave a single band in standard acrylamide gel electrophoresis (Canal Industrial Corp., 3 ma per tube at 0° to 4°C) and its specific activity was comparable to that of a sample (a gift from Dr. E. Steers, Jr.) which appeared homogeneous under several tests (Craven et al., 1965). Purified enzyme was stored under 40% saturated solution of ammonium sulfate at 4°C.

"Fresh" preparations of enzyme were obtained by disrupting in a French press cells of an i^- constitutive (strain 7-1) *E. coli* K12 grown in 5 *l* batches. All the steps in the following procedure were conducted between 0° and 4°C. The crude extracts were clarified by centrifugation at 25,000 *g* for 30 min followed by precipitation with $\frac{1}{3}$ of the vol of a saturated solution of ammonium sulfate (706 g dissolved in one liter of water) previously adjusted to pH 7.2 (23°C). The precipitate was spun down and the supernatant was precipitated by slowly adding a saturated solution of ammonium sulfate until a final concentration of 35% saturation was reached. The suspension was allowed to stand at 0°C for about 30 min and then the precipitate was collected by centrifugation, dissolved in a minimal vol of buffer B and dialysed against the same buffer for about 24 hr. The enzyme preparations obtained by this procedure were sterilized by filtration through a millipore membrane HA (previously washed with buffer B) and kept at 0°C. Their specific activities were about 40% of that of highly purified enzyme and analyses by acrylamide gel electrophoresis also indicated a 40% purity.

Ultimate purification of both fresh and old enzyme preparations was obtained by standard acrylamide gel electrophoresis in large slabs of gel (5 × 66 × 80 mm). The temperature during the electrophoresis was kept close to 0°C and the run lasted about 50 min. Subsequently, the position of the enzyme in the acrylamide gel was ascertained by incubating a portion of the slab in the presence of 5-bromo-4-chloro-3-indolyl-β-D-galactopyranoside for 5 min at 23°C. This resulted in the appearance of a sharp band of blue color at the position of the enzyme. In the remainder of the gel, the part containing β-galactosidase was removed and the enzyme extracted by allowing the gel to stand in buffer B overnight at 0°C. The entire procedure, starting from a bacterial culture and ending with electrophoretically pure enzyme, lasted about 24 hr. The specific activity of fresh enzyme purified by this method was 2.8 × 10⁵ units per optical density unit at 280 mμ. A maximum of about 3 mg of enzyme could be obtained in each run.

A crystalline β-galactosidase preparation, which had been stored for eight years under a 40% saturated solution of ammonium sulfate in a refrigerator, was obtained as a gift from Dr. D. Perrin.

Enzymatic Assays. The assay of β-galactosidase was done at 37°C in a 2 ml volume of buffer P containing 3 mM ONPG. The reaction was stopped when a visible yellow color appeared by adding 3 ml of 0.2 M Na_2CO_3. The optical density of the solution at 420 mμ was measured and then converted to o-nitrophenol concentration using a molar extinction coefficient (1 cm pathway) of 4700. An enzyme unit is defined as the amount of β-galactosidase which hydrolyzes 10^{-9} mole of substrate per min under the above conditions. One unit of β-galactosidase corresponds to 2.6 × 10⁹ molecules of enzyme (see Fig. 1).

Single Molecule Assay. A given dilution of an enzyme preparation mixed at 0°C with fluorescein-di-(β-D-galactopyranoside) to obtain a 0.1 mM solution of substrate was dispersed into silicone oil [type SF-96 (50),

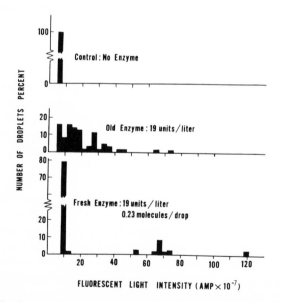

FIGURE 1. Distribution of fluorescence among microdroplets. Preparations containing the indicated units/l of β-galactosidase were dispersed into microdroplets, incubated and read in a microfluorimeter as indicated in Materials and Methods. The number of molecules/drop was calculated from the proportion of droplets without enzymatic activity. The preparation of old enzyme had been stored for eight years under ammonium sulfate.

General Electric] using the spray method of Collins, Mason and Perkins (1964). The detailed procedure for spraying and measuring microdroplets with discrete numbers of enzyme molecules has been described (Rotman, 1961). For the present investigation, two modifications were introduced; glass rings fused to microscope slides (A. D. Jones Optical Works, Inc.) were substituted for the original parafilm chambers, and a beam-splitting device (Barer, 1960) was used to select microdroplets of 20.34 μ average diameter. The standard deviation of the measurements of diameter of nine different droplets was less than 1%. The slides containing the droplets were incubated at 35°C for a given period of time which ranged from 16 to 20 hr for different experiments. However, within an experiment the incubation time did not vary by more than 30 min. The data are presented in the form of histograms which were obtained by means of a computer programmed to select statistically both the best class-width and the best interval between classes using as frame of reference the class of droplets without enzyme present in each histogram. The values used for the computation were not corrected by any factor, including time of incubation. An important step in all the experiments was to verify that a given number of enzyme units were recovered in terms of total rate of hydrolysis of the fluorogenic substrate calculated by adding the fluorescence of all the microdroplets measured.

EXPERIMENTAL RESULTS

The assay of enzymatic activity at the molecular level permits a rapid evaluation of a population of enzyme molecules in terms of three parameters, namely, (1) the number of enzyme molecules per unit volume; (2) the turnover number of individual enzyme molecules; and (3) the degree of heterogeneity in the population based on differences in turnover number of individual molecules.

Thus, the single molecule assay is particularly suited for studying mechanisms of enzyme inactivation since it can differentiate unambiguously partial, intramolecular inactivation from all-or-none effects.

The experimental procedure for comparing at the molecular level samples containing fully active enzyme with those of partially inactivated enzyme consisted of the following steps: (a) enzymatic assay of the samples by measuring the rate of hydrolysis of ONPG; (b) matching the enzyme units per ml of the samples by appropriate dilutions; (c) assay of the matched dilutions at the single molecule level by mixing each with fluorogenic substrate and dispersing into microdroplets; (d) measuring the individual fluorescence of a relatively large number (usually between 80 and 120) of microdroplets of the same diameter. The distribution of fluorescence among microdroplets was plotted in a histogram. The average number of enzyme molecules per microdroplet was calculated by Poisson's equation from the frequency of droplets without enzymatic activity, i.e., no significant fluorescence above the control microdroplets. The validity of this procedure was tested by determining the number of molecules present in a given solution of *purified* β-galactosidase, thereby estimating independently the mol wt of the enzyme. This was done by dividing the protein concentration of the enzyme dilution used for spraying (expressed in g/ml) by the average number of molecules per microdroplet and multiplying by both the vol of the microdroplet (4.4×10^{-9} ml) and Avogadro's number. Four independent determinations using different dilutions of a purified enzyme preparation obtained from Dr. I. Zabin gave an average value of 546,000 ($\pm$10%) comparable to the mol wt of 538,000 established by sedimentation equilibrium (Craven et al., 1965). Previous estimates of molecular weight of β-galactosidase by the single molecule method (Rotman, 1961) were high by about 15% because the protein concentration was not measured directly but calculated from the highest specific activity known at that time, which was off by a similar factor.

We describe below the results of experiments in which the assay of single molecules was used to compare β-galactosidase freshly extracted from bacteria with β-galactosidase which was partially inactivated due to storage under ammonium sulfate for three or more years. The results shown in Fig. 1 indicate that an 8 year old enzyme had significantly less activity per molecule than the fresh one since the frequency of the zero-molecule class of the former was 24% or less, while the latter was 79.5%. Converting these frequencies to average number of molecules per microdroplet, the values 1.45 and 0.23 were obtained for the aged and fresh enzyme solutions, respectively.

The results of experiments in which preparations of fresh and aged enzymes were assayed both separately and mixed are shown in Fig. 2. The data indicate that the lower activity found for the aged enzyme was not due to an inhibitor present in the preparation since the molecules of fresh enzyme had similar activity when assayed either separately or mixed with the aged enzyme.

In order to establish more accurately the extent of inactivation of the aged enzyme molecule, solutions containing fewer molecules were sprayed. From these experiments (Fig. 3), it was possible to calculate that some of the molecules of aged enzyme had as little as 5% of the activity of the fresh enzyme. In addition, the results of Fig. 3 indicate that the population of aged enzyme molecules was heterogeneous in that the activity of individual molecules varied by a factor as large as 4. In contrast, the molecules of fresh enzyme show variations of about 10% above that

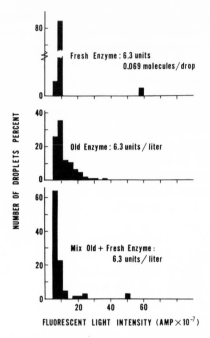

FIGURE 2. Experiment to show that mixing fresh and old preparations of β-galactosidase did not affect the activity of the former. Same procedure as in Fig. 1.

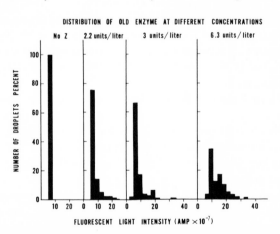

FIGURE 3. Distribution of fluorescence among microdroplets. The same preparation of old enzyme used for the experiment of Fig. 1 was dispersed into microdroplets at different concentrations, incubated and read as indicated for Fig. 1. Taking the class of droplets with the same fluorescence as that of the control without enzyme (no z) as zero-class, the number of molecules/droplet are 0.28, 0.385 and 0.94 for the preparations dispersed at 2.2, 3, and 6.3 units/l, respectively. These values correspond to 2.9×10^{10} molecules/unit of β-galactosidase for the first two dilutions and 3.4×10^{10} for the dilution with 6.3 units/l.

expected from the random error of the method. This error was established by measuring the fluorescence of microdroplets containing fluorescein (Rotman, 1961), which showed an average fluorescence value of 20 with a standard deviation of $\pm6.4\%$ for 16 different droplets.

Experiments designed to test whether aged enzyme molecules could be "rejuvenated" by dissociating the tetramer in urea and reassociating it by dialysis against 2-mercaptoethanol were conducted. The results of these experiments, shown in Fig. 4, indicate that dissociation and reassociation did not alter significantly the activity of the aged β-galactosidase molecules. Likewise, the activity of the fresh enzyme molecules remained the same after the urea-mercaptoethanol treatment. The aged enzyme preparation used for this experiment was a three-year-old preparation kept under 40% saturated ammonium sulfate.

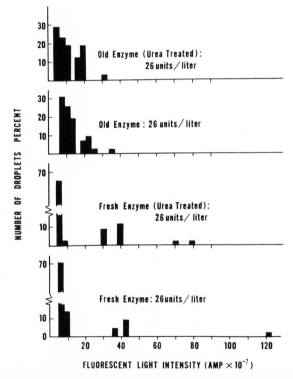

FIGURE 4. Effect of dissociation and re-association. Both old and fresh enzyme preparations were incubated at $0°C$ for 19 hr in the presence of 8 M urea. The enzymatic activity after this treatment was less than 0.01% of the original one for the fresh enzyme and less than 0.5% for the old enzyme. After urea treatment, the enzyme solutions were dialysed against buffer B for 15 hr, assayed, diluted to the indicated units/l and dispersed into microdroplets for the fluorogenic assay as indicated in Fig. 1. The old enzyme preparations used in this experiment had been stored for 3 yr.

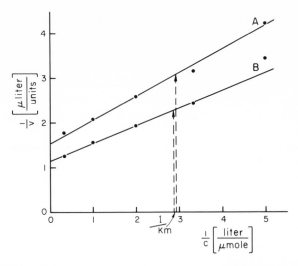

Figure 5. Effect of ONPG concentration in the assay of old and fresh preparations of β-galactosidase. Both preparations had been purified by acrylamide gel electrophoresis as indicated in Materials and Methods. Reciprocal units are used for both coordinates. Curve A: fresh enzyme; B: old enzyme.

In addition to the observations described above, we have recognized in the past that some enzyme solutions kept for months in the refrigerator exhibited molecules with less activity than those of fresh enzyme solutions. However, no systematic studies of enzyme inactivation under this condition were undertaken.

To date, all the experiments designed to test whether the aged preparations of β-galactosidase differ from fresh preparations in properties other than the turnover number have been negative. These experiments included mol wt determinations, electrophoretic mobility in standard acrylamide gel, Km determinations and inhibition by potassium. As shown in Fig. 5, the two enzyme preparations gave similar Km values when assayed with ONPG. The Km value using p-nitrophenyl-β-D-galactopyranoside as substrate was also the same for both enzymes.

DISCUSSION

We have shown above that the inactivation of β-galactosidase resulting from storage at low temperature for prolonged periods of time is due to partial loss of molecular activity. This must represent a different mechanism from that previously shown to obtain during thermal inactivation, since molecules in a heat inactivated population are either fully active or completely inactive (Rotman, 1961).

The decreased enzymatic activity of aged preparations was not correlated with changes in physical properties of the enzyme such as mol wt, electrophoretic mobility and affinity for substrates. These observations, and the fact that the number of enzyme molecules per unit of protein remained roughly the same with aging, indicate that no significant proteolytic attack had occurred during storage. The stability of the aged enzyme during the fluorogenic assay appeared to be essentially the same as that of fresh enzyme since both exhibited the same recovery of enzyme units in terms of fluorescent yield. It should be noted that the fresh enzyme has been shown to have a linear rate of hydrolysis of the fluorogenic substrate under our assay conditions (Rotman, 1961).

A straightforward hypothesis accounting for these results would be to assume that some side group of an amino acid(s) of the enzyme had been altered during storage. Considering the size of β-galactosidase, it would be difficult to rule out this possibility at the present time. A drawback of this hypothesis is that it does not offer a simple explanation for our observation that the *degree* of inactivation per molecule appears to be a function of storage time. One might expect that chemical alterations would inactivate an enzyme in discrete steps rather than in a continuous fashion.

Another possibility would be that the loss of one or more molecules of bound water caused changes in the three-dimensional structure of the enzyme. There is crystallographic evidence from studies on collagen and carboxypeptidase A that water is firmly bound to these macromolecules and is found in an ordered state (Ramachandran, 1969).

We find more challenging the alternative hypothesis that molecules of aged enzyme are in a state of lower total free energy than those of freshly synthesized enzyme. This implies that different *active* conformational states can be obtained with identical amino acid sequences.

Our assumption would apparently contradict the generally accepted hypothesis that the amino acid sequence is the sole determinant of the active three-dimensional configuration of an enzyme (Epstein, Goldberger, Young, and Anfinsen, 1962). However, it is possible to reconcile the two hypotheses by postulating that polypeptides may exist in metastable conformations of higher free energy than the minimal energy imparted by a given primary structure if disturbing forces occur during biosynthesis. A simple example of such a force is the assumption that the end of the polypeptide hanging free of the polyribosome folds in such a configuration that makes further alterations difficult (Levinthal, 1966). It would follow from this hypothesis that, for each polypeptide species, the probability of folding while attached to a polyribosome is a function of both the length of the molecule and the rate of its synthesis as compared with the folding rate. For relatively small enzymes, such as ribonuclease, the chances of folding during synthesis would be small; therefore, these enzymes would not exhibit more than one active configuration. For larger proteins, the active three-dimensional structure would be determined by both the primary structure and the partial amino acid sequence between the NH_2-terminus and some amino acid within the molecule. The formation of other active configurations would depend on the stability of the initial structure.

For enzymes with subunits, it is plausible that completed monomers influence the folding of monomers which are being synthesized.

Our hypothesis that old and fresh enzymes differ in terms of total free energy predicts that the same molecule should be obtained after unfolding and refolding either enzyme. The results of experiments with urea shown above would seem to contradict this prediction. However, there is no evidence that urea causes a complete unfolding of a protein. On the contrary, guanidine HCl appears to be a stronger unfolding agent for β-galactosidase than urea (Ullmann and Monod, 1969).

SUMMARY

Inactivation of β-galactosidase from *Escherichia coli* caused by prolonged storage at low temperature is shown to occur by a mechanism different from that of thermal inactivation. The latter causes an all-or-none loss of activity per molecule while the former produces a partial loss of activity in individual molecules which results in a population of enzyme molecules with heterogeneous activity.

Among other possibilities, this result could be explained by the assumption that the newly synthesized enzyme does not represent the conformation with minimal total free energy. An hypothesis is presented which reconciles this assumption with the evidence supporting the idea that the amino acid sequence is the unique determinant of the three-dimensional structure.

ACKNOWLEDGMENTS

This work was partially supported by grant GM-14198 from the National Institutes of Health, U.S. Public Health Service, and grant GB-5533 from the National Science Foundation.

We want to thank Drs. D. Perrin, E. Steers, Jr., and I. Zabin for generous gifts of crystalline β-galactosidase.

The able technical assistance of Miss Adriana Gonzalez is gratefully acknowledged.

REFERENCES

BARER, R. 1960. A new micrometer microscope. Nature. *188:* 398.

COLLINS, J. F., D. B. MASON, and W. F. PERKINS. 1964. A microphotometric method for the estimation of penicillinase in single bacteria. J. Gen. Microbiol. *34:* 353.

CRAVEN, G. R., E. STEERS, Jr., and C. B. ANFINSEN. 1965. Purification, composition, and molecular weight of the β-galactosidase of *Escherichia coli* K12. J. Biol. Chem. *240:* 2468.

DAVIS, B. D. 1949. Isolation of biochemically deficient mutants of bacteria by means of penicillin. Proc. Nat. Acad. Sci. *35:* 1.

EPSTEIN, C. J., R. F. GOLDBERGER, D. M. YOUNG, and C. B. ANFINSEN. 1962. A study of the factors influencing the rate and extent of enzymic reactivation during reoxidation of reduced ribonuclease. Arch. Biochem. Biophys. Suppl. *1:* 223.

LEVINTHAL, C. 1966. Molecular model-building by computer. Scientific American. *June:* 42.

RAMACHANDRAN, G. N. 1969. Stereochemistry of biopolymer conformation, p. 79. *In* A. Engstrom and B. Strandberg [ed.] Symmetry and function of biological systems at the macromolecular level. Nobel Symposium 11. Wiley & Sons, New York.

ROTMAN, B. 1961. Measurement of activity of single molecules of β-galactosidase. Proc. Nat. Acad. Sci. *47:* 1981.

ROTMAN, B., J. A. ZDERIC, and M. EDELSTEIN. 1963. Fluorogenic substrates for β-galactosidases and phosphatases derived from fluorescein (3,6-dihydroxy-fluoran) and its monomethyl ether. Proc. Nat. Acad. Sci. *50:* 1.

ULLMANN, A. and J. MONOD. 1969. The effect of divalent cations and protein concentration upon renaturation of β-galactosidase from *E. coli*. Biochem. Biophys. Res. Commun. *35:* 35.

Antibody Mediated Activation of a Defective β-galactosidase (AMEF). Characteristics of Binding and Activation Processes

FRANCO CELADA, ROBERTO STROM* and KERSTIN BODLUND

Department of Tumor Biology
Karolinska Institutet
Stockholm, Sweden

INTRODUCTION

Recently Rotman and Celada (1968) described the activating effect of anti-β-galactosidase serum on AMEF, the gene product of a lac^- point mutant E. coli (lac 201, W6101). The magnitude of the activation is between 500 and 1000 times over the low native enzyme activity of AMEF. The specificity of the site(s) of attachment of the activating antibodies on the enzyme molecule is demonstrated by the fact that antisera obtained by injecting mutant enzyme, and undistinguishable from anti-z by immunodiffusion, are not activating (Celada, Ellis, Bodlund, and Rotman, in prep.). The molecular mechanism of activation is not known; it probably involves a conformational change of the AMEF tetramer. In view of the interest of such a phenomenon both from a physico-chemical and an immunological point of view, we have done experiments to determine (a) whether divalent antibodies are required to bring about activation, (b) the effect of varying antibody concentration on the enzyme activity reached by a given amount of AMEF, and (c) the kinetics of activation of antibody-AMEF mixtures. To interpret the results of (b)-type experiments, we also present a theoretical treatment of the data following lines suggested to us by Jeffries Wyman.

*On leave from Istituto di Chimica Biologica, Università di Roma, Italy.

MATERIALS AND METHODS

1. *Buffers and solutions*. Buffer B contained 10 mM tris (hydroxymethyl) aminomethane, 10 mM $MgCl_2$, 0.1 M Na Cl and 0.05M 2-mercaptoethanol and its pH was adjusted to 7.05 (23°C) with acetic acid. The complete buffer was prepared daily by adding mercaptoethanol to a stock salt solution. For papain cleavage of antibodies, the following solutions were used:

Solution I: 1M Tris acetic acid buffer, pH 6.5, 100 ml; 0.15M Na Cl 900 ml with final 0.002 M EDTA.

Solution II: 0.1M Tris-H Cl pH 7.2, 100 ml, phosphate buffer 1/15M pH 7.4, 100 ml; 0.14 M NaCl 800 ml.

2. *Chemicals*. Inducer (isopropyl-β-D-thiogalactopyranoside-ITPG) and substrate (O-nitrophenyl-γ-D-galactopyranoside-ONPG) of z were purchased from Mann Research Lab., N.Y. Tris (3-hydroxymethyl) aminomethane, papain 2xcrystallized and cystein, free base were obtained from Sigma, St. Louis, Mo. Iodacetamide was obtained from Fluka A.G.

3. *Bacterial strains and conditions of culture*. The constitutive mutants E. coli 3300($i^-z^+y^+$) grown in tryptone-lactate broth was used for the production of normal β-galactosidase. Cells of W6101 (F^- *lac* 201) were cultured in minimal medium containing 0.4% Na lactate, and 5×10^{-4}M isopropyl-β-D-galactopyranoside as inducer. Bacterial cultures were grown under shaking in 2–4 liter batches for 12–15 hrs at 37°C.

4. *Purification of z and AMEF*. These procedures are described in detail elsewhere (Rotman and Celada, 1968; Celada, Ellis, Bodlund, and Rotman, 1969). Both proteins were kept at 4°C under 40% saturated ammonium sulphate. Aliquots were dissolved in buffer B and freed from the salt as needed.

5. *Quantitative precipitation assay*. A given amount of z, usually between 100 and 1000 enzyme units in 0.3 ml is added to each of a series of tubes containing 0.2 ml of progressive dilutions of the antiserum to be tested and the mixtures were incubated first for 30 min at 37°C, then for 60 min at 4°C, the tubes were centrifuged at 48,000 g for 30 min. The supernatant of each tube was assayed for β-galactosidase activity. The latter was expressed in percent of the total content of the same tube prior to centrifugation (s). 100-s was taken as the precipitated fraction. Under these conditions a complete titration of an antiserum shows an antibody excess, an equivalence, and an antigen excess zone. The titer of a serum was determined by taking the last tube, in slight antigen excess, where more than 50% of the z was precipitated. The titer was expressed as E.U. precipitated by 1 μl of undiluted serum in these conditions, by correcting for amount and concentration in the reaction mixture.

6. Activation of AMEF assay. Titration of antiserum for activation capacity was done by incubating at 37°C for 30 min mixtures containing one volume of an AMEF preparation and one volume of antiserum dilution. Normal serum and a standard antiserum were used as negative and positive controls, respectively. After the incubation time, a sample from the mixtures was assayed for β-galactosidase activity. The activating titer of a serum was defined by the increase of enzymatic activity elicited by 1 μl of antiserum incubated with an excess of AMEF, and readily calculated by the formula:

$$\text{Titer} = \text{EU}_{\text{Exp}} - \text{EU}_{\text{con}} \times \frac{df}{1000}$$

where Eu is the number of enzyme units obtained from 1 ml of the AMEF preparation after reaction with 1 ml of serum, and df is the dilution factor of the antiserum. The calculation is done by taking the tube with the highest dilution of serum still containing enzyme activity significantly higher than the negative control.

7. Rabbits. Male and female rabbits of various breeds, weighing between 2 and 5 kg were obtained from commercial sources. Immunization was done by injecting in the subscapular region 3-20 mg of z or AMEF emulsified with incomplete or complete Freund's adjuvant (Difco) in a total volume of 2 ml. The same route was used for secondary injections. Bleedings were done by ear or heart puncture.

8. Papain cleavage of antibodies. 150 mg of γ-globulins from a rabbit anti-z serum, separated by ammonium sulphate precipitation were dissolved in solution I (see Buffers and solutions) and incubated for 16 hrs at 37°C with agitation in the presence of 1.5 mg of papain, 0.02 M cystein, and 0.002 EDTA(Porter, 1959; Putnam, Tan, Lynn, Easley, and Migita, 1962). The digestion was stopped by addition of iodacetamide (final concentration 0.015M): the sample was dialyzed against solution II and then applied on a Sephadex G100 column (2.5 × 45 cm). Elution was followed with a LKB Uvicord I, and the fractions containing the second peak were recycled in the same order (see Fig. 1). The final fractions were pooled and concentrated by ultradialysis. After 24 hrs storage at 4°C, the crystallized Fc was discarded by centrifugation.

RESULTS

(A) Activation of AMEF by monovalent antibody fragments. Figure 1 shows the separation on Sephadex G100 of the products of papain digestion of the γ globulins obtained from an anti-z serum. The pooled effluent fractions pertaining to the second peak were compared with the original

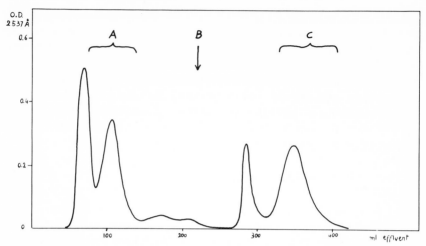

FIGURE 1. Separation of the products of papain digestion of anti-z γ-globulin on Sephadex G100. The front peak contains uncleaved γ-globulin, the second Fab and Fc fragments. A = Fractions recycled. B = Starting of recycling. C = Fractions collected. Ordinate: $OD_{2537Å}$. Abscissa: ml effluent.

γ globulin for activating and precipitating capacity. Table 1 shows their respective titers. The specific activating activity is somewhat higher in the Fab, which is devoid of precipitating capacity. Figure 2 shows a complete titration against a fixed amount of AMEF of the same γ globulin and Fab preparations obtained by recording the enzyme activity reached at equilibrium. Both the total activity and that expressed by soluble antigen-antibody complexes are shown. As expected, the complex formed by intact antibody molecules precipitates at equivalence and can be easily separated by centrifugation, while the Fab-AMEF complex does not.

TABLE 1.

Activating and precipitating capacity of an antiserum and its monovalent Fab

		TITER		
Source of antibody	Protein concentrat.	Activation	Spec.* activ.	Precipitation of z
Intact antiserum	n.d. (15µg/µl)	300	n.d.	600
γ globulin	54.6µg/µl	750	13.8	1000
FAB	28.4µg/µl	500	17.9	0

*Specific activating capacity is expressed in EU produced for 1 µg ab-protein.

(B) Effect of antibody concentration on the activation of a given amount of AMEF. Increase of the antibody concentration in the ab-AMEF mixture results in an increase in the enzyme activity reached at equilibrium, until a plateau is attained (Fig. 2). In AMEF excess, the increase in total activity may be proportional to the antibody concentration (a straight line with slope $\simeq 1$ in a log EU/log [Ab] plot) or less than proportional (a straight line with slope $\ll 1$). Hyperimmune sera are usually of the first type (as for example, the curves in Fig. 2), while sera taken early after immunization or obtained in semi-tolerant rabbits are of the second type.

In separate experiments (Celada, 1969, unpublished data) we were able to show that the activating capacity of the sera with a slope (Δlog EU/Δ log [ab]) $\ll 1$ decreases drastically with decreasing antigen concentration; this indicates that their combining affinity is low. We shall consider here the case of high affinity, and shall compare the experimental curves with the theoretical expectations for various possibilities of activating binding.

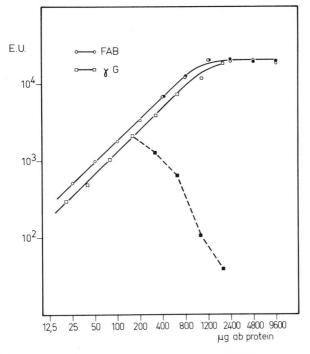

Figure 2. Rate of enzymatic activity of AMEF (EU/ml) over antibody concentration (μg/ml). Circles: using Fab. Squares: using intact γ-globulin. Clear symbols: total activity. Black symbols: supernatant activity after centrifugation. Ordinate: log EU/ml. Abscissa: log [ab].

The following symbols shall be used:

p = probability of a site being vacant

q = probability of a site being occupied

t = total number of sites per AMEF molecule

$$y = \frac{\text{amount of antibody added}}{\text{total amount of antibody required for 100\% activation}}$$

$\bar{Y}$ = fractional saturation of sites with antibody.

As "binding sites" we consider only those sites whose occupation can bring about activation of the enzyme. If $\bar{Y} = ky$, where k expresses the tightness of the binding, the frequency (P_r) of molecules in which r sites are occupied is given by the rth term of the expansion $(q + p)^t$, where

$$q = \bar{Y} = ky, \text{ and } p = 1 - \bar{Y} = 1 - ky.$$

There are two possibilities:

(1) The enzyme activation is an "all-or-none" event. It occurs when a number of sites $r \geq n$ (n being a positive integer $\leq t$) has been occupied, and the extent of activation of the single molecule is independent from the value of r (provided only that $r \geq n$).

In this case we can say that

$$\text{enzyme activity} = \text{constant} \cdot \sum_{r=n}^{t} (P_r)$$

This can be expressed as:

$$\text{e.a.} = \text{const} \cdot \left[\binom{t}{0} \bar{Y}^t + \binom{t}{1} \bar{Y}^{(t-1)}(1 - \bar{Y}) + \binom{t}{2} \bar{Y}^{(t-2)}(1 - \bar{Y})^2 + \right.$$

$$\left. + \cdots + \binom{t}{t-n} \bar{Y}^n \cdot (1 - \bar{Y})^{(t-n)} \right]$$

where

$$\binom{t}{n} = \frac{t!}{n!(t-n)!} = \frac{t(t-1)(t-2)\cdots(t-n+1)}{n!},$$

$$\binom{t}{0} = 1, \text{ and } \binom{t}{t-n} = \frac{t!}{n!(t-n)!}$$

We have, therefore, families of curves (see graphs in Fig. 3) according to the values of t and n. In the log (enzyme activity) vs. log (100.y) plot,

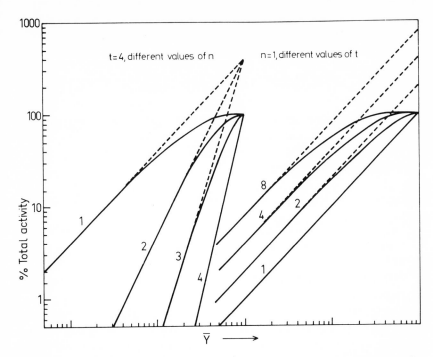

FIGURE 3. Theoretical curves according to an "all-or-none" activation model. Different values of t (total number of antigenic determinants potentially involved with activation) and of n (number of determinants which must be covered to bring about activation). Ordinate: log % EU Abscissa: log fractional saturation of sites with antibody. A comparison of these curves with the results in Fig. 2 shows that only values of n = 1 and of t comprised between 1 and 4 are compatible with the data.

all these curves have a longer or shorter linear part, since when $y \ll 1$ (i.e. also $\bar{Y} \ll 1$), the curves are simplified by taking into consideration only the $\bar{Y}$ term with the minimum value of the exponent, as:

$$\text{enzyme activity} = \left(\frac{t}{t-n}\right) \cdot \bar{Y}^n \cdot \text{constant}$$

i.e. $\log (\text{enzyme activity}) = n \log \bar{Y} + \log\left(\frac{t}{t-n}\right) + \text{constant}'$

$\log (\text{enzyme activity}) = n \log y + \log k + \log\left(\frac{t}{t-n}\right) + \text{constant}'.$

It can be seen from these formulas that:

(a) a change in the value of k does not change the slope of the curve

(b) if *all* the sites t have to be occupied in order to make the AMEF active (i.e. if n = t), then the general curve becomes:

$$\text{enzyme activity} = \text{constant} \cdot \binom{t}{0} \cdot k^t \cdot y^t$$

i.e. log (enzyme activity) = t log y + t log k + constant' which is *always* a straight line with slope t (see Fig. 3).

(c) if *one* occupied site is enough for full activation (i.e. if n = 1) then the linear part of the curve is

$$\log (\text{enzyme activity}) = \log y + \log k + \log \binom{t}{t-1} + \text{constant}'$$

i.e. log (enzyme activity) = log y + log k + log t + constant'. The slope is therefore 1, but the difference for different values of t is in the non-linearity at values of $\overline{Y}$ approaching 1 (for Graph 2). The extrapolation of the linear portion value on the ordinate axis, for $\overline{Y} = 1$, is equal to log t.

(2) The second possibility is that the participation of any AMEF molecule to the activity is proportional, *to some power s* (s being any positive, even non integer, number) of the number of sites occupied by the antibody. This can be expressed by the formula

$$\text{enzyme activity} = \text{constant} \cdot \sum_{r=0}^{t} r^s \cdot (P_r)$$

i.e.
$$\text{enzyme activity} = \text{constant} \cdot \sum_{r=0}^{t} r^s \cdot \binom{t}{r} \cdot p^{(t-r)} \cdot q^r$$

or
$$\text{enzyme activity} = \text{constant} \cdot \sum_{r=0}^{t} r^s \cdot \binom{t}{r} \overline{Y}^r \cdot \left(1 - \overline{Y}\right)^{(t-r)}$$

Of these families of curves, only those having s = 1 are straight lines. All the curves obtained with s = 1 have, independently of the value of t, slope 1 and cannot, therefore, be distinguished from the simple case of t = 1 (i.e. one site per AMEF molecule).

For s ≠ 1, the curves have only very short linear portions (see Fig. 4). But in all of those for $\overline{Y} \ll 1$, the slope tends to be 1, since the formula can be simplified as:

$$\lim_{\overline{Y} \to 0} (\text{enzyme activity}) = \text{constant} \cdot t \cdot \overline{Y}, \text{ since}$$

only the factor $(t \cdot y^r)$ having r − 1 becomes significant with respect to

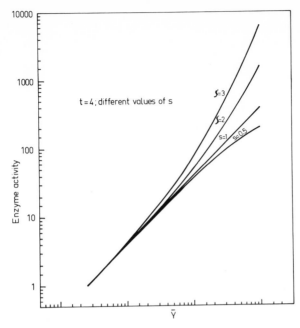

FIGURE 4. Theoretical curves according to a model postulating activation to be proportional to a power s of the number of antigenic sites of AMEF occupied by the antibody. Total number of sites (t) = 4. Different values of s (see text). Ordinate: log EU Abscissa: log fractional saturation of sites with antibody. Only the case of s = 1 results in a curve similar to the experimental one.

the others. Anyhow, in all these cases the deviation from linearity, in the log vs. log plot, are large.

(C) *Kinetics of AMEF activation.* The increase of β-galactosidase activity after contact with antibody is a relatively slow process reaching completion in 200–250 min at 37°C. This rate is identical for different sera and within certain limits is independent of the antibody concentration. Figure 5a illustrates the kinetics of activation of AMEF mixed with two antisera, one (M7) having a higher titer and higher affinity than the other (M3). The plot of the same data in Fig. 5b shows that the log of $EU_{max} - EU_t$ is proportional to $-t$. Thus, the rate-limiting step of activation is apparently a first-order reaction.

DISCUSSION

The findings presented in this article are concerned with the mechanism by which the defective AMEF molecules regain part of the enzymatic activity after contact with a specific antibody.

The digestion by papain, which reduces the antibody molecule to mono-

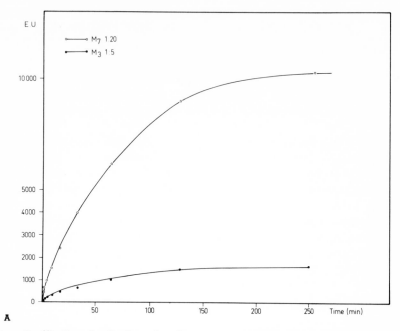

A

FIGURE 5a. Kinetics of activation of a given amount of AMEF by two anti-z sera. From independent experiments we know that M_7 (open circles) has a higher affinity than M_3. Ordinate: EU/ml. Abscissa: time in min. after AMEF-serum mixing.

valent fragments with unimpaired combining ability, did not interfere with the process of enzyme activation. It had previously been shown that activation occurs even in great antigen excess, where no precipitating complexes are formed (Rotman and Celada, 1968). Still it was conceivable that the role of antibody would be to bridge or pull together two AMEF molecules or two parts of the same tetramer. The present experiment clearly shows that a simple binding interaction is sufficient for the activation, and that one activated center contains a single AMEF tetramer.

The next questions were: (1) how many antibody molecules are needed to activate one AMEF, (2) how many antigenic determinants—the binding of which may cause activation—exist on AMEF, and (3) is activation an all-or-none event or does one AMEF molecule exhibit a degree of activity as a function of the number of ligands? It was feasible to obtain an answer by studying the effect of antibody concentration on the activity obtainable from a given amount of AMEF. Such titrations of activating antiserum result in a characteristic curve (see Rotman and Celada, 1968, and Fig. 2 of this article), which must reflect the mode of antibody-antigen combination. We calculated the probability of a site being vacant or occupied by antibody for each fractional saturation, and constructed curves of the activity expected according to a number of activating binding hypotheses. The theoretical model that best fits the experimental curves considers activation an all-or-none event, triggered by a single antibody hitting the AMEF molecule; the number of epitopes capable of binding the activating antibody would be one to four per AMEF tetramer, meaning that either a single determinant results from the tetrameric structure, or is carried by each dimer, or by each monomer. These are small numbers, if we consider that a protein molecule of 135,000 mol wt is expected to express between 10 and 20 different antigenic sites. In agreement with the present conclusions is the high specificity of the activating antigen-antibody reaction, demonstrated by the failure of producing activity by conjugating AMEF with a hapten (DNP) and adding anti-DNP antiserum (Celada, 1968, unpublished observation) and by the finding that only a minority of the anti-z antibodies capable of reacting with the AMEF molecules are engaged in its activation, as shown by the existence of antisera (directed against mutant β-galactosidases) which heavily crossreact with anti-z in precipitation but do not activate AMEF (Celada, Ellis, Bodlund, and Rotman, 1969).

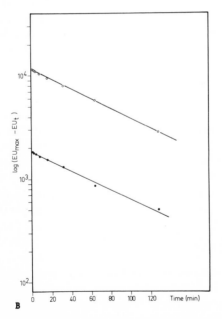

FIGURE 5b. The kinetics is identical for the two sera. The same data of Fig. 5a plotted to test whether activity increase is a first-order reaction. Ordinate: log (maximal activity minus activity at time t). Abscissa: time in min.

However, despite these corroborating facts and the intriguing correlation between the maximum postulated number of "activating" epitopes and the number of mutated sites per tetramer, one should keep in mind that while the determination of the slope $\Delta \log EU/\Delta \log [ab]$, and therefore, of n is unambiguous, the values in the region where activity reaches its asymptote are difficult to determine with precision. Thus, it would be desirable to check the present estimate of t by independent ways.

The kinetic study in the last section of "Results" shows that the formation of activity that we measure after admixture of antibody to AMEF is a first-order process with a half-completion time of ∼45 minutes. Since this is true also of near antigen-antibody equivalence, where one would expect a second-order kinetics and because of the very slow rate, we visualize a series of at least 2 events: first, the binding of the activating antibody to its specific site on the AMEF molecules; since we know that the precipitation of AMEF by antibody takes about 500 milliseconds in appropriate conditions (Antonini and Celada, 1969, unpublished observation), the binding should be completed in less than that time; second, a conformational change of the AMEF-activating antibody complex, thereby passing from no activity or low activity to the active state. The latter is, under our conditions, the rate-limiting step. It is of interest that a similar transition (with $t\frac{1}{2}$ of 30 min.) has been described by Craven (this symposium) for urea-treated wild type β-galactosidase molecules regaining their tetrameric form and in a subsequent step their enzymatic activity, upon lowering the concentration of urea by dilution.

SUMMARY

The β-galactosidase activity of the mutant AMEF is increased about 10^3 times by contact with anti-z antibody. The activating interaction involves a single antibody site and one out of a small number of specific determinants on the AMEF tetramer (1–4). The gain of enzymatic activity is a relatively slow process with a first-order kinetics, presumably brought about by a conformational change of the AMEF-antibody complex.

ACKNOWLEDGMENTS

We would like to thank Jeffries Wyman for stimulating discussions and for suggesting the mathematical treatment of the activation data. The excellent technical assistance of Lena Fält, Birgitta Åsjö and Margareta Ihre is gratefully acknowledged.

This work has been supported by the Swedish Cancer Society, the Swedish Medical Research Council and the Sir Samuel Scott of Yews Trust.

REFERENCES

CELADA, F., J. ELLIS, K. BODLUND, and B. ROTMAN. (In prep.) Antibody mediated activation of a defective β-galactosidase (AMEF). II. Immunological relationship between the normal and the defective enzyme.

PORTER, R. R. 1959. The hydrolysis of rabbit γ-globulin and antibodies with crystalline papain. Biochem J. *73:* 119.

PUTNAM, F. W., M. TAN, L. T., LYNN, C. W. EASLEY, and S. MIGITA. 1962. The cleavage of rabbit γ-globulin by papain. J. Biol. Chem. *237:* 717.

ROTMAN, B. and F. CELADA. 1968. Formation of β-D-galactosidase mediated by specific antibody in a soluble extract of E. coli containing a defective z gene product. Proc. Nat. Acad. Sci. *60:* 660.

The Activation of Mutant β-galactosidase by Specific Antibodies

WALTER MESSER and FRITZ MELCHERS

Max-Planck-Institut für Molekulare Genetik
Berlin, West Germany

Immunological studies with wild-type and mutant β-galactosidase have been used for the investigation of the structure, activity and mode of synthesis of this enzyme. Antibodies directed against β-galactosidase precipitate but do not inactivate the enzyme (Cohn and Torriani, 1952). The distribution of antigenic sites to which precipitating antibodies are bound has been studied with a series of nonsense, missense and deletion mutants (Fowler and Zabin, 1968). Anti β-galactosidase serum has been found to activate latent enzyme. Enzyme activity in growing β-galactosidase polypeptide chains on ribosomes could be increased 2-fold by addition of anti β-galactosidase antibodies (Lederberg et al., 1964). A lac^- mutant has been described producing β-galactosidase crossreacting material which could be activated to enzyme activity by the addition of anti β-galactosidase antiserum. The activation, up to 550-fold above background, was proportional to the antibody concentration (Rotman and Celada, 1968).

Such mutants are of interest in two areas of research:

(1) Further information about the structure and activity of β-galactosidase may be obtained by understanding the mechanism of this activation due to the binding of specific antibodies at its corresponding antigenic site.

(2) Mutant proteins of this kind seem to be powerful tools in detecting antibodies against a specific antigenic determinant on a protein molecule. An assay for cells producing and secreting such antibodies seems possible. Antibody-like receptors on the surface of lymphoid cells, sensitive to this antigenic site, may be localized.

With these problems in mind, we have isolated eleven mutants producing an inactive β-galactosidase which is activated by specific antiserum. The mutants are classified (a) on the basis of their position on a genetic map, (b) by the patterns of activation of their mutant proteins by different populations of antibodies.

The correlation between active site, antigenic site and site of mutation will be discussed.

ISOLATION OF *LAC*$^-_{aba}$*-MUTANTS

Lac$^-$ mutants of *E. coli* K12 Hfr C have been isolated after mutagenesis with N-Methyl-N'-nitro-N-nitroso-guanidine. β-galactosidase activity in extracts of these mutants was determined with and without the addition of antiserum prepared against wild-type β-galactosidase. The antiserum used was that of one rabbit only (No. 23) throughout all experiments reported in this paper.

Out of 480 mutants, 100 were found to be activated 2- to 10-fold and four mutants 10- to 30-fold over background. Eleven mutants upon addition of specific antiserum showed an enhancement in enzyme activity of 50-fold or more (Table 1). This report will describe experiments with these eleven mutants.

GENETIC GROUPS OF *LAC*$^-_{aba}$-MUTANTS

The possible identity of sites of the eleven *lac*$^-_{aba}$-mutants within the z gene† has been determined by transducing the marker of one mutant to another mutant with the generalized transducing phage P1kc. Relative frequencies of wild-type recombinants between the mutants are given in Table 2. They have been used to arrange the mutants on a map (Fig. 1). Seven of them fall into one group (1), two other mutants into another group (2). Two mutants map at sites different from the two groups. The orders cannot accurately be determined from these data (see Beckwith, this volume).

SEPARATION OF ANTIBODIES ACTIVATING THE DIFFERENT MUTANT PROTEINS

Serum from one rabbit immunized against wild-type β-galactosidase was fractionated to obtain serum fractions with higher specific activating activity (per mg of protein), and to test whether different serum fractions had similar or different activating capacities with our eleven mutant

---

* *lac*$^-$ antibody activatable
† Structural gene for β-galactosidase

Table 1. The activation of lac_{aba}^--mutants by rabbit anti-β-galactosidase serum

Extracts from mutant No.	0.9% NaCl	Rabbit anti-ovalbumin serum (1:5 diluted)	Rabbit anti-β-galactosidase serum (1:5 diluted)	Activation factor over background (0.9% NaCl)
		(activated β-galactosidase units/ml)		
13	25	15	6950	280
40	70	90	3700	53
71	20	35	8800	440
429	15	20	6400	428
627	10	30	3600	360
630	8	15	4520	565
645	7	15	4830	690
779	20	15	6550	327
918	80	120	4200	53
950	35	45	2620	75
959	21	35	5740	275

A stationary phase culture of *E. coli K12 Hfr C i⁻z⁺* in Nutrient Broth (Difco) was mutagenized with 1 mg/ml N-methyl-N'-nitro-N-nitroso-guanidine for 60 min at 37°C. The cells were grown for a few generations to allow for the segregation of the mutants. They were then plated on Nutrient Agar plates (Difco) and *lac⁻* mutants were isolated using the staining procedure of Messer and Vielmetter (1965). Extracts from mutants, grown to stationary in the medium described by Craven et al. (1965) and concentrated to 5×10^{10} cells/ml in 0.01 M Tris-Acetate, pH 7.1, 0.1 M NaCl, 0.1 M mercaptoethanol, 5×10^{-4} M MgCl$_2$, were prepared fresh by sonic disruption with the MSE sonicator for 6 min at maximal amplitude under cooling in ice using the microprobe (end diameter $\frac{1}{8}$″).

All studies reported in this paper were performed with serum of one rabbit (No. 23) immunized over a period of 4 months with purified β-galactosidase in Freund's incomplete adjuvant (Difco) by intramuscular infection of 5 mg at day 0 and day 14 and 2 mg each week thereafter. β-galactosidase was purified from *E. coli K12 Hfr C* cells according to Craven et al. (1965). An enzyme preparation with a specific activity of 5×10^5 units/mg protein was obtained and used for immunization and precipitation tests.

In this table values for maximum activation of the mutant proteins are given which were obtained with 1:5 diluted antiserum. In all tests 0.05 ml of mutant extract were mixed with 0.05 ml of suitable dilutions of anti-β-galactosidase serum or serum fractions and incubated for 30 min at 37°C. Then 0.25 ml p-nitrophenyl-β-D-galactopyranoside (Serva Entwicklungslabor, Heidelberg, Germany), 3.3 mg/ml in 0.1 M phosphate-citrate buffer, pH 6.3 (Hughes and Jeanloz, 1964), was added and the mixture incubated for a desired length of time (5–30 min) at 37°C. The reaction was stopped by adding 3.0 ml of cold 0.1 M sodium carbonate buffer, pH 9.4. Absorption at 430 mμ was measured. A coefficient of $\epsilon_{430m\mu}^{\mu Mol} = 2.0 \times 10^9$ as given for o-nitrophenol (Hughes and Jeanloz, 1964) was used to convert measurements at 430 mμ into p-nitrophenol concentrations. One unit of β-galactosidase is defined as the amount of enzyme splitting 1 nMol p-nitrophenyl-β-D-galactopyranoside per minute at 37°C (Lederberg et al., 1964). Controls contained 0.9% NaCl or rabbit anti-ovalbumin serum in 1:5 dilution instead of anti-β-galactosidase serum.

Table 2. Relative recombination frequencies between *lac⁻*$_{aba}$-mutants

	Recip. donor	Group 1							Group 2			
		13	71	429	630	645	779	950	40	918	627	959
Group 1	13	2	0	0	1	2	2	—	262	146	29	39
	71	2	0	0	1	1	3	—	122	108	28	8
	429	1	0	0	0	4	2	—	151	264	37	27
	630	2	0	3	1	4	1	—	346	511	57	61
	645	3	0	1	0	0	3	—	149	241	27	23
	779	4	0	0	1	6	1	—	440	390	57	84
	950	1	5	0	0	4	0	—	366	265	98	42
Group 2	40	173	255	197	234	128	108	—	1	2	198	107
	918	181	124	156	360	237	136	—	3	1	193	106
	627	76	57	81	67	79	40	—	332	227	4	112
	959	—	—	—	—	—	—	—	—	—	—	—

The marker of one mutant was transduced to another mutant using P1kc. To account for possible differences in the efficiency of transduction in the different recipients, transductions have been done using P1 grown on wild-type Hfr C under identical conditions. The results in the table are expressed as number of *lac⁺* recombinants per 1000 *lac⁺* recombinants in the control experiment on the same recipient. Each frequency is the average out of 3 to 5 different experiments. The number of *lac⁺* recombinants with P1(*lac⁺*) used for normalization in an experiment was about 2500 for each recipient.

Lysates were prepared and transduction was done as described by Wolf et al., (1968). Transduced cells were irradiated with 16 erg × mm² × sec⁻¹ of UV to increase the recombination frequency.

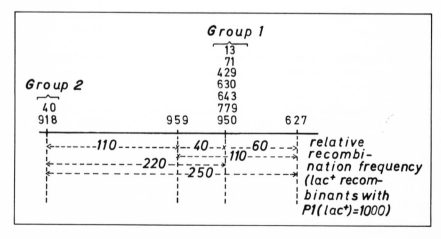

FIGURE 1. Relative distances between *lac⁻*$_{aba}$-mutants as taken from the results in Table 2.

proteins. The serum fraction obtained by 50% $(NH_4)_2SO_4$ precipitation was subjected to ion-exchange chromatography on CM-** and DEAE***-cellulose columns (Figs. 2 and 3). On both columns a considerable enrichment of activating antibodies as expressed in activated enzyme units per $A_{280\ m\mu}$-unit of protein is observed (Table 3).

The eleven mutant proteins can be distinguished in two groups (A and B) on the basis of their pattern of activation obtained with antibodies eluted from both columns. Mutant proteins 71, 630, 645, 779, and 950 show activation patterns very similar to those shown in Figs. 2 and 3 for mutant protein 13 (Group A). Mutant proteins 40 and 918 show activation patterns very similar to each other (Group B) and clearly distinct from Group A patterns (Figs. 2 and 3, mutant protein 40). The activation patterns of mutant proteins 429, 627, and 959 are similar to the pattern of Group A mutant proteins. Certain of the CM- and DEAE-cellulose column fractions, however, show either a higher or a lower activating capacity when compared with Group A mutant protein activation patterns. A detailed evaluation of these experiments will be reported elsewhere (Melchers and Messer, in prep.).

All fractions of the CM- and the DEAE-cellulose columns activating either mutant protein have been found to precipitate wild-type β-galactosidase as well as mutant proteins (Table 3). A 400-fold enrichment in activating activity per $A_{280\ m\mu}$-unit of protein could be obtained over that of unfractionated antiserum by successive chromatography on CM- and DEAE-cellulose columns. These successive chromatographies also yielded antibody fractions precipitating wild-type β-galactosidase as well as mutant proteins but not activating mutant proteins.

DISCUSSION

For a discussion of the properties of lac^-_{aba}-mutants we may consider three different functional sites in the β-galactosidase mutant protein which are essential in the activation reaction: the active site, the antigenic site and the site of mutation. We will present arguments that these functionally defined sites are in fact different structures on the molecule.

Antibodies prepared in rabbits against wild-type β-galactosidase do not change the activity of the wild-type enzyme (Cohn and Torriani, 1952). Therefore, antibodies directed against the active site do not exist in such animals. The antigenic site combining with the antibody must, therefore, be some distance apart from the active site.

** Carboxymethyl-
*** Diethylaminoethyl-

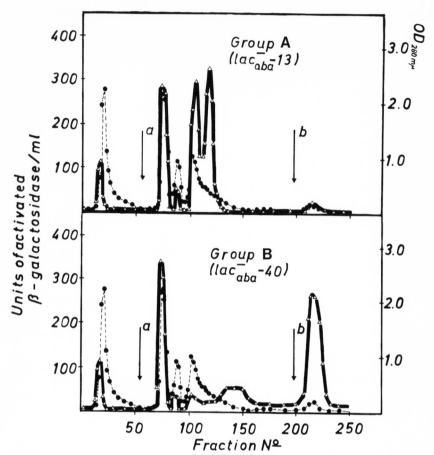

FIGURE 2. Protein was precipitated from anti-β-galactosidase serum of one rabbit by adding $(NH_4)_2SO_4$ to 50% saturation in the cold. The precipitate was collected by centrifugation, washed once with 50% saturated $(NH_4)_2SO_4$ solution, dissolved in and dialysed against 0.001 M potassium phosphate, pH 8.0.

A 11 ml aliquot of this solution with 19.8 $A_{280 m\mu}$-units/ml was brought to pH 7.1 with H_3PO_4 at room temperature. It was then applied to a 3 × 28 cm CM-cellulose column equilibrated at room temperature with 0.001 M potassium phosphate, pH 6.7. After washing the column with 225 ml 0.001 M potassium phosphate, pH 6.7, a linear concentration gradient from 0.001 M to 0.2 M potassium phosphate, pH 6.4 (when measured at a phosphate concentration of 0.5 M) was applied for elution in two steps (from 0.001 M to 0.01 M: fractions 55–85; from 0.01 M to 0.2 M: fractions 86–195) (a). At the end of the gradient more material was eluted from the column with 1.0 M potassium phosphate, pH 8.0 (b). Eluted fractions (volume 5 ml) were measured for protein content by their absorption at 280 mμ (– – ● – –) and tested for their ability to activate mutant protein 13 (representative for Group A mutants; upper part) and mutant protein 40 (representative for Group B mutants, lower part) to β-galactosidase activity (—△—). Recovery of protein as measured by its absorption at 280 mμ was 88%.

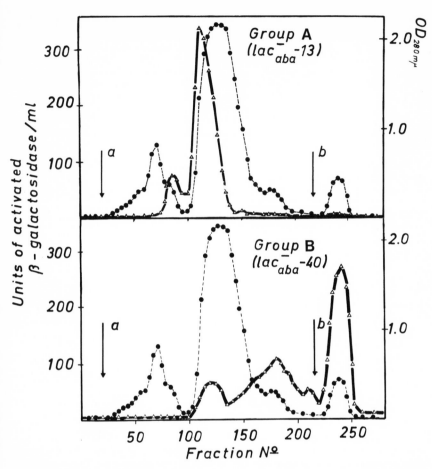

FIGURE 3. A 22 ml aliquot of the solution containing the 50% $(NH_4)_2SO_4$ precipitate with 19.8 $A_{280 m\mu}$-units/ml in 0.001 M potassium phosphate, pH 8.0 was applied to a 3 × 28 cm DEAE-cellulose column equilibrated with 0.001 M potassium phosphate, pH 8.0, in the cold. A linear concentration gradient from 500 ml 0.001 M to 500 ml 0.5 M potassium phosphate, pH 8.0, was applied for elution (a). At the end of the gradient more material was eluted from the column by the addition of 2.0 M NaCl in 0.5 M potassium phosphate, pH 4.2 (b). Eluted fractions (5 ml) were tested as described for the CM-cellulose column in Fig. 2 (‑ ‑ ●‑ ‑ $A_{280 m\mu}$; ■‑△‑■ activated β-galactosidase activity). Recovery of protein from the column was 80%.

The activation of the mutant proteins by antibody to enzyme activity may suggest that the mutations did not occur at the active site. The observed activation with the antibody, however, amounts to only 1–10% of the specific activity of the wild-type enzyme (wild-type enzyme: 5×10^5 units/mg, mutant protein No. 13: $5 \times 10^3 - 5 \times 10^4$ units/mg, unpub-

Messer and Melchers

Table 3. Precipitating and activating activity of rabbit anti-β-galactosidase antibodies in different fractions from the CM- and DEAE-cellulose columns.

Fraction No.	Precipitating activity	Activating activity	
	wild-type β-galactosidase units per $A_{280\,m\mu}$-unit	activated β-galactosidase units per $A_{280\,m\mu}$-unit mutant protein	
		13	40
unfractionated rabbit anti- β-galactosidase serum	1000	30	15
CM-cellulose column (Fig. 2)			
18	1300	125	125
76	2800	90	95
106	3700	205	20
118	4700	725	10
214	3000	85	680
DEAE-cellulose column (Fig. 3)			
86	1200	180	$<$1
112	4500	85	15
180	3700	1	250
240	3400	5	410

Quantitative immune precipitations of wild-type β-galactosidase or mutant proteins were done as described by Melchers and Knopf (1967). Assays for activating antibodies in the different column fractions were done in antigen excess as described in the legend to Table 1. The washed immune precipitates were tested for β-galactosidase enzyme activity. Controls were performed by adding ovalbumin to the extracts, precipitating with rabbit anti-ovalbumin serum and sheep anti-rabbit γ-globulin serum, and testing the washed precipitates for β-galactosidase activity.

lished results). We do not know whether all mutant protein molecules or only some are activated within a population. We, therefore, cannot rule out that the mutations did occur within the active site of the enzyme, impairing, for example, the substrate binding (Langridge, 1968).

Examination of precipitin lines in Ouchterlony immunodiffusion tests of nonsense, missense and deletion mutants have suggested three classes of antigenic sites on the β-galactosidase molecule. (Fowler and Zabin, 1968). Approximately one third of our 480 *lac*⁻ mutant extracts showed strong precipitin lines in Ouchterlony immunodiffusion tests; another fifth, weak lines with antiserum prepared against wild-type β-galactosidase.

These mutant proteins were therefore precipitated, but not activated, by specific antiserum. One can conclude that in addition to the antigenic sites, to which activating antibodies are bound, other antigenic sites exist on the β-galactosidase molecule.

Mutations which allow the synthesis of a protein activatable by specific antibodies occur at least at four different sites. Data with more mutants may reveal more sites responsible for this phenotype. The P1 transduction experiments cannot decide whether mutant proteins of mutants within one group are identical. Different, independently isolated mutants within Group 1 (seven mutants) or Group 2 (two mutants) may map at identical sites or some distance apart, giving recombination frequencies below the level of detectability.

An immunopotent site on the wild-type enzyme gives rise to an antibody population which will recognize this site as being antigenic on wild-type as well as on mutant protein. Since the antigenic site is present on both types of molecules, it is unlikely that this site is altered by mutation. If the site is changed, however, by mutation in such a way that binding of antibody will still occur, but with different affinity, a difference in the binding constants of the antibody with the two antigens should be observed.

Antibody populations activating mutant proteins of Group A on the one hand and of Group B on the other hand have been found to be different. One possible explanation for this difference is that parts of the total population of activating antibodies from one animal can bind and/or activate at the same antigenic site(s) of the two groups of mutant proteins with different efficiency. Another explanation is that the antigenic sites, through which antibody activates, are different on the two groups of mutant proteins. The groups of mutants genetically not distinguishable by P1 transduction (1 and 2) are correlated to the groups of mutant proteins activated by the same population of antibodies (A and B). This implies that two sites of mutations (1 and 2) are correlated either to one antigenic site responding with different efficiency to the total population of activating antibodies or to two antigenic sites—or two sets of antigenic sites. Since mutants 627 and 959 are genetically distinct from Group 1 mutants but produce proteins with activation patterns very similar to Group A proteins, we are lead to think that more than one site of mutation may be correlated to an antigenic site.

In summary, we think that it is unlikely that mutation has occurred directly at the active site of the enzyme or at the antigenic site binding the activating antibody. As one possible conclusion we, therefore, like to suggest that for each group of activatable mutants there is a correlated antigenic site to which antibody is bound.

Surprising remains the finding that the antibody populations activating the different mutants can be separated, presumably by their net charge difference. While the serum fraction applied to the DEAE- and CM-cellulose columns did not contain detectable amounts of 19 S antibody, possible class differences between the different activating antibodies may still exist within the 7 S classes. A charge difference of antibody molecules produced against the same haptenic group on differently charged carriers has been observed (Sela and Moses, 1966). In our case, there is only one carrier molecule (β-galactosidase). If there exist two antigenic determinants binding the different populations of antibodies, this would mean that this molecule carries two different immunopotent determinants. If one assigns carrier functions to limited parts of the β-galactosidase molecule, possibly in the neighborhood of the immunopotent determinant, the observed charge differences of the antibody molecules could indicate charge differences in different regions of the β-galactosidase molecule.

SUMMARY

Eleven *lac⁻* mutants have been isolated producing β-galactosidase mutant proteins, which can be activated to enzyme activity upon addition of anti β-galactosidase antibodies. A preliminary mapping of the mutants has been done, using P1 transduction. Seven of them fall into one group (1), two others into another group (2). Two mutants map at sites different from the two groups.

Mutant proteins within one group are activated by the same population of antibodies. The two populations of antibodies activating the two groups of mutants are distinguishable by their chromatographic behavior on DEAE- and CM-cellulose. Our results suggest that two different antigenic sites on the β-galactosidase molecule bind two different populations of activating antibodies. One group of mutants is correlated to one antigenic site. It is discussed, whether the sites of mutation are different from their corresponding antigenic sites and from the active site of the enzyme.

ACKNOWLEDGMENTS

We thank Thomas Trautner, Christof Spatz, Gisela Nass and Paul Knopf for stimulating discussions. We are grateful to Mrs. R. Lochmann who helped to isolate the mutants, and to Miss D. Jablonski and Miss M. Hübener for their able technical assistance.

REFERENCES

COHN, M. and A. M. TORRIANI. 1952. Immunochemical studies with the β-galactosidase and structurally related proteins of *Escherichia coli.* J. Immunol. *69:* 471.

CRAVEN, R. G., E. STEERS, Jr., and C. B. ANFINSEN. 1965. Purification, composition and molecular weight of the β-galactosidase of *Escherichia coli* K12. J. Biol. Chem. *240:* 2468.

FOWLER, A. V. and I. ZABIN. 1968. β-galactosidase: Immunological studies of non-sense, missense and deletion mutants. J. Mol. Biol. *33:* 35.

HUGHES, R. C. and R. W. JEANLOZ. 1964. The extracellular glycosidases of *Diplococcus pneumoniae*. I. Purification and properties of a neuraminidase and a β-galactosidase. Action on the α_1-acid glycoprotein of human plasma. Biochemistry *3:* 1535.

LANGRIDGE, J. 1968. Genetic evidence for the disposition of the substrate binding site of β-galactosidase. Proc. Nat. Acad. Sci. *60:* 1260.

LEDERBERG, S., B. ROTMAN, and V. LEDERBERG. 1964. Distribution and activity of single β-galactosidase centers among ribosomes of *Escherichia coli*. J. Biol. Chem. *239:* 54.

MELCHERS, F. and P. M. KNOPF. Biosynthesis of the carbohydrate portion of immunoglobulin chains: possible relation to secretion. Cold Spring Harbor Symp. Quant. Biol. *32:* 255.

MESSER, W. and W. VIELMETTER. 1965. High resolution colony staining for the detection of bacterial growth requirement mutants using naphthol azo-dye techniques. Biochem. Biophys. Res. Commun. *21:* 182.

ROTMAN, M. B. and F. CELADA. 1968. Antibody-mediated activation of a defective β-galactosidase extracted from an *Escherichia coli* mutant. Proc. Nat. Acad. Sci. *60:* 660.

SELA, M. and E. MOSES. 1966. Dependence of the chemical nature of antibodies on the net electrical charge of antigens. Proc. Nat. Acad. Sci. *55:* 445.

WOLF, B., A. NEWMAN and D. A. GLASER. 1968. On the origin and direction of replication of the *E. coli* K12 chromosome. J. Mol. Biol. *32:* 611.

Is Subunit Assembly a Rate-Limiting Factor on Induction?

LUCILLE ADAMSON, CAROL GROSS, and AARON NOVICK

Institute of Molecular Biology
University of Oregon
Eugene, Oregon

INTRODUCTION

The basal or uninduced rate of formation of β-galactosidase is extremely low and can be accounted for by the production of less than one messenger for β-galactosidase per cell per generation (Rotman, pers. commun.). Since the concentration of subunits resulting from one messenger molecule per cell would be less than 10^{-7}M, we wondered whether the assembly of these subunits to the active tetrameric enzyme would require a relatively long time. Were a long time necessary, one might expect to see an increase in the time required (the lag) to establish the ultimate rate of β-galactosidase synthesis when a culture is induced with low concentrations of inducer.

The lag on induction should include in addition to the time for assembly of β-galactosidase subunits contributions from (a) the time needed after addition of inducer for the fraction of operators free of repressor to reach steady state values, and (b) the time to transcribe and translate the gene for β-galactosidase. An effect of slow assembly would be seen only if the other two processes were relatively fast and independent of the rate of synthesis of β-galactosidase.

Unhappily, there is lack of agreement in published reports on the observed values of the lag at low rates of synthesis. In one case, it has been reported that the lag did not increase as the inducer concentration was reduced below saturation values (Pardee and Prestidge, 1961). In another case, it has been reported that the lag did increase at lower concentrations of inducer (Boezie and Cowie, 1961). More recently, this

317

observation has been attributed to the slow rate of dissociation of the operator-repressor complex at low concentrations of inducer (Gilbert and Müller-Hill, 1967). Were this theoretical analysis correct, it would not be possible to study the dependence of the rate of assembly on subunit concentration in this system.

We have repeated the theoretical analysis of the lag expected from the time required for dissociation of the operator-repressor complex. We find that the analysis by Gilbert and Müller-Hill (1967) is in error since they have ignored the process which determines the time constant, the re-association of free operator with repressor. The expression we have derived shows that the time required for the concentration of free operators to approach the steady state becomes constant as inducer concentration is lowered.

We have also repeated the measurements of lag time after induction by low concentrations of inducer and have extended these studies to extremely low rates of synthesis. We find that the lag time does not increase even when the induced rate is less than twice the basal rate of β-galactosidase synthesis.

THEORETICAL

The definitions and assumptions used in our derivation of the relationship between the ultimate rate of synthesis and lag expected from the time required for the fraction of free operators to reach the steady state value are given below. They are all included among those made in the earlier analysis (Gilbert and Müller-Hill, 1967).

a) The total concentration of repressor is R_0. It is either free (R), bound to inducer (RI), or bound to operator (RD). It is assumed that the amount of repressor bound to operator is small compared with R + RI so that $R + RI = R_0$.

b) The rate-limiting step is assumed to be the interaction of repressor with operator, the rate of β-galactosidase synthesis being given by the fraction of operators free of repressor ($=D$). The fraction of operators bound to repressor includes that associated with repressor alone (DR) and that with repressor plus inducer (DRI). Hence $D + DR + DRI = 1$.

c) It is assumed that there is a rapid equilibrium between inducer and repressor, whether the repressor is free or bound to operator. Thus,

$$R + I \rightleftharpoons RI \quad \text{with} \quad (R)(I) = K(RI)$$

and

$$DR + I \rightleftharpoons DRI \quad \text{with} \quad (DR)(I) = K(DRI)$$

d) Equilibrium is reached more slowly between operator and repressor with

$$DR \underset{k_{-s}}{\overset{k_s}{\rightleftharpoons}} D + R \text{ and at equilibrium } \frac{(D)(R)}{(DR)} = K_0$$

and

$$DRI \underset{k_{-f}}{\overset{k_f}{\rightleftharpoons}} D + RI \text{ and at equilibrium } \frac{(D)(RI)}{(DRI)} = \tilde{K}_0$$

It is assumed that $k_{-s} = k_{-f} \equiv k_b$.

e) When $I = O$, $R = R_0$ and r_B (basal rate) $= 1/1 + R_0/K_0 \cong K_0/R_0$. In the presence of inducer, the ultimate rate of synthesis, r_E is expressed by $r_E = 1/1 + R/K_0$.

A measure for the lag on induction can be found in how quickly $r_E(=D)$ approaches its ultimate value. Following addition of inducer, the change in fraction of operators which are free is given by

(1) $$\frac{dD}{dt} = k_s(DR) + k_f(DRI) - [k_b(D)(R) + k_b(D)(RI)]$$

This differs from the rate expression used by Gilbert and Müller-Hill by the inclusion of the terms involving D, which account for the re-association of operator with repressor.

Upon substitution for DR and DRI from (b) and (c) one has

(2) $$\frac{dD}{dt} = k_s(1-D)\frac{R}{R_0} + k_f\frac{I}{K}(1-D)\frac{R}{R_0} - k_b R_0 D$$

Then using (c) and (e) one can replace I and R in terms of the ultimate rate of synthesis r_E and R_0 in terms of r_B.

(3) $$\frac{dD}{dt} = k_s\frac{r_B - r_B r_E}{r_B} + k_f\frac{r_E - r_B + r_B r_E}{r_E}$$

$$-D\left[k_s\frac{r_B - r_B r_E}{r_B} + k_f\frac{r_E - r_B + r_B r_E}{r_E} + k_b\frac{K_0}{r_B}\right]$$

This is the form

(4) $$\frac{dD}{dt} = M - D(M + Q)$$

with r_E being given by the value of D when $dD/dt = 0$ or

(5) $$r_E = \frac{M}{M + Q}$$

One measure of the lag in question is the time (T) required for r to reach $1 - e^{-1}$ of its ultimate value. From (4)

(6)
$$T = \frac{1}{M + Q} = \frac{r_E}{M}$$

Since from (5) $M = r_E Q / 1 - r_E$, one has

(7)
$$T = \frac{r_B}{k_b K_0} (1 - r_E)$$

The expression derived above makes explicit predictions concerning the variation of lag time with r_E, assuming that the interaction of inducer with repressor-operator complex is the rate-limiting step. It can be seen from the expression for T that a sharp increase is expected initially as one goes to values of r_E below its maximum value. Further decreases in r_E should have relatively little effect on the lag time since the function approaches a constant value for $r_E \ll 1$.

Thus, the lag should remain unchanged as r_E falls further toward r_B. Therefore, processes other than the interaction of inducer with the repressor-operator complex would be revealed if they become rate-limiting at low rates of synthesis, provided, of course, that they require more than the four minutes of lag time seen at the maximum rate of synthesis.

LAG ON INDUCTION

The kinetics of induction were measured in the standard way. An appropriate concentration of inducer (IPTG) was added to an exponentially growing culture of an *E. coli* strain lacking the β-galactoside permease. Samples were then removed periodically for measurement of bacterial density and β-galactosidase activity. It is well documented that approximately four minutes are required to reach the steady state rate of β-galactosidase synthesis following addition of a concentration of IPTG leading to the maximum rate of synthesis. Our results in this concentration range gave the expected lag and are not presented here. As the concentration of inducer was lowered, the expected sharp decrease in ultimate rate of synthesis was observed, but the lag time was essentially unchanged in agreement with one of the earlier reports (Pardee and Prestidge, 1961). Furthermore, we have gone to extremely low concentrations of inducer; and even at the lowest rates of enzyme synthesis studied, corresponding to less than twice the basal rate, the lag remains about four minutes, as can be seen in Fig. 1 and 2 where results for two strains (including the ML 3 strain used by Boezie and Cowie) are presented.

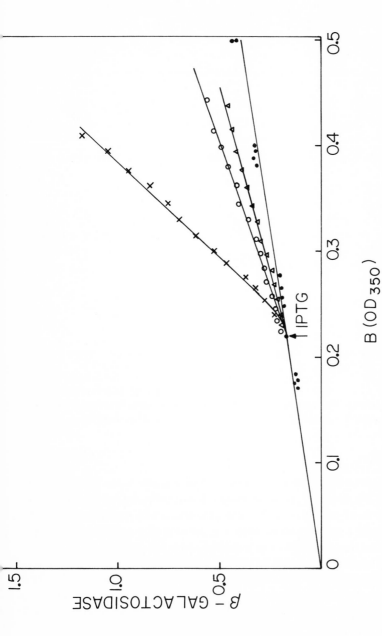

FIGURE 1. Strain ML-3, an *E. coli* prototroph lacking the *β*-galactoside permease, was grown for at least ten doublings in a glycerol-salts medium (Sadler & Novick 1965) at 37°C in a rotary shaker. The culture was split into four parts and, at the point indicated by the arrow, IPTG was added to a final concentration of 8×10^{-6}M (Δ-Δ-Δ), 10^{-5}M (0-0-0), or 2×10^{-5}M (X-X-X). The observed *β*-galactosidase per ml is plotted as a function of bacterial growth (measured as OD_{350}) for each sample. The basal rate of *β*-galactosidase synthesis is given by (●-●-●).

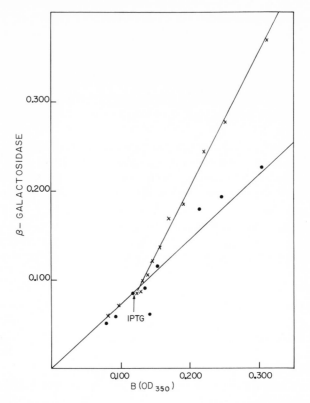

FIGURE 2. Strain 2241, an *E. coli* prototroph lacking the β-galactoside permease was grown for at least ten doublings in a glycerol-salts medium (Sadler & Novick 1965) at 37°C in a rotary shaker. The culture was split in half and at the point indicated by the arrow, IPTG was added to one flask at a final concentration of 10^{-5}M (X-X-X). The observed β-galactosidase per ml is plotted as a function of bacterial growth (measured as OD_{350}) for each sample. The basal rate of β-galactosidase synthesis is given by (●—●—●).

DISCUSSION

It is apparent from the measurement of lag times reported here that no very slow process, such as might have been expected for subunit assembly, is evident. Thus, the rate of assembly of β-galactosidase subunits is quite fast even when they are present at a concentration corresponding to the products of one mRNA molecule per cell.

Regulatory proteins, such as the *lac* repressor, are also present at very low concentrations in the cell (Müller-Hill, Crapo, and Gilbert, 1968). If one assumes that the results obtained for β-galactosidase are applicable to other subunit proteins as well, one may conclude that their rate of assembly is, likewise, quite rapid under in vivo conditions.

It might be argued that our conclusions should be qualified by the fact that β-galactosidase was determined directly in toluenized bacteria in the experiments reported in Fig. 1 and 2. Although toluenization destroys the bacterial permeability barrier, most β-galactosidase remains within the bacteria (unpublished experiments by us and others). Polymerization of enzyme subunits might occur in the toluenized bacteria during the assay for enzyme. Since between ten and twenty hours are required to assay the low levels of activity being studied here, an increase in polymerization time of up to thirty or forty minutes might go unnoticed in the experiments reported above. To test this point, we have repeated the present studies using sonication to liberate the enzyme from the bacteria. In this case, polymerization would be effectively stopped by dilution. Again, we find no increase in lag at the lowest rates of synthesis.

It can be concluded that assembly of protein subunits is a very rapid process even at the lowest concentration at which the subunits could *ever* occur in a bacterium (i.e., that resulting from the products of one mRNA molecule per cell.)

Since this was submitted for publication, it has been called to our attention that similar results, both theoretical and experimental, were reported by E. W. Branscombe and R. N. Stuart in Biochemical Biophysical Research Communication, *32:* 731 (1968).

ACKNOWLEDGMENTS

This work was supported by grants from the NIH 872-1 P01 GM 15423-03 and the NSF 1068 GB 5679. The authors are grateful for the technical assistance of Pam Riley.

L. A. is the recipient of a Stipend from a Public Health Service Training Grant No. 5T01GM00715-11.

C. G. is the recipient of a Public Health Service Postdoctoral Research Grant No. 1F02GM43987-01.

REFERENCES

BOEZIE, J. A. and D. B. COWIE. 1961. Kinetic studies of β-galactosidase induction. Biophys. J. *1:* 639.

GILBERT, W. and B. MÜLLER-HILL. 1967. The lac operator is DNA. Proc. Nat. Acad. Sci. *58:* 2415.

MÜLLER-HILL, B., L. CRAPO, and W. GILBERT. 1968. Mutants that make more lac repressor. Proc. Nat. Acad. Sci. *59:* 1259.

PARDEE, A. and L. PRESTIDGE. 1961. The initial kinetics of enzyme induction. Biochim. Biophys. Acta *49:* 77.

SADLER, J. R. and A. NOVICK. 1965. The properties of repressor and the kinetics of its action. J. Mol. Biol. *12:* 305.

Superrepressors of the *lac* Operon

SUZANNE BOURGEOIS and ALAN JOBE

The Salk Institute for Biological Studies
San Diego, California
and University of California
San Diego Medical School

INTRODUCTION

Two superrepressed (i^s) mutants of the *lac* operon have been described so far (Willson, Perrin, Cohn, Jacob and Monod, 1964). They behave as noninducible mutants whose *lac* negative phenotype is dominant over the wild-type inducible one. Their dominance characteristics as well as their reversion pattern to the *lac* positive constitutive phenotype were interpreted as the result of a mutation in the regulatory gene *i* inactivating the inducer recognition site of the repressor (R) but leaving the operator (O) binding site intact. The discovery of i^s mutations has been the crucial genetic argument that the *i* gene product, R, recognizes the inducers directly and specifically, making it very likely, therefore, that R is a regulatory protein.

We have isolated a family of *lac* negative mutants which behave like i^s in all dominance tests and in their reversion pattern. However, we found that most of these new mutants, although noninducible by lactose, still respond to other *lac* inducers but at concentrations higher than those required by the wild type: they range in their induction capacity from nondetectably inducible, to different levels of partial inducibility, to almost normal inducibility by IPTG. They seemed to represent, therefore, inducer affinity mutants of R.

The i^s mutations could also, however, have increased the affinity of R for O and/or have altered the allosteric properties of R in such a way that, although having retained inducer binding capacity, the inducers could no longer catalyze the release of R from O. In vivo studies could not distinguish between these different possibilities.

Thanks to the pioneer work of Gilbert and Müller-Hill (1966, 1967) and

325

$K = \frac{kd}{kf}$

to convenient techniques developed in our laboratory (Riggs and Bourgeois, 1968; Riggs, Bourgeois, Newby and Cohn, 1968), the wild-type *lac* repressor became amenable to in vitro studies. It is a protein of M. W. $\sim$ 150,000 (Gilbert and Müller-Hill, 1966; Riggs and Bourgeois, 1968) having distinct sites for binding IPTG and operator. It is made up of four subunits of M. W. $\sim$ 38,000 which have been isolated in a form still able to bind IPTG but not O (Riggs, Suzuki and Bourgeois, 1970). Its affinity for the operator is very high with a dissociation constant of the order of 10^{-13}M (Gilbert and Müller-Hill, 1967; Riggs, Suzuki and Bourgeois, 1970). This very tight binding was confirmed by measuring the rate constants for RO association and dissociation (Riggs and Bourgeois, 1969; Riggs, Bourgeois and Cohn, in preparation). The association of R with O is a very fast process indeed, having a rate constant $k_f = 4$ to 8×10^9 M^{-1} sec^{-1}, while the dissociation of RO is slow and proceeds with a rate constant $k_b = 4$ to 6×10^{-4} sec^{-1}. The mechanism of inducer action was elucidated (Riggs and Bourgeois, 1969; Riggs, Newby and Bourgeois, in press) by showing that inducer interacts directly with the RO complex and catalyses its dissociation. These results have been recently summarized and discussed (Bourgeois and Monod, 1970).

There is obviously much to be learned from the in vitro study of repressor proteins altered by mutations. An i^t mutant was isolated by Gilbert and Müller-Hill (1966) who showed in vitro that its repressor had a binding constant (K_m) for IPTG of $\sim 6 \times 10^{-7}$ M differing by a factor of 2 from the $K_m = 1.3 \times 10^{-6}$ M measured for the wild-type repressor. On the other hand, the two i^s repressors which have been examined so far in vitro (Gilbert and Müller-Hill, 1966; Riggs and Bourgeois, 1968) did not show any detectable IPTG binding activity when tested by equilibrium dialysis or by antiserum assay.

We have developed new in vitro techniques which have allowed us to study the properties of the altered repressors, or superrepressors (R^s), of the family of i^s mutants we have isolated. We were able to examine directly their affinity for inducers and for the operator, as well as the interaction of IPTG with the different R^{s}O complexes.

EXPERIMENTAL RESULTS

IN VIVO STUDY

ISOLATION OF i^s MUTANTS

Strains C6000 or 2000 m (obtained from F. Jacob), made diploid for the wild-type *lac* operon by introduction of an F'*lac* episome, were used as parental strains.

After mutagenesis by U.V. irradiation or N-methyl-N'-nitro-N-nitro-soguanidine treatment (Adelberg, Mandel and Chein Ching Chem, 1965) the cells were grown for a few divisions in nutrient broth then plated on indicator plates containing lactose. Either one of the classical indicator media, "Eosine-Methylene Blue", "Mac Conkey Agar", or "Triphenyltetra-zolium" were used. After incubation *lac* negative colonies were picked up and reisolated on lactose indicator plates. The mutants so obtained segregate *lac*+ bacteria at very high frequency due to recombinations between the *lac* regions of the chromosome and of the episome. They were streaked out and reisolated until their *lac* phenotype was stable.

This diploid *lac* genome of the parental strain does quite efficiently screen against the recessive (z^- or y^-) *lac* negative mutations which have occurred. However, some recessive *lac*- mutants did show up as homo-genotes and had to be discarded. So were a great number of *lac*- strains carrying mutations outside of the *lac* region and resulting in the pleiotropic loss of the capacity to utilize a great many sugars, including glucose.

Eight new i^s mutants were obtained, six after U.V. irradiation and two resulting from nitrosoguanidine treatment.

INDUCTION SPECTRUM OF i^s MUTANTS

Selected to be poorly or not induced in the presence of lactose the i^s mutants obtained were tested for their capacity to be induced by different sugars known to be inducers of the wild-type *lac*+ strains. Their induction characteristics, compared to those of the wild type and of the strains i^s_{Y18} and i^s_{YA694} previously isolated (Willson, Perrin, Cohn, Jacob and Monod, 1964) are summarized in Table 1.

All mutants show, within a factor of two, the same basal level of β-galactosidase in the absence of inducer as the wild type. They range in inducibility from a normal response to 10^{-3} M IPTG to a total incapacity to be induced even by 10^{-1} M IPTG. Their deficiency in induction shows up clearly in all the strains, however, when inducers less active than IPTG are used. The inducers of the wild type, i^+, can be arranged into an unambiguous heirarchical order from the best one, IPTG, to the poorest one, melibiose. The family of i^s mutants can be ordered in a parallel fashion, in that any one unable to be induced by a galactoside high on the list is also non-inducible by all galactosides lower on the list. The fact that the i^s mutants can be arranged, without exception, in the hierarchy, predicted by the order of inducibility of the wild type proves that this protein recognizes the inducer.

We have checked that, as expected from regulatory mutations, their effect is pleiotropic in that the characteristic induction pattern for β-galactosidase also extends to the β-galactoside permease and thiogalac-toside transacetylase.

Table 1. Induction spectrum of i^s mutants

i gene	No inducer	IPTG 10^{-1}M	IPTG 10^{-3}M	nPTG 10^{-3}M	TMG 10^{-3}M	BuTG 10^{-3}M	GTG 10^{-3}M	GTG 10^{-4}M	GTG 10^{-5}M	βMG 10^{-3}M	lac 10^{-3}M	Mel 10^{-3}M
i^+	3	—	4120	5500	4420	4150	3910	3740	2670	845	695	715
i^s 44	3	—	3670	3070	2780	3020	—	201	—	114	230	2
i^s 2A	3	—	3840	3320	2040	1410	—	283	—	77	89	3
i^s 16Z	2	—	3690	2840	3060	610	—	400	—	37	13	2
i^s 14A	3	—	4390	3140	2830	500	—	372	—	28	17	2
i^s N2	5	2780	18	10	6	3	4	3	—	7	4	6
i^s 43	3	1010	3	3	3	3	3	2	—	4	3	3
i^s Y18	3	162	4	4	6	3	3	3	—	6	11	5
i^s YA694	3	150	3	3	3	<1	—	—	—	2	3	3
i^s 45	3	8	6	3	3	2	3	3	—	3	2	2
i^s N1	5	2	2	2	6	2	2	2	—	5	5	5

β-galactosidase activity (units/mgr bacteria) of i^+ and i^s strains grown exponentially in minimum medium containing glycerol (2 gr/L) as a carbon source and inducers as indicated in the table. β-galactosidase assay and units are described elsewhere (Willson, Perrin, Cohn, Jacob and Monod, 1964).

DOMINANCE CHARACTERISTICS OF i^s MUTANTS

The behavior of all these i^s mutations in the presence of the alleles i^+, i^-, and o^c was analyzed quantitatively in diploid strains obtained either by transfer of the episomes carrying the i^s mutation into the proper recipients or, after curing the diploid i^s homogenotes from their episome by treatment with acridine orange (Hirota, 1960), by using the resulting haploids as recipients for F'*lac* episomes of known genotype.

Table 2 summarizes the results obtained in the case of i^s_{43} as an example to illustrate dominance characteristics which turned out to be the same for all i^s mutants. Complete dominance data have been presented elsewhere (Bourgeois, 1966).

Table 2, line 3, shows the dominance of i^s over the wild-type allele i^+. This dominance is not absolute since the $i^s/F'i^+$ strain is more inducible than the $i^s/F'i^s$ one. This seems best explained by intracistronic complementation between the products of the i^s and the i^+ gene alleles leading to hybrid repressor molecules made of i^s and i^+ repressor subunits. The same partial dominance was observed in a rec$^-i^s/F'i^+$ diploid, ruling out that it might be due to the presence of $i^+/F'i^+$ homogenotes in the population.

The dominance of i^s over i^-, illustrated in line 6, is not complete either, the diploid $i^s/F'i^-$ being partially constitutive. Partial dominance could result either from intracistronic complementation or from an operator gene dosage effect since, in this case, 2 or 3 operators must be turned off by the amount of repressor produced by only one i^s gene.

Although we did not find total dominance of i^s over i^+ or i^- as described by Willson, Perrin, Cohn, Jacob and Monod (1964) in the case of i^s_{Y18},

Table 2. Dominance characteristics of i^s_{43}

Genotype	No inducer	IPTG 10⁻⁴M	IPTG 10⁻³M	BuTG 10⁻³M
1 $i^s/F'i^s$	5	—	5	4
2 $i^+/F'i^+$	4	—	11200	—
3 $i^s/F'i^+$	5	—	641	133
4 *lac* deletion$/F'i^-_3$	8110	7350	—	—
5 $i^+/F'i^-_3$	675	7220	—	—
6 $i^s/F'i^-_3$	615	668	—	—
7 $i^+o^+/F'i^+o^c$	1180	—	10900	—
8 $i^so^+/F'i^+o^c$	1970	—	7200	3400

β-galactosidase activity (units/mgr bacteria) of diploid strains measured as described in the legend of Table 1.

our results are qualitatively similar in showing partial dominance of the superrepressors.

As shown in line 8, the o^c allele is expressed in the presence of an i^s gene. The i^s repressor must, like the wild-type repressor, have a decreased affinity for an o^c operator resulting in a higher inducibility of the $i^s o^+ / F' i^+ o^c$ than of the $i^s o^+ / F' i^+ o^+$ (line 3) strain, in agreement with the observation (Willson, Perrin, Cohn, Jacob and Monod, 1964) that lower concentrations of inducer are required to induce $i^+ o^c$ mutants than are required by the wild type.

REVERSION OF i^s MUTANTS TO THE lac^+ PHENOTYPE

As it has been observed previously in the case of i^s_{Y18} (Willson, Perrin, Cohn, Jacob and Monod, 1964), all the i^s mutants isolated in this study, when reverting to a lac^+ phenotype give rise predominantly to constitutive strains either i^- or o^c, rather than to true inducible i^+ revertants. This is certainly one of the typical and expected features of i^s mutations that their effect be abolished by superimposing upon them either an i^- mutation which inactivates the superrepressor or an o^c mutation which makes the superrepressor inefficient by weakening its binding to the operator. This pattern of reversion argues strongly that R recognizes O itself or possibly its RNA product.

A large number of i^- and o^c constitutive mutants derived from i^s_{43} has been isolated and studied in further detail.

Of 1100 lac^+ phenotypic revertants of i^s_{43}, 975 were $i^s i^-$ and only 125, or about 13%, were $i^s o^c$.

The $i^s i^-$ double mutants turned out to be an excellent tool which allowed us to show (Bourgeois, Cohn and Orgel, 1965), suppression of i^- mutations by suppressors of chain terminating mutations as well as the polymeric nature of the repressor. Suppression of such i^- mutations restore the i^s lac negative dominant phenotype, demonstrating that the repressor is a protein whose properties can be affected by either i^s or i^- mutations.

Out of the 975 $i^s i^-$ mutants tested for suppressibility only 24 were suppressed, but this must be taken as a minimum figure since weak suppressibility could have been missed upon scoring on triphenyltetrazolium plates for the restored i^s phenotype in su^+ strains.

These $i^s i^-$ double mutations, carried by an episome, could be transferred into strains carrying the different amber or ochre su^+ genes whose mode of action had been precisely elucidated (Capecchi and Gussin, 1965; Brenner, Stretton and Kaplan, 1965; Weigert and Garen, 1965). This provides us today with a family of strains in which we can, at will, substitute in the same position of the superrepressor protein either a serine, a glutamine or a tyrosine residue by suppressing them by su^+_1, su^+_2, or su^+_3, respectively, and this might be of some use in the detailed in vitro study of repressor structure and properties.

Two non-suppressible $i^s i^-$ mutants showed clear complementation with the product of an i^+ gene, the resulting $(i^s i^-)$ (i^+) hybrid repressor manifesting itself by the superrepressibility of the $i^+/F'i^s i^-$ diploids (Bourgeois, Cohn and Orgel, 1965). The very low frequency (2/975) of i^- missense mutations able to be complemented by i^+ is a strong argument that the i gene has only one cistron and, therefore, that the repressor subunits (Riggs and Bourgeois, 1968; Riggs, Suzuki and Bourgeois, 1970) are identical.

Of the total of 670 $i^s o^c$ double mutants tested, none could be suppressed, an argument, negative as it is, in favor of the idea that the operator region is not translated, at least into a biologically active protein.

IN VITRO STUDY

IPTG BINDING BY SUPERREPRESSORS

Since the superrepressors are expected to show a low affinity for IPTG, a new technique was worked out which is more sensitive than equilibrium dialysis for the testing of binding over a wide range of IPTG concentrations in the presence of small amounts of repressor. Its principle consists in precipitating with ammonium sulfate the proteins of a bacterial extract containing repressor and ^{14}C-labeled IPTG. Bound ligand is specifically retained in the precipitate even after the washing necessary to eliminate the excess of free labeled IPTG and lower the background.

A Scatchard plot of the results obtained by this technique in the case of a wild-type repressor is shown in Fig. 1.

The apparent association constant for IPTG measured by ammonium sulfate precipitation is 10^7 M or about ten times higher than the value of $\sim 1 \times 10^6$ M observed by equilibrium dialysis (Gilbert and Müller-Hill, 1966; Riggs and Bourgeois, 1968), a feature of the ammonium sulfate technique favoring the detection of low affinity binding. The data from both the ammonium sulfate experiment and equilibrium dialysis extrapolate to intercept the abcissa at the same value of 4.7 for the maximum number of IPTG/0 binding sites.

The K_{diss} for IPTG obtained for the superrepressors are listed in Table 3 (column 2). All superrepressors show a decreased binding affinity for IPTG which could be measured quantitatively in the case of $i^s 44$, $i^s 2A$, $i^s 16Z$ and $i^s 14A$. However, binding constants lower than 5×10^4 M could not be estimated quantitatively in crude preparations where repressor concentration is of the order of 10^{-7} M.

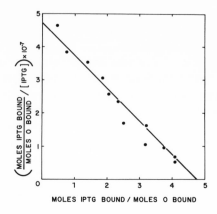

y-axis: $\left(\dfrac{\text{MOLES IPTG BOUND}}{\text{MOLES O BOUND}} \middle/ [\text{IPTG}]\right) \times 10^{-7}$

x-axis: MOLES IPTG BOUND / MOLES O BOUND

FIGURE 1. IPTG binding by i^+ repressor extract using the ammonium sulfate technique. 50 μl of an extract of C_{6000} $i^+/F'i^+$, fractionated as described in Table 3, were added to increasing amounts of ^{14}C-IPTG (Cal Biochem-25mc/m mole) in the presence and the absence of 1×10^{-3} M unlabeled IPTG, and brought to 50% saturation of ammonium sulfate. The resulting precipitate is centrifuged and washed twice with a 50% saturated ammonium sulfate solution containing no IPTG. The precipitate is dissolved in 0.01 M KOH and counted. The samples containing both labeled and unlabeled IPTG represent the nonspecific background which has been subtracted. The moles of $\lambda\phi80$ *dlac* DNA bound by this extract were measured in a separate experiment of the type described in Fig. 2.

Table 3. In Vitro Characteristics of Superrepressors

i gene	K_d for IPTG of free R	$t_{1/2}$ of RO in minutes	K_d for IPTG of RO complexes
i^+	1×10^{-7}M	45	1.7×10^{-6}M
i^s44	3×10^{-7}M	33	2.7×10^{-6}M
i^s2A	4.3×10^{-7}M	35	1.8×10^{-6}M
i^s16Z	8×10^{-7}M	43	1.9×10^{-5}M
i^s14A	9×10^{-7}M	42	1.8×10^{-5}M
i^sN2	$>5 \times 10^{-4}$M	50	2.3×10^{-3}M
i^s43	$>5 \times 10^{-4}$M	38	2.2×10^{-3}M
i^sY18	$>5 \times 10^{-4}$M	50	6×10^{-3}M
i^s45	$>5 \times 10^{-4}$M	43	1×10^{-4}M
i^sN1	$>5 \times 10^{-4}$M	105	1×10^{-1}M

All strains are diploid $i^s/F'i^s$ homogenotes derived from strain $C_{6000}i^+/F'i^+$ as described in the text.

For all in vitro experiments, bacteria were grown in a medium containing 1.1% K_2HPO_4, 0.85% KH_2PO_4, 0.6% Difco yeast extract, and 1% glucose. They were suspended in 0.2 M Tris, 0.01 M magnesium acetate, 0.0001 M EDTA, 0.006 M mercaptoethanol at pH 7.4 and treated in a French press. The resulting extract was centrifuged and the supernatant was fractionated by ammonium sulfate as described before (Riggs and Bourgeois, 1968). The fraction precipitating between 23 and 35% saturation in ammonium sulfate was redissolved in 0.01 M Tris, 0.01 M magnesium acetate, 0.0001 M EDTA, 0.006 M mercaptoethanol, and 0.2 M KCl at pH 7.4 and assayed as described in the text and the legends of the figures.

Superrepressors of the lac Operon **333**

OPERATOR BINDING BY SUPERREPRESSORS

The weak or undetectable binding of IPTG by the different superrepressors would make their purification difficult to follow. We have adapted the membrane filter technique described previously (Riggs, Bourgeois, Newby and Cohn, 1968) to allow the assay of operator binding by superrepressors in crude preparations. The modification consists, essentially, in the addition to the extract of a large excess of unlabeled DNA which does not contain the *lac* region and absorbs proteins of the extract which bind DNA at non-operator regions and with low affinity. At the concentrations of unlabeled DNA used, the superrepressors themselves present at low concentration, do not bind significantly the foreign DNA. Their specific binding to ^{32}P-labeled $\lambda\phi80$ d*lac* DNA can then be measured by trapping the R^{s}O complexes on membrane filters in the usual way.

Although the background counts of ^{32}P-$\lambda\phi80$ d*lac* DNA retained non-specifically on the filter are fairly high and increase linearly with the amount of extract used, specific binding of R to O can easily be detected. Figure 2 illustrates the binding curve obtained. The amount of labeled RO retained on the filter is plotted against an increasing amount of a crude preparation of wild-type repressor.

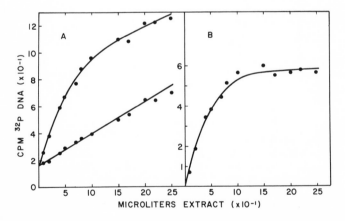

FIGURE 2. DNA binding curve of i^+ repressor extract. The i^+ extract is prepared as described in Table 3. It is diluted to an OD$_{280}$ of about 0.4 in binding buffer, BB, (Riggs, Suzuki and Bourgeois, 1970) containing 25 μg/ml BSA. The abscissa indicates the amount of this diluted extract added per 3.2 ml of total reaction mixture, containing 0.08 μg/ml ^{32}P-$\lambda\phi80$ d*lac* DNA and 140 μg/ml unlabeled DNA from *E. coli* strain 2000 × 74m that is deleted for the entire *lac* region. Each point is the average CPM retained by filtering a 1 ml aliquot of the reaction mixture in triplicate on 25 mm Schleicher and Schuell B6 filters. The background is determined at each point in the presence of 1.5×10^{-3} M IPTG; the lower part of curve A is background, and the upper part is total counts. B represents the data with background subtracted.

Binding curves comparable to the one observed for wild type were obtained when extracts of all i^s mutants were prepared and tested similarly, indicating that all the superrepressor preparations contained about the same operator binding activity with respect to OD_{280} as does the wild type. No attempt was made to determine an accurate DNA binding constant for the mutants because of the difficulties involved (Riggs, Suzuki and Bourgeois, 1970).

However, quantitative estimates of the affinity of the different R^s for O can be obtained by measuring the half-life of each of the R^sO complexes by using the membrane filter technique to follow the *rate* of dissociation of R^sO in the presence of an excess of competing unlabeled $\lambda\phi80$ *dlac*

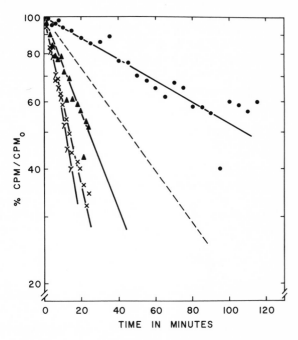

FIGURE 3. Rate of dissociation of RO and R^sO complexes. Extract of C_{6000} $i^sN1/F'i^sN1$ is added so as to just saturate 10^{-12} M ^{32}P-$\lambda\phi80$ *dlac* DNA in BB containing 7 μg/ml of unlabeled "chicken blood" DNA (Cal Biochem.). At time zero, 2 μg/ml of a mixture of unlabeled $\lambda\phi80$ and $\lambda\phi80$ *dlac* DNA is added, corresponding to a 25-fold excess of unlabeled *dlac* DNA. Aliquots of 1 ml are filtered in duplicate at various times. The results are expressed as percent of RO present at time zero.

(– – – –) A previously determined curve for C_{6000} $i^+/F'i^+$ extract
(-●-●-) i^sN1 repressor extract
(▲-▲) i^sN1 repressor extract + 10^{-3} M IPTG
(-x-x-) i^sN1 repressor extract + 10^{-2} M IPTG
(-y-y-) i^sN1 repressor extract + 10^{-1} M IPTG

DNA. This technique, which has allowed us to study the kinetics of the interaction of purified wild-type R with O (Riggs and Bourgeois, 1969; Riggs, Bourgeois and Cohn, in preparation) has only to be modified as mentioned above to be applicable in crude repressor preparations. The value for the rate of dissociation of the R^sO complexes will be a measure of the affinity of the different R^s for O if we make the assumption that their *rate of association* with O is for all of them the same as for the wild-type R. This assumption is very likely since we know (Riggs and Bourgeois, 1969; Riggs, Bourgeois and Cohn, in preparation) that the association of R with O is extremely fast and diffusion limited with a rate constant of $k_f = 4$ to 8×10^9 M^{-1} sec^{-1}.

The values obtained for the half-life of the R^sO complexes compared to the half-life of the RO complex measured in the same conditions are summarized in Table 3 (column 3).

Most R^sO complexes appear to have approximately the same stability as RO, within experimental errors, except for i^s_{N1} which (assuming k_f is the same) has a higher binding affinity for the operator than the wild-type repressor. The data obtained for i^s_{N1} and the details of the method can be seen in Fig. 3.

INTERACTION OF IPTG WITH THE R^sO COMPLEXES

The superrepressors have thus far been characterized as to their affinity for IPTG and for O. Yet we know that IPTG not only binds to free R but also interacts directly with the RO complex (Riggs and Bourgeois, 1969; Riggs, Newby and Bourgeois, in press). The following experiments characterize this interaction in the case of the i^s mutants either by determining the amount of R^sO formed at equilibrium in the presence of increasing concentrations of IPTG or by measuring the effect of IPTG on the *rate* of dissociation of the R^sO complexes.

Table 3 (column 4) shows the concentrations of IPTG required to inhibit 50% the formation of the different R^sO complexes. Release curves for RO and R^sO are illustrated in Fig. 4.

All superrepressors, except those from i^s_{45} and i^s_{N1}, show release curves parallel to the one obtained for wild-type R, only displaced to higher IPTG concentrations. An example of such a case is illustrated in Figure 4 by the curve obtained for R^s_{43}. However, release curves for the R^sO complexes formed by R^s_{45} and R^s_{N1} have different slopes from that of the wild-type RO.

Direct interaction of IPTG with $R^s_{45}O$ and $R^s_{N1}O$ can be shown by its effect on the rate of dissociation of these complexes. As can be seen in Fig. 3, the half-life of the $R^s_{N1}O$ complex decreases from 105 minutes to 24 minutes by addition of 10^{-3} M IPTG. The same concentration of IPTG brings the half-life of $R^s_{45}O$ from 45 minutes to 5 minutes.

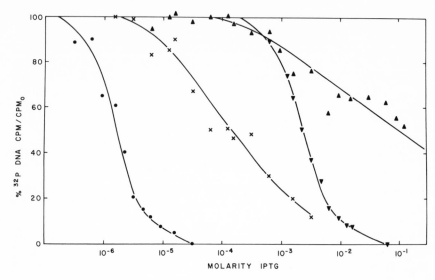

FIGURE 4. Effect of IPTG on the R-O binding equilibrium. Repressor, $^{32}P\text{-}\lambda\phi80$ d*lac* DNA, and unlabeled "chicken blood" DNA concentrations are the same as described under Fig. 3. The binding of R to O is allowed to occur in the presence of varying amounts of IPTG. The points are the average of triplicate filtrations of 1 ml aliquots at each IPTG concentration. The data has been normalized; 100 represents the amount of RO complex in the absence of IPTG, and zero is an endpoint determined in the presence of excess unlabeled O and high IPTG concentrations.

(–•–•–) i^+ repressor extract
(–x–x–) i^s45 Repressor extract
(–▼–▼–) i^s43 repressor extract
(▲–▲) i^sN1 repressor extract

CONCLUSIONS AND DISCUSSION

We have been analyzing the in vivo and in vitro behavior of a series of superrepressed (i^s) mutants. The parallelism between these two systems gives confidence that the in vitro situation accurately reflects the in vivo one.

The in vivo study has led to the following conclusions:

1. *The product of the* i *gene locus is a regulatory protein* (R) which recognizes both the inducer and the operator.
2. *The* i *gene locus is a single cistron* showing intracistronic complementation, implying that its product, R, is a polymer of identical subunits.
3. *The* o *gene is probably not translated* into biologically active protein.

The in vitro study has extended these conclusions in the following way:

1. R HAS FOUR IDENTICAL AND INDEPENDENT I BINDING SITES FOR EACH O BINDING SITE.

Since it is known (Riggs and Bourgeois, 1968; Riggs, Suzuki and Bourgeois, 1970) that the O binding activity of purified R decays rapidly compared to its I binding activity and that this differential decay can be accompanied by the dissociation of R into subunits, it was important to examine the binding properties of unpurified wild-type R. This became possible thanks to new techniques allowing to assay for I as well as O binding properties in the crude extract, the closest we could come to intact cells. This analysis gives rise to a clearly linear Scatchard plot (Fig. 1), extrapolating to 4.7 I binding sites per O binding site. A small loss ($\sim$10%) of O binding activity, relative to I binding activity, is likely to be responsible for the ratio being slightly higher than 4.0. This result implies that the *i* gene product, R, is present in the cell in the active tetrameric form with four I binding per one O binding site.

The association constant of each I site is 10^7, apparently identical for each subunit in the tetramer. While this result argues also that the subunits are identical, it is surprising that no cooperativity in I binding is observed. However, it should be stressed that induction occurs at the level of the RO complex, not free R, so that it is in the I-RO interaction that cooperativity should be sought.

Whereas equilibrium dialysis gives an association constant for the RI complex of 10^6, the ammonium sulfate technique used here gives a value of 10^7, an order of magnitude higher. Possibly high salt or the insoluble state of R is responsible for this useful artifact. In any case, the value of 10^6 is more likely to be close to the in vivo situation.

2. i^s MUTATIONS ALTER THE AFFINITY OF R FOR ITS LIGANDS.

The affinity of the wild type and i^s mutant R for its ligands, I and O, has been measured, the former directly using the ammonium sulfate technique, and the latter by the half-life of the different RO complexes.

Eight of the nine i^s mutants have a repressor with an affinity for I lower than wild type while their O binding affinity is unaltered. This differential alteration of I and O binding properties as a result of mutation confirms that the I and O sites are distinct and non-overlapping, as already indicated by their differential decay in vitro.

The ninth mutant repressor (i^s_{N1}) has, in addition to a lowered affinity for I, an increased affinity for O with a half life for the RO complex of 105 minutes as compared to 45 minutes for the wild type. Interestingly enough, the value of 105 minutes is also observed for the half life of the wild-type RO complex in the presence of the anti-inducer ONPF measured in the same conditions (Jobe, Riggs and Bourgeois, in preparation). The altered repressor of i^s_{N1}, which has minimal affinity for I and maximal affinity for O, results in vivo in a completely uninducible phenotype. However, besides altered binding properties, the i^s_{N1} repressor also shows altered allosteric properties which we shall now describe before trying to give a possible interpretation of the i^s_{N1} mutation at the molecular level.

3. i^s MUTATIONS CAN ALTER THE ALLOSTERIC PROPERTIES OF R.

Since the I and O binding sites of R are distinct and nonoverlapping, the effect of I on the binding of O clearly matches the definition of an allosteric interaction (Monod, Changeux and Jacob, 1963), whatever detailed model one wants to propose for it. The mechanism of this effect in the particular case of the wild-type *lac* R has been elucidated by showing that I interacts directly with the RO complex, accelerating its dissociation (Riggs and Bourgeois, 1969; Riggs, Newby and Bourgeois, in press). The inducer appears to act, at least in part, as a *catalyst* in the transition of R from the bound to the free state. This mechanism, so far unique for allosteric proteins, has been discussed elsewhere (Bourgeois and Monod, 1970).

One can extend the Monod, Wyman, Changeux (1965) model by postulating the following equilibria which describe the reactions we observe in this case.

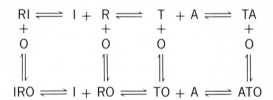

I is an inducer such as IPTG and A an anti-inducer such as ONPF. The R and T forms would have the following properties:

AFFINITY OF BINDING SITES FOR

	I	A	O
R	maximum	minimum	minimum
T	minimum	maximum	maximum

According to the allosteric model (Monod, Wyman and Changeux, 1965), several constants determine the apparent affinity of the repressor for IPTG, the intrinsic dissociation constants of the R and T forms for their ligands and the allosteric constant (L) governing the equilibrium between R and T. The i^s mutants could have altered repressors in which either or both these constants are affected, i.e. they could be simple affinity mutants unchanged in their allosteric properties or allosteric mutants in which the constant L is changed.

As expected, some i^s mutations appear to alter the allosteric properties of R quite independently of its binding properties. As a measure of this effect, let us consider the slopes of the curves relating the amount of RO complex formed at equilibrium with IPTG concentration (Fig. 4).

Seven i^s mutants out of nine show RO equilibrium release curves parallel to the one observed for the wild-type RO complex, only displaced by several orders of magnitude to higher IPTG concentrations. Therefore, these mutations could affect either the affinity or allosteric constants.

In contrast, the repressors from two strains, i^s_{45} and i^s_{N1}, give rise to RO release slopes drastically different from wild type. Of these two, the i^s_{45} repressor has unaltered O binding affinity. The concentration of IPTG needed in vitro to reduce one half the equilibrium concentration of RO is, in the case of i^s_{45}, 1×10^{-4} M, a factor of ~ 20 lower than that required for the same effect on i^s_{N2} repressor (see Table 3). Yet, in vivo i^s_{45} is non-inducible whereas i^s_{N2} is reasonably well induced at high IPTG concentrations. This is a consequence of the flattened RO release curve resulting from the i^s_{45} mutation. On the other hand, the i^s_{N1} repressor has a maximal O binding affinity, as described in the preceding section, and might therefore be visualized as a mutation which freezes the repressor in the T conformation. If such is the case, one might predict that the i^s_{N1} repressor should have a maximal affinity for ONPF. However, the interpretation of the RO release curves at equilibrium as a function of IPTG concentration is made difficult by the fact that they reflect both the effect of IPTG on the final equilibrium and the catalytic effect of IPTG on the dissociation of the RO complex. Some i^s repressors, such as in the case of i^s_{N1}, could be modified in this latter property. Further insight into the mechanism of inducer, repressor and operator interaction would come from the demonstration of two postulated conformations of the repressor and the i^s repressors could help in the characterization of their properties.

Altogether, the hierarchical ordering of the i^s mutants in vivo is confirmed by the in vitro analysis of their repressors showing that they can be altered in their allosteric properties as well as their binding properties.

SUMMARY

A family of regulatory mutants of the *lac* operon, superrepressed to different extents, has been isolated and their dominance and reversion characteristics are described.

New techniques have been developed which allowed us to specify the properties of their altered repressor proteins or superrepressors (R^s).

All R^s have a decreased affinity for IPTG. In eight of them no change in affinity of R^s for O, as compared to the wild type, could be detected. One of them (R^s_{N1}) appears to have an affinity for O increased by about a factor of 2 over the wild-type R.

IPTG interacts with all R^sO complexes. In seven cases the interaction looks qualitatively the same as wild type, only taking place at higher IPTG concentrations. Two of the mutants (i^s_{45} and i^s_{N1}) give rise to *slopes* of the IPTG-R^sO release curves drastically different from wild type. This indicates that these i^s mutations have deeply altered the allosteric properties of the repressor protein.

ACKNOWLEDGMENTS

This work was started at the Pasteur Institute of Paris, where it was inspired by Professors Jacques Monod and François Jacob who guided its first steps. We want to thank them very gratefully. It was pursued at the Salk Institute for Biological Studies, in La Jolla, in the laboratory of Dr. Melvin Cohn whose inestimable contribution is heartily acknowledged. We also owe many thanks to Drs. Niels Kjeldgaard, Arthur Riggs and Hiromi Suzuki for the suggestions and help they generously gave us.

This work was supported by a National Science Foundation Grant, and a Department of Health, Education and Welfare Training Grant from the National Cancer Institute, to Dr. Melvin Cohn.

ABBREVIATIONS

βMG, methyl-β-D-galactoside; BSA, bovine serum albumin; BuTG, butyl-β-D-thiogalactoside; EDTA, ethylenediaminetetracetid acid; GTG, 1-O-glycerol-β-D-thiogalactoside; IPTG, isopropyl-β-D-thiogalactoside; *lac*, lactose; Mel, melibiose; nPTG, n-propyl-β-D-thiogalactoside; TMG, methyl-β-D-thiogalactoside.

REFERENCES

ADELBERG, E. A., M. MANDEL, and G. CHEIN CHING CHEM. 1965. Optimal conditions for mutagenesis by N-methyl-N'-nitro-N-nitrosoguanidine in *Escherichia coli* K$_{12}$. Biochem. Biophys. Res. Commun. *18:* 788.

BOURGEOIS, S., M. COHN, and L. E. ORGEL. 1965. Suppression of and complementation among mutants of the regulatory gene of the Lactose operon of *Escherichia coli*. J. Mol. Biol. *14:* 300.

BOURGEOIS, S. 1966. Sur la nature du répresseur de l'opéron Lactose d'*Escherichia coli*. Doctorat dissertation at the University of Paris.

BOURGEOIS, S. and J. MONOD. 1970. In vitro studies of the *lac* operon regulatory system, p. 3. *In* G. E. W. Wolstenholme and J. Knight [ed.] Ciba Symposium on Control Processes in Multicellular Organisms. J. & A. Churchill, Ltd., London.

BRENNER, S., A. O. W. STRETTON, and S. KAPLAN. 1965. Genetic code: The nonsense triplets for chain termination and their suppression. Nature *206:* 994.

CAPECCHI, M. R. and G. N. GUSSIN. 1965. Suppression *in vitro:* Identification of a serine-sRNA as a "nonsense" suppressor. Science *149:* 417.

GILBERT, W. and B. MÜLLER-HILL. 1966. Isolation of the *lac* repressor. Proc. Nat. Acad. Sci. U.S. *56:* 1891.

GILBERT, W. and B. MÜLLER-HILL. 1967. The *lac* operator is DNA. Proc. Nat. Acad. Sci. U.S. *58:* 2415.

HIROTA, Y. 1960. The effect of acridine dyes on mating type factors in *Escherichia coli*. Genetics *46:* 57.

JOBE, A., A. D. RIGGS, and S. BOURGEOIS. The *lac* repressor-operator interaction V. Characterization of superrepressors. Manuscript in preparation.

MONOD, J., J. P. CHANGEUX, and F. JACOB. 1963. Allosteric proteins and cellular control systems. J. Mol. Biol. *6:* 306.

MONOD, J., J. WYMAN, and J. P. CHANGEUX. 1965. On the nature of allosteric transitions: A plausible model. J. Mol. Biol. *12:* 88.

RIGGS, A. D. and S. BOURGEOIS. 1968. On the assay, isolation and characterization of the *lac* repressor. J. Mol. Biol. *34:* 361.

RIGGS, A. D., S. BOURGEOIS, R. F. NEWBY, and M. COHN. 1968. DNA binding of the *lac* repressor. J. Mol. Biol. *34:* 365.

RIGGS, A. D. and S. BOURGEOIS. 1969. On the *lac* repressor-operator interaction and the purification of the *lac* operator. Biophys. J. *9:* A84.

RIGGS, A. D., H. SUZUKI, and S. BOURGEOIS. 1970. The *lac* repressor-operator interaction I. Equilibrium studies. J. Mol. Biol. *48:* 67.

RIGGS, A. D., R. F. NEWBY, and S. BOURGEOIS. The *lac* repressor-operator interaction. II. The effect of galactosides and other ligands. J. Mol. Biol. in press.

RIGGS, A. D., S. BOURGEOIS, and M. COHN. The *lac* repressor-operator interaction III. Kinetic studies. In prep.

WEIGERT, M. G. and A. GAREN. 1965. Amino acid substitutions resulting from suppression of "nonsense" mutations. J. Mol. Biol. *12:* 448.

WILLSON, C., D. PERRIN, M. COHN, F. JACOB, and J. MONOD. 1964. Non-inducible mutants of the regulator gene in the lactose system of *Escherichia coli*. J. Mol. Biol. *8:* 582.

Strains with the Promoter Deletion L1 Synthesize An Altered *lac* Repressor

JEFFREY H. MILLER, TERRY PLATT,* and KLAUS WEBER*

Department of Bacteriology and Immunology
Harvard Medical School, Boston, Massachusetts
*Department of Biochemistry and Molecular Biology
Harvard University, Cambridge, Massachusetts

INTRODUCTION

Several mutations in the *lac* promoter of *E. coli* have been isolated (Scaife and Beckwith, 1966; Ippen, Miller, Scaife, and Beckwith, 1968). Three of these, L8, L29, and L37 have been shown to be point mutations of the transition class (Arditti, Scaife, and Beckwith, 1968). A fourth mutation, L1, has been postulated to be a deletion of part of the *lac* promoter (Miller, Ippen, Scaife, and Beckwith, 1968). L1 does not recombine with either of the three promoter point mutations. In addition, strains with L1 are almost completely constitutive for the *lac* enzymes. In the presence of IPTG there is only a slight increase in the amount of β-galactosidase, while wild type is induced nearly 1000-fold. This is consistent with L1 being a deletion extending from the i gene into the *lac* promoter.

In this paper we show that the constitutivity of the *lac* operon in strains with L1 is indeed due to a lesion on the i gene, the structural gene for the *lac* repressor. We report genetic evidence which demonstrates the existence of an altered *lac* repressor in strains with L1. This molecule can be detected in vitro and partially purified. We offer an experiment which shows that the L1-repressor is physically different from the wild-type repressor.

MATERIALS AND METHODS

Strains: The construction of F'*lacpro* episomes with i^Q, and the double mutation i^Q,L1 has been described (Miller, Müller-Hill, and Beckwith, 1968). 115, and SQ are mutations which allow an overproduction of the *lac* repressor by 35- and 50-fold, respectively (Miller and Platt, in prep.). Starting with the mutations L1; i^Q,L1; and 115,Q,L1 the z^- derivatives were prepared as described in the text. The construction of 115,Q,L1 is described in Miller and Platt (in prep.) as is the construction of various mutants on the $\phi 80lac\lambda c_{I\ 857}$ t68 prophage.

β-galactosidase assay: The assay is the same as in Pardee, Jacob, and Monod (1959) and the units are the same as in Miller, Müller-Hill, and Beckwith, (1968).

Repressor assay: The equilibrium dialysis method was exactly the same as in Gilbert and Müller-Hill (1966). Specific activity equals the % excess counts of C^{14}-IPTG divided by the protein concentration in mg/ml. C^{14}-IPTG, 25mC/mM, was obtained from Calbiochem.

Media and Buffers: 2YT media contains per liter 5 grams of sodium chloride, 10 grams of yeast extract, and 16 grams of tryptone. TMS buffer is 0.2M KCl, 0.01M tris HCl, 0.01M magnesium acetate, 0.006M b-mercaptoethanol, and 10^{-4}M EDTA. The pH is 7.6 at 4°C. Breaking buffer contains 0.2M KCl, 0.2M tris HCl, 0.01M magnesium acetate, 3×10^{-4}M Cleland's reagent, and 5% glycerol. The pH is 7.6 at 4°C.

Binding curve: The points were obtained by dialysis of 0.25 ml aliquots of the respective extracts against 20 ml of TMS buffer containing C^{14}-labelled + cold IPTG at various concentrations, at 4°C. After equilibrium was attained (dialysis was carried out for three hours in #20 dialysis tubing), the sacs were opened and $200\mu 1$ of each sample was counted and compared to an equal volume of the liquid outside the sac. The protein concentrations, as determined by the Biuret method, were all between 20–30 mg/ml. For each point, C^{14}-IPTG was present at 1×10^{-7}M, with the balance made up by cold IPTG. The starting concentrations outside were 1.1 and 3.1×10^{-6}M, and 1.0, 2.0, and 4.0×10^{-5}M.

Sucrose gradient: Parallel cultures of the two strains were grown up, induced, frozen, and broken by alumina grinding. Conditions for induction are described in Miller and Platt (in prep.). The ribosomes and cell debris were spun out, and an 0.3 ml sample of each extract was layered on a 5 ml gradient, 5 to 20% sucrose, in the same breaking buffer. The wild-type sample had a specific activity for repressor of 21, and a protein concentration of 7 mg/ml; and the L1 sample had a specific activity of 4.5 and a protein concentration of 20 mg/ml. Thus about 50% more wild-type repressor than L1 was applied to the gradient, and the areas under the respective peaks are consistent with this ratio. The gradients were run at 200,000 $\times$ g for 16 hours at 4°C, then twenty fractions of 0.25 ml each were collected from each gradient, and to each was added 0.25ml of C^{14}-IPTG at 2×10^{-6}M. After a few minutes incubation period at room temperature, the entire sample was applied to a 25mmHAWP Millipore filter (boiled three times in distilled water, and presoaked in 10^{-3}M cold IPTG), and rinsed through with 2 ml of the breaking buffer. This assay is a modified version of that used by Riggs and Bourgeois (1968). The assay is linear in this range, even in crude extracts if repressor is present in greater amounts than 0.1% of the total protein. Each filter was counted in scintillation fluid, and the average background of 100 cpm has been subtracted from each sample.

RESULTS

The *lac* repressor is normally present at 10 to 30 molecules per cell (Gilbert and Müller-Hill, 1966). One can increase the amount of *lac* repressor 20-fold by inducing a defective prophage containing the wild-type *lac* operon (Müller-Hill, Crapo, and Gilbert, 1968). Further increases can be obtained by introducing different mutations into the *i* promoter. These are Q, which synthesizes 10 times more repressor than wild type (Müller-Hill, Crapo, and Gilbert, 1968), the double mutant Q,115, which makes 35 times more repressor, and SQ, which synthesizes 50 times more than wild type (Miller and Platt, in prep.).

Strains carrying the L1 deletion have lower maximal levels and higher basal levels than normal strains (Scaife and Beckwith, 1966; see Table 1). The lower maximal levels are due to a defective *lac* promoter (Miller, Ippen, Scaife, and Beckwith, 1968). Although the inducibility is less than 2-fold, this is most plausibly accounted for by a partially defective *lac* repressor. This was tested by constructing diploids carrying different *i* promoters on an L1,z^- episome, and an i deletion, z^+ on the chromosome (see Fig. 2). The construction of z^- episomes carrying the L1, the i^Q, L1, and the i^Q,115,L1 mutations is discussed and diagramed in Fig. 1. The only source of repressor is the episome, which carries the L1 mutation. Functional β-galactosidase can only be synthesized from the chromosome. The operator region on the chromosome is normal, so the only effect observed is due to interactions between i^Q, L1 repressor and wild-type *lac*

Table 1. β-galactosidase levels in L1 and wild type

	β-galactosidase specific activity	
	No IPTG	IPTG
Wild type	1.5–3.0	1500
L1	25–30	40–45

Strains were grown in glucose-M63 synthetic media (Pardee, Jacob, and Monod, 1959) either with or without inducer (1×10^{-3}M IPTG). The strains used contained an F'*lacpro* episome. They harbored a *lacpro* deletion on the chromosome.

Chromosome

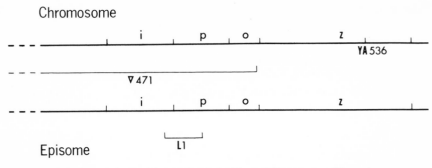

Episome

FIGURE 1. Deletion strain used to construct double mutations on an F'*lac* episome.
In constructing strains with multiple mutations in the *lac* region, we have used the same principle throughout. The figure above depicts a strain containing the chromosomal deletion #471 (also referred to as X7713, Reznikoff and Beckwith, 1969). This deletion removes all of the *i* gene, the *lac* promoter, and at least part of the *lac* operator. In addition, we have crossed a z^- point mutation into this strain. This is now a double mutation, a point mutation plus a deletion. We can cross the point mutation onto an episome carrying the *lac* genes by homogenotizing for z^-. No marker on the episome which is covered by the 471 deletion can be affected. Thus, as shown in Fig. 1, L1 cannot be crossed out from the episome. Using this technique, one can construct the double mutant L1, z^-; the triple mutant i^q,L1,z^-, and also i^q,115,L1,z^-. The z^- mutation used here is the amber mutation, YA536 (Newton, Beckwith, Zipser, and Brenner, 1965).

operator. The data presented in Table 2 show that the L1 mutant exhibits a 1.8-fold repression ratio in *trans,* but that as the amount of L1 repressor is increased, the amount of repression also increases. However, full repression is still not achieved even though the double mutant Q,115 synthesizes 35 times more L1 repressor than normal. Thus, either the L1 mutation leads to the synthesis of greatly reduced amounts of a normal repressor, or to the synthesis of an altered repressor.

IPTG BINDING

Since L1 strains exhibit both repressor activity and a sensitivity to IPTG in vivo, it is reasonable to expect IPTG binding activity in vitro. Gilbert

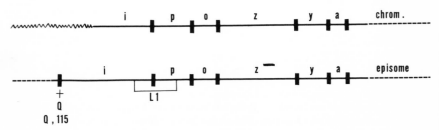

FIGURE 2. Diploid used for *trans* repression test of L1.

Table 2. Repression in *trans* of an i⁻z⁺ strain

| | *β*-galactosidase specific activity | |
Episome	No IPTG	IPTG
i⁺, p⁺, z⁻	0.6	550
(+), L1, z⁻	300	550
Q, L1, z⁻	29	550
Q, 115, L1, z⁻	9	—

The episome used is an F'*lacpro* episome, and the female harbors a deletion of the *lacpro* region. The chromosomal *lac* region has been transposed to a region near the *tryp* operon, to enable the selection of deletions ending in the *i* gene, but leaving the rest of the operon intact (Miller, Müller-Hill, and Beckwith, 1968). Segregants are eliminated by growth in media without proline. The proportion of z⁺/z⁺ homogenotes can be determined by observing single colonies on glucose minimal plates containing 5-bromo-4-chloro-indoxyl-beta-D-galactoside (40 ug/ml). These colonies would be dark blue. In addition, homogenotes in which L1 has been crossed out can also be observed, since these appear white on these plates. Neither class was present in a significant percentage.

and Müller-Hill (1966) have shown that the *lac* repressor is the only protein which can bind IPTG with high enough affinity to be detected by equilibrium dialysis. The effect of L1 on the level of binding activity is shown in Table 3. The defective, heat-inducible prophage mentioned previously was used in all four cases, in order to provide the highest repressor levels possible. There is significant IPTG binding activity present, but L1 extracts consistently yield only 6% to 12% of the wild-type levels for a given *i* promoter, as measured by equilibrium dialysis. The possibility that the L1 repressor is present in the same amounts as wild-type repressor, but with a much lower affinity for IPTG, is ruled out by the experiment shown in Fig. 3. This is a Scatchard plot of the IPTG binding activity present in crude extracts of L1 and wild type. The binding constants obtained from the slopes of these curves are 1.3×10^{-6}M for wild type, and 1.5×10^{-6}M

Table 3. IPTG binding activity of L1 and wild type as determined by equilibrium dialysis.

Strain	Repressor specific activity
iQ	6.0–8.0
iQ, L1	0.6–0.8
isQ	30.0–50.0
isQ, L1	3.0–5.0

This measurement was done on the crude extracts of induced strains in rich (2YT) media. See Materials and Methods. The values given represent the average of several experiments.

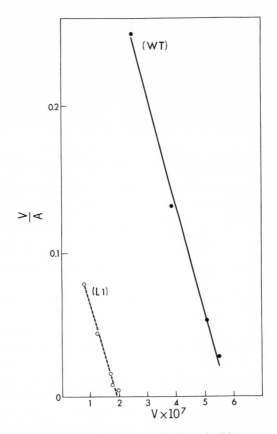

Figure 3. Scatchard plot of IPTG binding activity in L1 and wild type.

The horizontal axis, V, represents the concentration excess of IPTG inside the dialysis sac divided by the protein concentration outside. For the vertical axis, A is the final IPTG concentration outside, calculated from the ratio of starting cpm to final cpm.

for L1. Th two molecules thus bind IPTG with essentially the same affinity, and hence L1 repressor must be present in reduced amounts relative to wild type.

Sucrose Gradient Studies

A sucrose gradient on crude extracts from cultures in which the prophage carrying the repressor gene has been heat-induced is shown in Fig. 4. The fractions were assayed for IPTG binding activity by the millipore filter technique (see Materials and Methods), and hemoglobin (4.1 S) was used as a marker. Wild-type repressor, a tetramer of molecular weight 160,000, sediments with a value of 7.6 S (Gilbert and Müller-Hill, 1966). The L1 protein sediments at about 5 S, which corresponds to a molecular

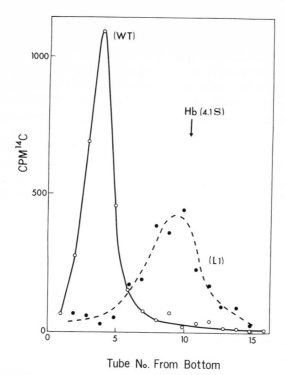

Tube No. From Bottom

FIGURE 4. Sucrose gradient analysis of IPTG binding activity in L1 and wild type.

weight of roughly 80,000 for a globular protein. This clearly reflects a structural difference of the L1 repressor, but does not allow a prediction of the size of the L1 polypeptide chain. Preliminary results, however, (Rosenbusch, Platt, and Weber, unpubl.), show that the L1 polypeptide chain is approximately the same size as that of normal repressor. Thus, the gradient results suggest that L1 repressor exists predominantly as a dimer in the crude extract, under conditions in which wild type moves as a tetramer, although this data does not rule out a rapid equilibrium between monomer, dimer, and tetramer forms.

DISCUSSION

These experiments show that the repressor from strains with L1 is different in structure and repressor activity from that of wild type. Since the IPTG binding is apparently not affected by the mutation, specific activity measurements based on IPTG affinity directly reflect the amounts of either repressor present. L1 crude extracts normally yield about 10%

of the wild-type IPTG binding activity, but even 35 times more L1 repressor does not restore full repression in vivo (Table 2). This must represent a substantial drop in the ability of the altered repressor to bind to the *lac* operator. The explanation for the reduced amounts of L1 repressor has not been established, but one possibility is that proteolytic enzymes partially degrade altered proteins of this type. Alternatively, a certain percentage of the molecules might fold incorrectly and possess no activity whatsoever.

Since transcription of the *i* gene is in the same direction as the structural genes of the *lac* operon (Miller, Müller-Hill, and Beckwith, 1968), a deletion like L1 should eliminate both transcriptional and translational stop signals at the end of the *i* gene. When the Q mutation, which increases the level of *i* gene transcription, is combined with L1, read-through into the *lac* genes occurs, and β-galactosidase is produced in higher amounts (Miller, Müller-Hill, and Beckwith, 1968). If L1 is not present, Q has no detectable effect. These results suggest that the mRNA stop signal at the end of the *i* gene is missing, and that possibly the *i* message in strains with L1 includes the *lac* genes. Other evidence that L1 eliminates the mRNA stop signal has been found in *trp i* gene fusion strains (Reznikoff, Miller, Scaife, and Beckwith, 1969). Since the L1 repressor is physically altered, the structural part of the *i* gene must be affected. The translation termination signal must therefore be deleted, and amino acids encoded by the promoter and operator should be added on to the end of the uncompleted repressor polypeptide chain until a nonsense codon is encountered. Thus, the sequence of the carboxyl-terminal part of such an altered repressor should reflect the base sequence of whatever portions of the promoter and operator are translated. A number of such deletions in different phases should permit the determination of the primary structure of the promoter and the operator. Further purification of L1 repressor, and experiments to establish its carboxyl-terminal sequence are in progress, as well as a search for additional deletions similar to L1.

SUMMARY

The deletion L1, which fuses the *i* gene to the *lac* promoter, results in the synthesis of an altered repressor molecule. This repressor is only partially functional, and is recovered at about 10% of the level of wild type. The molecule sediments as a dimer under conditions in which the wild type is a tetramer.

ACKNOWLEDGMENTS

We should like to thank Prof. Walter Gilbert for many helpful discussions, and Miss Diane Gartner for excellent technical assistance.

T. P. was supported by a pre-doctoral fellowship from the National Science Foundation, and J. H. M. by a training grant from the National Institutes of Health to the Department of Biochemistry and Molecular Biology, Harvard University.

REFERENCES

ARDITTI, R. R., J. G. SCAIFE, and J. R. BECKWITH. 1968. The nature of mutants in the *lac* promoter region. J. Mol. Biol. *38:* 421.

GILBERT, W. and B. MÜLLER-HILL. 1966. Isolation of the *lac* repressor. Proc. Nat. Acad. Sci. *56:* 1891.

IPPEN, K., J. H. Miller, J. G. SCAIFE, and J. R. BECKWITH. 1968. New controlling element in the *lac* operon of *E. coli.* Nature *217:* 825.

MILLER, J. H., K. IPPEN, J. G. SCAIFE, and J. R. BECKWITH. 1968. The promoter-operator region of the *lac* operon of *E. coli.* J. Mol. Biol. *38:* 413.

MILLER, J. H., B. MÜLLER-HILL, and J. R. BECKWITH. 1968. Direction of transcription of a regulatory gene in *E. coli.* Nature *220:* 1287.

MÜLLER-HILL, B., L. CRAPO, and W. GILBERT. 1968. Mutants that make more *lac* repressor. Proc. Nat. Acad. Sci., *59:* 1259.

NEWTON, W. A., J. R. BECKWITH, D. ZIPSER, and S. BRENNER. 1965. Nonsense mutants and polarity in the *lac* operon of *E. coli.* J. Mol. Biol. *14:* 290.

PARDEE, A. B., F. JACOB, and J. MONOD. 1959. The genetic control and cytoplasmic expression of "inducibility" in the synthesis of β-galactosidase by *E. coli.* J. Mol. Biol. *11:* 23.

RIGGS, A. and S. BOURGEOIS. 1968. On the assay, isolation and characterization of the *lac* repressor. J. Mol. Biol. *34:* 361.

REZNIKOFF, W. S. and J. R. BECKWITH. 1969. Genetic evidence that the operator locus is distinct from the z gene in the *lac* operon of *E. coli.* J. Mol. Biol. *43:* 215.

REZNIKOFF, W. S., J. H. MILLER, J. G. SCAIFE, and J. R. BECKWITH. 1969. A mechanism for repressor action. J. Mol. Biol. *43:* 201.

SCAIFE, J. G. and J. R. BECKWITH. 1966. Mutational alteration of the maximal of *lac* operon expression. Cold Spring Harbor Symp. Quant. Biol. *31:* 403.

Deletion of Translational Start Signals in the *lac* Operon of *E. coli*

LARRY ERON, JONATHAN R. BECKWITH and FRANÇOIS JACOB

Department of Bacteriology and Immunology
Harvard Medical School
Boston, Massachusetts
and Institut Pasteur
Paris, France

The order of genetic elements in the *lac* operon of *E. coli* is *p-o-z-y-a* (Miller, Ippen, Scaife, and Beckwith, 1968), where *p*, the promoter, is the region of initiation of transcription of the operon; *o*, the operator, is the site of action of the *lac* repressor; and *z*, *y*, and *a* are structural genes coding for the proteins β-galactosidase, permease or M-protein and thiogalactoside transacetylase, respectively. The nearby *i* gene, codes for the structure of the repressor protein. Since transcription begins in the promoter region, it seems likely that the operator is *transcribed* as part of the *lac* mRNA. However, evidence has been presented that the operator is not *translated* as part of the first structural gene, *z*, and it is possible that the operator is not translated at all (Reznikoff and Beckwith, 1969; Bhorjee, Fowler, and Zabin, 1969). If this is so, then translation of the operon mRNA would begin at the *z* gene. It may be asked, then, whether there is a special translation start signal at the beginning of the *z* gene-copy in the mRNA which is different from internal start signals or whether the signals at the beginning of *z*, *y* and *a* are identical. In this paper, we present evidence that there is no such site in the *o-z* boundary region which is essential for operon expression.

Previous results suggested the existence of a region essential to the expression of the *lac* operon lying between (or including the end of) the operator and the beginning of the *z* gene (Jacob, Ullmann, and Monod, 1964). Since transcription is initiated before the operator, it was suggested that the *o-z* boundary might represent a special translation initiation

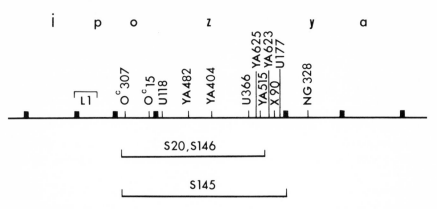

FIGURE 1. Recombination tests with z^- mutations were done by crossing Hfr Hayes Sm^s derivatives of the z^- point mutants with females of genetic constitution *lac$^-$* (*o-z* deletion), *proC$^-$*, *trp$^-$*Sm^r. A drop of a log phase culture of donor and recipient were mixed on lactose-minimal plates containing streptomycin and tryptophan, and, after two days, the plates scored for *lac$^+$* recombinants. The same type of mating was also done between F'*lac* donor strains carrying the deletions and female strains carrying the z^- point mutations. Both types of matings gave the same results. The z^- point mutations are described in Newton, Beckwith, Zipser, and Brenner (1965). The distance from the z^- mutation U366 to the C-terminal end of the *z* structural gene is approximately 24% of the gene based on the data of Fowler and Zabin (1966). Further analysis of their data, indicates that the deletion ends of S20 and S146 must be between 10 and 24% distant from the end of *z* and S145 less than 10% distant.

sequence, the "starter" (Davies and Jacob, 1968). The existence of this latter site was suggested by the failure to find a class of deletions which extend from the operator into the *z* gene. These deletions were sought under conditions where they would have been found if they permitted expression of the *y* gene. As a result of a more extensive analysis, we report here the isolation of such deletions.

To detect *o-z* deletions which are *y$^+$*, the following technique is used: strains carrying an *i^s* (super-repressed) mutation (Willson, Perrin, Cohn, Jacob, and Monod, 1964) are *lac$^-$* and *mel$^-$* (at 42°C) due to the non-inducibility of β-galactosidase and the *lac* permease. In a strain diploid for the *i^s* mutation, revertants isolated on melibiose-synthetic agar at 42°C will, in general, have restored permease activity due to mutations altering the operator causing insensitivity to repressor. Among the *o^{c}y$^+$* revertants, most are *lac$^+$*, but a small proportion are *o^{c}z$^-$y$^+$*. Of 67 *o^{c}z$^-$y$^+$* revertants described previously (Jacob, et al., 1964), all were due to deletions which extended from the *z* gene into or beyond the *i* gene, thus removing the *lac p* and *o* regions. The *y* gene in these strains probably functions as a result of fusion to a nearby gene or operon.

We have now carried out a more extensive screening for *o^{c}z$^-$y$^+$* deletions which do not extend out of the operon. Of 300 spontaneous $o^c z^- y^+$ revertants of the diploid F'*lac* i^s/*lac* i^s strain, we have found 3 which retain the *lac i* gene and promoter intact. The presence of the *i* gene in these 3 deletions is shown by transferring the episome carrying the deletions into a *lac*$^+$ (i^+) strain; the presence of the episome results in a *lac*$^-$ (dominant) character in such diploids. Thus, the episomes must still carry the dominant i^s mutation.

For further studies, the i^s mutation was replaced with a wild-type allele (i^+) by recombination. Recombination studies with a series of z^- mutations showed that the 3 revertants are the result of deletions which extend far into the z gene (Fig. 1). Bacterial crosses between the 3 deletions and a strain carrying a partial deletion of the p region, L1 (Miller, et al., 1968), show that the *lac* promoter was at least partially intact in the strains (Table 1). Finally, the 3 deletions fail to give recombinants with two o^c mutants, $o^c{}_{15}$ and $o^c{}_{307}$ (Table 1). Since it may be difficult or impossible to detect recombination between point mutants and a deletion end which

Table 1   Recombination frequency with

	p^-L1	$o^c{}_{15}$	o_{307}
S20	.006	$<5 \times 10^{-5}$	$<6 \times 10^{-5}$
S145	.006	$<4 \times 10^{-5}$	$<5 \times 10^{-5}$
S146	.006	$<8 \times 10^{-5}$	$<10 \times 10^{-5}$

To replace the i^s mutation in the three deletions with the wild-type (i^+) allele, the following steps were carried out: 1) the F'*lac* carrying a deletion was crossed into a *lac*$^+$ *proC*$^-$*trp*$^-$ recipient to give F'$i^s\Delta o$-z/$i^+o^+z^+$ heterogenotes. The heterogenotes were *lac*$^-$ due to the presence of the i^s mutation. 2) From the heterogenotes, *lac*$^+$ (i^+/i^+) recombinants were picked up on *lac*-tetrazolium agar and screened for those ($i^+\Delta o$-z/i^+z^+) which threw off *lac*$^-$ homogenotes. 3) The $i^+\Delta o$-z homogenotes were cured of the episome by treatment with acridine orange. An Hfr carrying the L1 mutation was crossed with these F$^-$ strains. The frequencies represent the percentage of *proC*$^+$ recombinants which are *lac*$^+$. Mapping of the o^c mutants with the o-z deletions was done by constructing diploids of the following sort F'*lac*$^+o^c$*proA*, B$^+$/Δ(*lac*-*pro*)$^-$$_{X111}\phi80$ *lac* (Δo-z) *gal*E$^-$Sm^r. Aliquots of 4 cultures from independent colonies of the 6 possible diploids were plated at 42°C on glucose-minimal agar containing 0.03% phenyl-β-D-galactoside and 5-bromo-4-chloro-3-indolyl-β-D-galactoside. The cultures were titered on glucose-minimal agar at 42°C. If any o^+ recombinants were formed from recombination between the two *lac* regions, these would survive on these plates and would exhibit a pale blue color (see Miller, et al., 1968). Possible o^+ recombinants were picked, purified and assayed for β-galactosidase activity with and without the inducer isopropyl-β-D-thiogalactoside. None of the possibilities turned out to have o^+ character. The frequency of recombination with the o^c mutations is presented as the percentage of colonies plated which were o^+. See Miller, et al. (1968) for representative frequencies of recombination between o^c mutations and other deletions. Other techniques and media may be found in Reznikoff, Miller, Scaife, and Beckwith (1969). The o^c mutants have been mapped by Davies and Jacob (1968).

Table 2

Thiogalactoside transacetylase activities of *o-z* deletion strains		
	− inducer	+ inducer
S20	5	12
S145	43	88
S146	31	54
Wild-type	0.2	100

Values are presented as percentage of the fully induced wild-type control. The assays were done in isogenic strains which are ϕ80 *lac* lysogens carrying the *lac* region only on the phage; the normal *lac* region is deleted. The enzyme is assayed according to Epstein (1967) using 2×10^{-3} M isopropyl-β-D-thiogalactoside (Mann Chemical) as inducer. Assays were done on two independent cultures for each value with an average error of less than 3%, except for the very low values which had somewhat larger errors.

An i^-a^+ control exhibited no effect of inducer on transacetylase activity.

maps very close to them, these results indicate that the deletions either extend very close to or past the mutant sites.

Although all three strains grow on melibiose as sole carbon source, indicating *y* gene activity, one, S20, grew very slowly. To determine accurately the level of operon expression in the *o-z* deletion strains, the specific activity of the enzyme thiogalactoside transacetylase was measured. None of the deletion strains make normal levels of the enzyme (Table 2). The strain, S20, which appeared to have low permease activity also exhibited low transacetylase activity.

The consistent finding of an approximately 2-fold induction ratio for all 3 deletions suggests that deletion of at least two o^c sites in this region does not completely eliminate repressor binding.

The finding of 3 deletions which extend from the *lac* operator into the *z* gene and which exhibit substantial levels of *lac* permease shows that there is no region covered by the deletion which is essential for *lac* expression. This conclusion suggests several features of *lac* operon structure. First, it strongly supports the suggestion that the operator is transcribed as part of the operon mRNA. If mRNA synthesis were started rather at the beginning of the *z* gene, the elimination of this region by deletion should abolish operon expression. This is not the case. Second, there is no special translation start signal at the beginning of the *z* gene, which is essential for the translation of the entire operon mRNA. However, a notable feature of the 3 deletions is that they all extend very close to the start of the *y* gene. Although, 3 is a small number to base conclusions on, the finding does raise the possibility that only *o-z* deletions of this length allow *y* and *a* gene expression. Further support for this idea comes from the finding that the two shorter deletions (S20 and S146) make lower levels of transacetylase. The following hypothesis could account for these findings: the z, y and a genes each have the same translation start signal. The reason translation can be initiated at the z gene-copy in the mRNA is that the start signal is very close to the 5′ end of the mRNA. If this signal is eliminated by deletion, translation cannot begin at the y gene-copy unless it also lies close to the 5′ end of the mRNA. Thus, only o-z deletions which bring the y gene close to the beginning of the message will exhibit y and a gene activity. Explanations for why short o-z deletions would not have distal gene activity would be parallel to those used to account for polarity mutations (Zipser, 1969).

We recognize that there are alternative explanations for the restoration of permease activity by these deletions. It is conceivable that the activity of y and a genes is due to creation by the deletion of a new transcription start signal formed by joining two nucleotide sequences. However, it seems too fortuitous that all 3 deletions happen to have one end in the o region and the other very late in z. Other explanations raise similar difficulties.

ACKNOWLEDGMENTS

The work was supported by a Career Development award and a research grant from the National Institutes of Health to J. R. Beckwith and by grants from the National Institutes of Health (AI-07885), Délégation Générale à la Recherche Scientifique et Technique, Centre National de la Recherche Scientifique and Commissariat à l'Energie Atomique to F. Jacob. We thank Miss Veronica MacGillivray for excellent technical assistance.

REFERENCES

BHORJEE, J. S., A. V. FOWLER, and I. ZABIN. 1969. Biochemical evidence that the operator locus is distinct from the z gene in the lac operon of Escherichia coli. J. Mol. Biol. 43: 219.

DAVIES, J. and F. JACOB. 1968. Genetic mapping of the regulator and operator genes of the lac operon. J. Mol. Biol. 36: 413.

EPSTEIN, W. 1967. Transposition of the lac region of Escherichia coli. IV. Escape from repression in bacteriophage-carried lac genes. J. Mol. Biol. 30: 529.

FOWLER, A. V., and I. ZABIN. 1966. Colinearity of β-galactosidase with its gene by immunological detection of incomplete polypeptide chains. Science 154: 1027.

JACOB, F., A. ULLMANN, and J. MONOD. 1964. Le promoteur, élément génétique necéssaire à l'expression d'un opéron. C. R. Acad. Sci. 258: 3125.

REZNIKOFF, W. S., and J. R. BECKWITH. 1969. Genetic evidence that the operator locus is distinct from the z gene in the lac operon of Escherichia coli. J. Mol. Biol. 43: 215.

REZNIKOFF, W. S., J. H. MILLER, J. G. SCAIFE, and J. R. BECKWITH. 1969. A mechanism for repressor action. J. Mol. Biol. *43:* 201.

MILLER, J. H., K. IPPEN, J. G. SCAIFE, and J. R. BECKWITH. 1968. The promoter-operator region of the *lac* operon of *Escherichia coli.* J. Mol. Biol. *38:* 413.

NEWTON, W. A., J. R. BECKWITH, D. ZIPSER, and S. BRENNER. 1965. Nonsense mutants and polarity in the *lac* operon of *Escherichia coli.* J. Mol. Biol. *14:* 290.

WILLSON, C., D. PERRIN, M. COHN, F. JACOB, and J. MONOD. 1964. Noninducible mutants of the regulator gene in the lactose system of *Escherichia coli.* J. Mol. Biol. *8:* 582.

ZIPSER, D., S. ZABELL, J. ROTHMAN, T. GRODZICKER, M. WENK, and M. NOVITSKI. The fine structure of the gradient of polarity in the z gene of the *lac* operon of *E. coli.* J. Mol. Biol. (in press).

Some Properties of Insertion Mutations in the *lac* Operon

MICHAEL H. MALAMY

Department of Molecular Biology and Microbiology
Tufts University, School of Medicine
Boston, Massachusetts

We have described the isolation and properties of spontaneous mutations in the lactose operon (Malamy, 1966). Using the fact that cells deficient in the enzyme UDPGal 4-epimerase are caused to lyse when growing in the presence of galactose or lactose, we determined plating conditions which only allowed the survival of *lac** non-fermenting mutants (as well as secondary mutations in the *gal** system) arising spontaneously in the population. Several different types of mutants were isolated including complete and partial deletions of the *lac* genes. However, reverting mutations mapping throughout the *z* and *y* genes were predominant. We have emphasized the unique polarity properties of certain of these reverting mutations mapping in the ω region of the *z* gene (Ullmann, Perrin, Jacob, and Monod, 1965). Fourteen out of eighteen strains examined, mapping at many sites within the ω segment (Fig. 1), exhibit a complete polar effect in contrast to all other reverting mutations in this segment, nonsense and missense, (Newton, Beckwith, Zipser, and Brenner, 1965; Perrin, 1963). The complete polar spontaneous mutants fail to synthesize any detectable permease or transacetylase activity (Malamy, 1966). Other studies with these complete polar mutants indicate that they possess a functioning *i* gene (Malamy, unpubl.) and are able to synthesize almost normal amounts of the early β-galactosidase peptides α and β (Morrison and Malamy, unpubl.).

On the basis of mutagen-induced reversions and the lack of response to nonsense suppressors, it was concluded that the complete polar muta-

---

*Abbreviations listed at end of article.

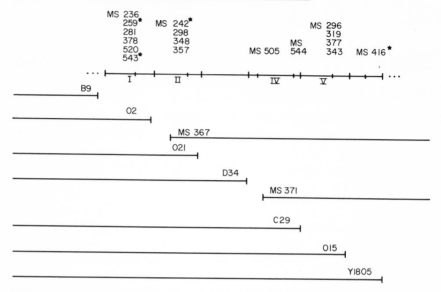

FIGURE 1. Map of spontaneous mutants in ω. Most of this data is taken from Malamy (1966). Additional strains have been mapped as previously described. All mutants except those marked with an asterisk fail to synthesize any detectable amounts of transacetylase. The division of ω into segments has been done arbitrarily.

tions in the ω segment were of the frameshift class and that the polarity effect was solely a result of changes in the reading frame during translation (Malamy, 1966). The studies included in this report have revealed that the complete polar mutations in ω are insertion mutations and result from the insertion of large pieces of DNA into the ω region. Although changes in the reading frame may result from the insertion of DNA into the gene, this explanation is clearly not the only factor involved in determining the degree of polarity exhibited by these strains.

Using a similar selection procedure for spontaneous mutants, Shapiro (1967) and Jordan, Saedler, and Starlinger (1967) isolated complete polar mutants in the transferase gene of the galactose operon. Shapiro (1969) showed that the complete polar mutants in the *gal* system were insertions by comparing the density of transducing phage λdg*al* containing nonsense or complete polar mutations. An increase in the density of λdg*al* containing complete polar mutations was observed and assumed to be the result of an increase in the DNA content of the phage. These results have been confirmed and extended by Starlinger's group (Jordan et al., 1968).

In order to determine if the *lac* operon complete polar mutations were insertions, it was necessary to incorporate these mutations into derivatives of the transducing phage ϕ80d*lac*. In addition to determining the density of ϕ80d*lac* containing different types of *lac* operon mutations, it was also desired to examine other physical properties of the phages to prove that an increased density was related to an increase in the size of the DNA carried by the phage. To this end we developed procedures for isolating double lysogens which yield large amounts of transducing phage. With the availability of sufficient quantities of transducing phages, we were able to use the analytical centrifuge for precise determination of phage density, and to prepare DNA for sucrose gradient analysis.

MATERIALS AND METHODS

The origin of the MS mutations is described in Malamy (1966). Incorporation of these mutations into ϕ80d*lac*, and the production of Hft-yielding double lysogens is reported in Malamy (in prep.). (The wild-type phages used in these experiments were obtained from Dr. E. Signer and are actually λ-ϕ80 hybrids properly designated as $\lambda C_I 857h80$ and $\lambda C_I 857$-h80d*lac*$^+$. We will refer to these phages as ϕ80 and ϕ80d*lac*). To construct double lysogens we took advantage of the fact that all MS and nonsense mutations in ω synthesize the α peptide (Ullmann, Jacob, and Monod, 1967) of β-galactosidase and can complement with a strain carrying an α deletion. We transduced RV/F'M15 (α del.,β^+,ω^+,y$^+$) to *lac*$^+$ and isolated a series of strains of genotype RVϕ80,ϕ80d*lac*(α^+,β^+,ω^-)/F'M15. These strains (or derivatives having lost the F'M15 episome) could be used directly for phage production. All other bacterial strains carrying deletions or nonsense mutations were from the collection of the Pasteur Institute or were provided by Dr. J. Beckwith. The map positions of pertinent mutations are given in Fig. 1 and 5.

Media, indicator plates and genetic mapping procedures are given in Malamy (1966). Cultures for phage production were grown at 34°C in MLT medium which contained per liter: 10 g Difco Bacto-tryptone; 5 g Difco Yeast Extract; 5 g NaCl, and buffered with 0.01M Tris, pH 7.4.

VERIFICATION OF MUTATIONS CARRIED BY ϕ80d*lac*

The genetic identity of the mutation carried on the transducing phage with the mutation as originally isolated was confirmed in the following manner. Derivatives of RV lysogenic for ϕ80 and ϕ80d*lac* $\alpha\beta^+$,ω^- were mated with the identical series of mapping strains used to determine the ω position of the original mutant. Table 1 shows that, in every case, the ϕ80d*lac* derivative and the strain carrying the original mutation recombine with the same set of deletions and have the same map position. Transducing phages carrying suppressible nonsense mutations were verified by their ability to yield *lac*+ transductants with complete *lac* deletion strains carrying the appropriate nonsense suppressors. In every case, ϕ80d*lac* carrying mutations in ω were capable of yielding *lac*+ recombinants and complementing with recipients of genotype α^-, β^-, ω^+, y^+ or α^-, β^+, ω^+, y^+.

Table 1. Verification of mutations carried by ϕ80d*lac*. Equal volumes of donor strains grown at 37°C and recipients grown at 34° were mixed and incubated at 34° for 2 hr. The mating mixtures were plated on EMB*lac* plates and incubated at 34°. Map positions of donors and recipients are indicated in Fig. 1. C = complementation; R = recombination; — = no recombination (scored after 3 days of incubation at 34°).

	B9	O2	D34	C29	Y1805
2000K MS 348	C	R	—	—	—
RV(ϕ80,ϕ80d*lac*MS348)	C	R	—	—	—
2000K MS 505	C	R	R	—	—
RV(ϕ80,ϕ80d*lac*MS505)	C	R	R	—	—
2000K MS 319	C	R	R	R	—
RV(ϕ80,ϕ80d*lac*MS319)	C	R	R	R	—

DETERMINATION OF THE DENSITY OF ϕ80d*lac* CONTAINING ω MUTATIONS

Active and transducing phages were prepared from the double lysogens and the density of the transducing phages determined. Cultures were grown at 34°C in MLT medium buffered at pH 7.4 with Tris, and phage development was induced by heating the culture at 45°C for 10 to 15 min. Incubation at 37°C was continued until complete lysis of the culture had occurred. Phages were concentrated by centrifugation and further purified by two cycles of CsCl equilibrium centrifugation.

One method to demonstrate the difference in density of transducing phages containing nonsense and complete polar mutations, and the method used by Jordan et al. (1968), is to prepare differentially radioactive phages. A mixture of the labeled phages is then subjected to equilibrium centrifugation in CsCl and the distribution of radioactivity determined in the gradient. Figure 2 demonstrates the results of such an experiment and shows that ϕ80d*lac*MS348 has a greater density than ϕ80d*lac*YA623. The genetic marker carried by each phage was also determined in a separate experiment by transduction assays, as used by Shapiro (1969)

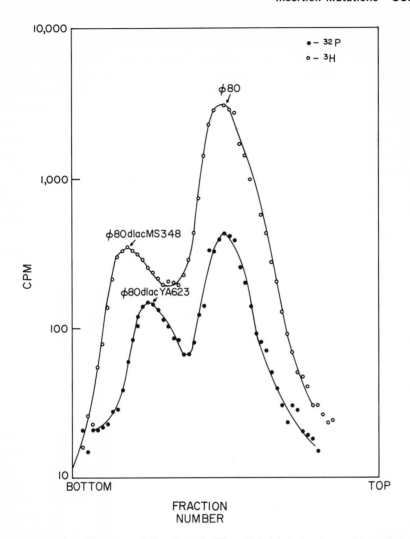

Figure 2. CsCl equilibrium centrifugation of differentially-labeled active and transducing phages. Strain RV(ϕ80,ϕ80dlacMS348) grown at 34°C in MLT was induced at 45°C and labeled with ³H-thymidine (1 μC/ml) in the presence of 250 μg/ml deoxyadenosine. After lysis, phages were purified through the first CsCl block gradient step. Strain RV(ϕ80, ϕ80dlacYA623) was labeled with ³²PO₄H₃ (3 μC/ml) at the time of induction and similarly purified. Mixtures containing 0.4 ml of the ³H-thymidine containing phages, 1.6 × 10⁴ cpm, and 0.1 ml of the ³²P-containing phages, 8 × 10³ cpm, were made up to 4 ml and the density of the solution adjusted to 1.500 with CsCl. Centrifugation was at 22,000 rpm, at 10°, for 48 hr in the SW65 rotor of the Spinco Model L-2 centrifuge. Fractions were dripped from the bottom of the tube directly onto glass fiber filters in vials, dried, and radioactivity measured in a scintillation counter using a toluene-based scintillation fluid.

in the *gal* system, since phages containing nonsense mutations can be differentially assayed in the presence of other ω mutations.

A simpler and more precise method for determining the density of any $\phi80dlac$ transducing phage utilizes the Model E analytical ultracentrifuge. Since transducing phages are present in amounts equivalent to active $\phi80$ in an Hft lysate, it was possible to directly analyze a phage preparation after the first CsCl block gradient centrifugation. Figure 3 illustrates the UV absorption photographs obtained after equilibrium was reached. The photographs of $\phi80$ and $\phi80lac^+$ and $\phi80$ and $\phi80dlacYA623$ (nonsense) show an identical separation between both phages, while the separation between $\phi80$ and $\phi80dlacMS348$ is greater. This difference is illustrated by the result obtained when a mixture of $\phi80$ and $\phi80dlacYA623$ and $\phi80dlacMS348$ is centrifuged to equilibrium. There is a clear separation between the two transducing phages. The density of each transducing phage was calculated according to the method of Szybalski (1968) after

A. $\phi80 + \phi80$dlac$^+$

B. $\phi80 + \phi80$dlac YA623

C. $\phi80 + \phi80$dlac YA623
   $+\phi80$dlac MS348

D. $\phi80 + \phi80$dlac MS348

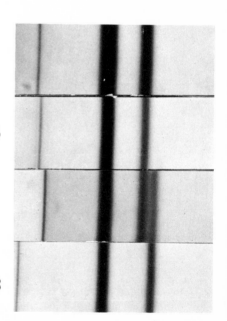

FIGURE 3. Determination of the density of $\phi80$ and $\phi80dlac$ in the analytical ultracentrifuge. Samples of phages purified through the CsCl block gradient step and containing 0.05–0.1 A_{260nm} absorbance units were adjusted to a density of 1.500 with CsCl using an Abbe refractometer.

A Spinco Model E analytical ultracentrifuge, equipped with UV optics and a rotating mask assembly enabled analysis of four samples during one run. A four-place ANF rotor and 12 mm Kel-F centerpieces were employed. Centrifugation was at 29,500 rpm for 18–22 hr with temperature automatically controlled at 20°C.

Table 2. Density of φ80dlac carrying ω mutations. RV derivatives lysogenic for φ80 and φ80dlac containing the mutations indicated were grown and purified as described. Conditions of centrifugation are described in Fig. 3. The density of each transducing phage was calculated using the density of φ80, 1.4953, as the standard.

Strain	Density difference (φ80 = 1.4953)
Wild-type	+0.0074
YA623	+0.0070
YA596	+0.0068
MS242	+0.0070
MS259	+0.0072
MS416	+0.0075
MS520	+0.0093
MS348	+0.0091
MS296	+0.0095
MS319	+0.0091
MS377	+0.0091
MS505	+0.0102
MS348 · MS319	+0.0111

the photographs had been traced on a Joyce-Loebl microdensitometer (made available for our use by Dr. D. Freifelder of Brandeis University). Table 2 summarizes the data obtained when many different ω mutations were analyzed in this manner. Three nonsense mutations (YA596, YA623, and MS416) and two frameshift mutations (MS242 and MS259; Malamy, unpubl.) have the same density as φ80dlac$^+$. Five complete polar mutations have a density 0.002 units greater than φ80dlac$^+$. One of the complete polar mutants, MS505, has a density increment of +0.003, which is greater than the other complete polar mutations. Included in the table is the result obtained with a strain containing two independent complete polar mutations, MS348 and MS319. The density increase of this strain is exactly the sum of the density increases observed with each mutation alone.

INSERTION MUTATIONS CONTAIN MORE DNA

Although the increased density of transducing phages carrying complete polar mutations strongly suggests that these mutations are insertions, it can be argued that the density increase is due to factors other than an increase in the DNA content of the phage. We have determined by CsCl equilibrium centrifugation that the *density* of DNA extracted from ϕ80d*lac*[+], ϕ80d*lac*YA623 and ϕ80d*lac*MS348 is the same. Therefore, the increased density of the phages is not due to a higher density (GC composition) of the DNA it contains. To prove that the DNA containing an insertion mutation has a *mass* greater than DNA from ϕ80d*lac*[+], we analyzed by zone centrifugation in sucrose the DNA from differentially-labeled phage preparations of ϕ80d*lac*[+] and ϕ80d*lac*MS348 · MS319. The following mixtures of DNA were analyzed: ^{32}P-labeled ϕ80DNA + ^{3}H-thymidine-labeled ϕ80d*lac*MS348 · MS319 DNA, and ^{3}H-thymidine-labeled ϕ80DNA + ^{32}P-labeled ϕ80d*lac*[+] DNA. The purification and separation of the phages and the extraction of DNA, as well as the details of sucrose gradient centrifugation, are reported in Malamy and Burgi (in prep.). From the relative mass of each DNA (Table 3) and taking a value of 28.2×10^6 for the mol wt of ϕ80 DNA, the molecular weight of the DNA contained in the transducing phages can be calculated. The increase in the mass of DNA in ϕ80d*lac*[+] transducing phage is greater than that expected from the increased density of the phage in CsCl using the equation of Weigle, Meselson, and Paigen (1959). This can be explained if the average GC composition of the substituted DNA in ϕ80d*lac*[+] is less than the phage DNA it replaces. The increase in DNA mass when the two insertions are added corresponds exactly to the density increase. We can conclude that the presence of two insertion mutations has led to an increase in the mass of the transducing DNA by 1.0×10^6. Since the density increase of each insertion mutation is the same, this indicates that each insertion was

Table 3. The size of DNA in ϕ80 and its derivatives. * For these experiments, ω mutant containing derivatives of a λ-ϕ80 hybrid containing the λ s cistron mutation t68 (Harris, Mount, Fuerst, and Siminovitch, 1967) were employed. Although the absolute densities of these phages differ from the phages used previously, the difference in density between the active and transducing phages are exactly the same.

The mol wt of ϕ80 DNA was determined by sucrose gradient analysis with DNA from λb[+]C$_{\text{I } 15}$, mol wt 31×10^6 as the standard (Burgi, pers. commun.).

Phage	Density difference* (ϕ80t68 = 1.492)	Relative DNA Mass	M. W. DNA	M. W. difference (M. W. DNA$_x$ —M. W. DNAϕ80)
		DNA$_x$/DNA$_{\phi80}$	x10^6	x10^6
ϕ80	—	1.00	28.2	—
ϕ80d*lac*[+]	+0.007	1.091	30.8	2.6
ϕ80d*lac* MS348 · MS319	+0.011	1.129	31.8	3.6

5×10^5 daltons, or approximately 750 nucleotide pairs (based on the weight of 664 for the average mass of one nucleotide pair). These results offer a direct confirmation of the hypothesis that the complete polar mutations in the ω region of the z gene are insertions of large pieces of DNA into the structural gene.

REVERSION OF COMPLETE POLAR MUTATIONS

All of the complete polar mutations in ω can revert spontaneously to *lac*+ but with frequencies differing by several orders of magnitude. We have previously reported (Malamy, 1966) that certain *lac*+ revertants were indistinguishable from the wild-type by the amounts and temperature stability of the β-galactosidase they synthesized. In addition, reversion to full *lac*+ was accompanied by restoration of permease activity (as judged by growth on melibiose plates) and the ability to synthesize wild-type levels of transacetylase (measured enzymatically). Other classes of revertants can be selected spontaneously; *mel*+, *lac*− revertants occur by deletions which may only include the region around the site of the original mutation, or may extend considerable distances from it within the z gene.

We have examined the density of several spontaneous *lac*+ revertants which synthesize wild-type levels of β-galactosidase. These revertants were selected in double lysogens containing the MS mutations. When phages are purified from these revertants and analyzed in the ultracentrifuge, it can be seen (Table 4 and Fig. 4B) that reversion to *lac*+ has been accompanied by a decrease in the density of the transducing phage to that found for ϕ80d*lac*+.

Table 4. Density of spontaneous *lac*+ revertants of insertion mutations. Cultures of RV(ϕ80,ϕ80d*lac*MS) were spread onto the surface of *lac* minimal medium plates and incubated at 34°C. Spontaneous *lac*+ revertants were purified on the same medium and cultures tested for β-galactosidase and transacetylase activity. Lysates were prepared from the revertants showing wild-type levels of both enzymes and the phage purified through the CsCl block gradient step. Density of transducing phages was determined as in Table 2.

Strain	Density difference (ϕ80 = 1.4953)
MS520	+0.0093
Spon. R-520	+0.0069
Ms348	+0.0091
Spon. R-348	+0.0069
MS319	+0.0091
Spon. R-319	+0.0068

A. φ80dlacYA623 +
    φ80dlacMS319

B. φ8dlac⁺ Spon R - 319 +
    φ80dlacMS319

C. φ80dlacYA623 +
    φ80dlac⁺ A.M. R-319

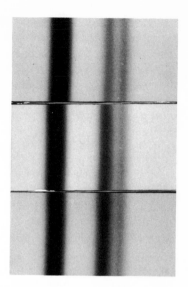

FIGURE 4. Density of φ80d*lac* containing full and partial *lac*⁺ revertants of insertion mutation MS319. Revertants were obtained as in Table 4. RV(φ80,φ80d*lac*MS319) was spread on *lac* minimal medium plates. One plate was treated with ICR 191 by placing a drop of a solution containing 1 mg/ml in the center of the dish. Colonies of *lac*⁺ revertants were purified after 2 to 3 days incubation at 34°C. Revertants were tested for enzyme levels and for the ability to transfer the *lac*⁺ character to a complete *lac* deletion strain by transduction. Phages were purified from full and partial revertants and the density of the transducing phage carrying the revertant determined. For this Figure, reference markers were added to the purified phages before centrifugation to clearly illustrate the difference in density between φ80d*lac*MS319 and the full *lac*⁺ revertant Spon-R-319 (B), and the preservation of the insertion density for φ80d*lac*AMR-319 (C). The densities reported were determined without the added markers.

Reversion frequencies of complete polar mutations in ω are unaffected by treatment with mutagens such as NTG or base analogs. We have reported (Malamy, 1966) that certain of the complete polar mutants do respond to the mutagen ICR 191, an acridine-half mustard. We have been able to stimulate the reversion frequency to *lac*⁺ of MS319 at least 100 times when a culture is treated with this mutagen on the surface of a *lac* minimal medium plate and incubated at 34°C. This response is observed with the original strain carrying the MS319 mutation as well as with the derivative carrying φ80d*lac*MS319. Most of the revertants capable of growth on *lac* minimal medium at 34°C fail to give a positive response when grown on indicator plates. We have measured the β-galactosidase and transacetylase levels in these strains and find them both to be about 2% of the wild-type levels. Complementation assays show that α and β peptides are made in normal amounts and respond to the normal *lac* repression system. When the density of transducing phages carrying the partial acridine-mustard-induced revertants is determined (Fig. 4C), the surprising result is that they still retain, to the limits of the centrifugal assay, the same increased density and therefore the same segment of inserted DNA. From the acridine-mustard partial *lac*+ revertants, spontaneous *mel*+ revertants can be selected. Some of these strains are now full *lac*+ revertants and have lost the increase in transducing phage density. Therefore, reversion to full *lac*+ can occur in one or several steps and results in the loss of the inserted DNA segment.

DISCUSSION

We have analyzed many different types of mutations in the ω segment of the z gene by determining the buoyant density in CsCl of $\phi80d$*lac* transducing phages carrying these mutations. Figure 5 summarizes the type and map position of those mutants reported in this communication. Of the reverting mutations, nonsense and frameshift mutations have exactly the same density as the wild-type $\phi80d$*lac*+. Only the complete polar mutations have a density greater than that of the wild type. We have also examined the density of transducing phages carrying deletion mutations

CLASSIFICATION OF OMEGA MUTANTS EXAMINED BY DENSITY OF $\phi80d$lac

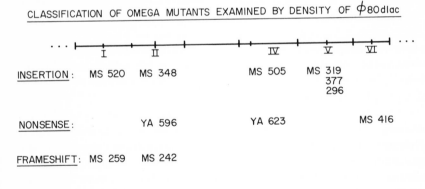

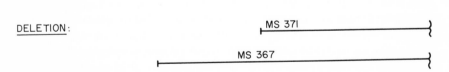

FIGURE 5. Classification of ω mutants examined by density of $\phi80d$*lac*. Map positions and types of mutations examined by density of $\phi80d$*lac* and reported in this communication are presented. Two deletions, MS371 and MS367, whose transducing phages are less dense than $\phi80d$*lac*+ are also included.

in the ω region. As could be expected, the mutants examined, MS367 and MS371, have a density less than ϕ80d*lac*$^+$. The results for these strains and a large series of deletions mapping throughout the *lac* operon will be reported in a future communication.

On the basis of the increased density of the phages containing complete polar mutations and the increase in the mass of DNA extracted from these phages, we can conclude that complete polar mutations in the ω segment of the *z* gene are a result of the insertion of DNA into the gene. Although the DNA can be inserted at many different regions in ω, in most cases the size of the insertion is the same—750 nucleotide pairs. The constant size of the insertion might indicate that the same piece of DNA is involved in the different mutations. However, the insertion mutations mapping throughout ω differ in many respects: reversion frequency to *lac*$^+$, response to acridine mustards as mutagens, ability to be suppressed by a suppressor of polarity, SuA (Beckwith 1963). The size of the *lac* operon insertions is similar to the size of the *gal* operon insertions (Shapiro, 1969; Jordan et al., 1968) although completely different strains were used as parental stocks. There are, however, several differences between the *lac* insertion mutations and the *gal* insertions reported by Shapiro (1969). All of the *lac* insertions revert to *lac*$^+$ spontaneously, whereas certain *gal* insertions have not been observed to yield *gal*$^+$ revertants. Acridine-half mustard ICR 191 is reported to be without effect on the *gal* operon insertions although it does increase the reversion frequency of many *lac* insertion mutations. Recently Michaelis, Saedler, Venkov, and Starlinger (1969) have reported that two insertion mutations in the *gal* operon, N 102 and N 116, although differing in size, contain common sequences as measured by DNA-RNA hybridization experiments.

There is still no explanation for the complete polar effect of insertion mutations. The size of the insertion cannot alone account for the polarity. A nonsense mutation situated the same distance from the beginning of the *y* gene as the beginning of the insertion DNA, approximately 750 nucleotides further than the map position of the mutation, would still synthesize appreciable permease and transacetylase (Newton et.al., 1965). The results with the acridine mustard partial revertants suggest that the sequence of bases within the insertion is responsible for the polarity effect. If the inserted DNA contained a punctuation signal for transcription termination, then no permease or transacetylase could be made. Alteration of these base sequences with mutagens might lead to partial revertants of the type containing a new low level promoter within the inserted DNA (see Morse and Yanofsky, 1969, for an example in the *trp* system).

Spontaneous reversion to full *lac*$^+$ occurs by a precise removal of the inserted DNA. Such a process would seem to require a specific recognition system and the involvement of host enzymes. At the present moment we can eliminate the involvement of the recA system, since reversion to full *lac*⁺ occurs equally well when the transducing phages are incorporated into a recA⁻ host. The insertion and removal of DNA seems analogous to the integration and detachment of substituted sex factors observed in the formation of Hfr donor strains. As a model system we have been studying the process of integration of Fts114*lac*⁺ in the system developed by Beckwith and Signer (1966).

In addition to integrations of Fts114*lac*⁺ at the T1 receptor site which lead to the formation of Hfr donor strains, we can isolate integrants which are *lac*⁺ at high temperature, are located at the T1 receptor locus, but retain no male properties. However, these abnormal integrants do lose the integrated Fts*lac*⁺ and give rise to *lac*⁻ segregants, in many cases at high frequency. Most normal and some abnormal integrants at the T1 receptor locus can give rise to chromosomal reversion; in none of these revertants has it been possible to demonstrate the reappearance of the autonomous episome.

The importance of insertion mutant formation is indicated by the fact that 14/18 or 80% of spontaneous mutants mapping in the ω region seem to be of this type. We have not yet established whether other spontaneous mutants in the α or β region of the z gene are insertions. It should be emphasized that the selection technique used to screen for *lac*⁻ mutants is biased in favor of the selection of mutants which inactivate the permease gene. This could occur by mutation in the y gene itself, or by the formation of polar mutations in the z gene. Since no other types of strong polar mutation seem to exist in the ω region, we greatly enriched our sample for insertion mutants in this region. This in no way detracts from the importance or generality of this type of mutation in bacterial evolution. The existence of partial *lac*⁺ revertants, which have 2% of the normal β-galactosidase activity but retain the inserted DNA, suggests that the process of insertion formation might not necessarily lead to the complete inactivation of the gene into which the DNA has been inserted. Under such circumstances, the cell would retain some of the old function but now would have the ability to evolve new functions, such as altered substrate affinities or reaction kinetics, by further alterations in the DNA of the insertion. These observations require that the inserted DNA be transcribed and translated in the partial revertants. This point is now under investigation.

The origin of the DNA which becomes inserted into the z gene is completely unknown. We do not know if it corresponds to another region of the bacterial chromosome or if it has an extra-chromosomal origin. The existence of extra-chromosomal plasmids in *E. coli* (Cozzarelli, Kelly, and

Kornberg, 1968) and *Shigella* strains (Rush and Warner, pers. commun.) makes it tempting to speculate that the inserted DNA arises from the integration of such a plasmid. However, no plasmids have yet been detected in our derivatives of *E. coli* K12. There is some indirect evidence that our parental strains, although females, might contain remnants of sex factors. Some of our female cells have the ability to control certain properties of an F'*gal* episome transferred to these strains by conjugation (Morrison and Malamy, unpubl.). These points will be answered by the characterization of the DNA contained in the inserted region or by finding a source of extra-chromosomal DNA in our strains. Work is in progress in our laboratory to answer these questions.

* ABBREVIATIONS:

lac, lactose; *gal*, galactose; NTG, N-methyl-N'-nitro-N-nitrosoguanidine; *trp*, tryptophan; *mel*, melibiose.

ACKNOWLEDGMENTS

The research reported in this paper was supported by grant GM14814, from the U.S. Public Health Service, National Institutes of Health, Division of General Medical Science. The author is a Faculty Research Associate of the American Cancer Society (PRA 46). Excellent technical assistance was rendered by Mrs. S. Riley and Miss M. Israel.

The author wishes to thank Dr. E. Signer and Dr. B. Müller-Hill for bacterial strains and viruses and for advice in the purification of ϕ80d*lac*. Dr. J. Beckwith has been more than generous in supplying bacterial strains.

REFERENCES

BECKWITH, J. R. 1963. Restoration of operon activity by suppressors. Biochim. Biophys. Acta 76: 162.

BECKWITH, J. R. and E. R. SIGNER. 1966. Transposition of the *lac* region of *E. coli*. I. Inversion of the *lac* operon and transduction of *lac* by ϕ80. J. Mol. Biol. 19: 254.

COZZARELLI, N., R. KELLY, and A. KORNBERG. 1968. A minute circular DNA from *E. coli* 15. Proc. Nat. Acad. Sci. 60: 992.

HARRIS, A. W., D. W. A. MOUNT, C. R. FUERST, and L. SIMINOVITCH. 1967. Mutations in bacteriophage λ affecting host cell lysis. Virology 32: 553.

JORDAN, E., H. SAEDLER, and P. STARLINGER. 1967. Strong polar mutations in the transferase gene of the galactose operon in *E. coli*. Mol. Gen. Genet. 100: 296.

———, ———, ———. 1968. 0° and strong polar mutations in the *gal* operon are insertions. Mol. Gen. Genet. 102: 353.

MALAMY, M. H. 1966. Frameshift mutations in the lactose operon of *E. coli.* Cold Spring Harbor Symp. Quant. Biol. *31:* 189.

MICHAELIS, G., H. SAEDLER, P. VENKOV, and P. STARLINGER. 1969. Two insertions in the galactose operon having different sizes but homologous DNA sequences. Mol. Gen. Genet. *104:* 371.

MORSE, D. E. and C. YANOFSKY. 1969. A transcription-initiating mutation within a structural gene of the tryptophan operon. J. Mol. Biol. *41:* 317.

NEWTON, W. A., J. R. BECKWITH, D. ZIPSER, and S. BRENNER. 1965. Nonsense mutants and polarity in the *lac* operon of *Escherichia coli.* J. Mol. Biol. *14:* 290.

PERRIN, D. 1963. Complementation between products of the β-galactosidase structural gene in *Escherichia coli.* Cold Spring Harbor Symp. Quant. Biol. *28:* 529.

SHAPIRO, J. A. 1967. The structure of the galactose operon of *E. coli* K12. Ph.D. Thesis, Univ. of Cambridge, England.

———. 1969. Mutations caused by the insertion of genetic material into the galactose operon of *Escherichia coli.* J. Mol. Biol. *40:* 93.

SZYBALSKI, W. 1968. Use of cesium sulfate for equilibrium density gradient centrifugation. *In* L. Grossman and K. Moldave [ed.] Methods in Enzymol. *12-B:* 330. Academic Press, New York.

WEIGLE, J., M. MESELSON, and K. PAIGEN. 1959. Density alterations associated with transducing ability in the bacteriophage λ. J. Mol. Biol. *1:* 379.

ULLMANN, A., D. PERRIN, F. JACOB, and J. MONOD. 1965. Identification par complémentation in vitro et purification d'un segment peptidique de la β-galactosidase d'*Escherichia coli.* J. Mol. Biol. *12:* 918.

ULLMANN, A., F. JACOB, and J. MONOD. 1967. Characterization by in vitro complementation of a peptide corresponding to an operator-proximal segment of the β-galactosidase structural gene of *Escherichia coli.* J. Mol. Biol. *24:* 339.

Cell-Free Studies on the Regulation of the *lac* Operon

G. ZUBAY, D. A. CHAMBERS and L. C. CHEONG

Department of Biological Sciences
Columbia University
New York City, New York

INTRODUCTION

The ideal test for a model of gene regulation would be the measurement of gene activity as a function of the concentration of each of the alleged regulating components. A cell-free system in which it would be possible to mix the required components in any amounts and observe the effects on gene activity would be most suitable for such studies. About four years ago our laboratory began developing such a cell-free system for the *lac* operon. At a minimum, demonstration of gene activity would require a system containing DNA, RNA polymerase, the substrates and cofactors for RNA synthesis, and a procedure for characterization of the RNA. In vitro systems that synthesize only the immediate RNA product of the gene have thus far proven ineffective for bacterial gene studies; for some unknown reason RNA polymerase in these systems does not function with sufficient discrimination. The result is a chaotic assemblage of RNA molecules whose synthesis is insensitive to in vivo gene regulating factors (Zubay, unpublished results).

Thus, the immediate challenge in developing a workable cell-free system lies in finding conditions under which RNA polymerase recognizes only true starts and true stops on the gene. In the cell-free system which we have developed, DNA-directed synthesis of the proteins of the *lac* operon has been studied. This system is quite complex, comprising a cell-free extract of *E. coli*, DNA from the defective transducing virus ϕ80d*lac* (although any DNA containing the *lac* operon is active) and the cofactors and substrates necessary for RNA and protein synthesis. We have chosen to characterize the secondary gene products or proteins rather than the

375

primary gene products or RNA because: (1) translatability supplies the most discriminating test for a particular RNA messenger and (2) an enzymatically active protein is easier to detect with high sensitivity than is an RNA. Once conditions for DNA-directed protein synthesis have been maximized, it is hoped that simplification of the system can be made so as to allow the study of DNA-directed RNA synthesis in the absence of translation.

DESCRIPTION OF THE DNA-DIRECTED CELL-FREE SYSTEM FOR β-GALACTOSIDASE SYNTHESIS

The composition of the cell-free system for β-galactosidase synthesis is given in Table 1. All the ingredients, except the cell-free bacterial extract (S-30), are mixed and preheated to 37°C. Synthesis is measured from the time of addition of S-30, 60 to 70 minutes being required for maximum synthesis. The amount of de novo synthesized β-galactosidase is quantitated by a colorimetric assay, which measures the hydrolysis of ortho-nitrophenyl-galactoside (ONPG). Two systems have been used in synthesis studies: The first system, referred to as the α-system, involves the use of S-30s containing a defective β-galactosidase protein in which a peptide segment from the operator-proximal part of the β-galactosidase polypeptide chain is deleted. When using this S-30 to produce active enzyme, only the first part of the chain of β-galactosidase, called α, need be synthesized since the de novo synthesized α-fragment can complement the defective β-galactosidase related protein present in the S-30 to produce active enzyme. The principal β-galactosidase active product of this system is believed to be a complex containing one de novo synthesized α-containing fragment and a defective dimer originating in the S-30 (de Vries and Zubay, 1969). The second synthetic system employs an S-30 prepared from a bacterial strain containing a deletion of the entire lac operon. Any enzymatic activity obtained from this system would require de novo synthesis of the complete β-galactosidase polypeptide chain essential for enzyme activity. The principal β-galactosidase active product of this system is believed to be a dimer which upon concentration is converted to a tetrameric form resembling the naturally occurring enzyme (Zubay and Chambers, 1969). Both the α-system and the lac-deletion system have been used to study lac operon activity. In each system the amount of active enzyme resulting from synthesis is proportional to the φ80 dlac DNA concentration over a wide range (at least 1 to 50 γDNA/ml). In Table 2, typical yields resulting from cell-free synthesis are indicated. The various experiments shown in Table 2 demonstrate that both transcription and translation are required to obtain β-galactosidase activity. Activities for the complete system are about 1000-fold greater than for controls in which an essential

Table 1

Composition of cell-free system

Component	Amount per ml. incubation mixture
tris-acetate, pH 8.2	44 μmoles
Dithiothreitol	1.4 μmoles
potassium acetate	55 μmoles
Twenty amino acids	0.22 μmoles
CTP, GTP, UTP	0.55 μmoles
ATP	2.2 μmoles
Trisodium phosphoenol pyruvate	21 μmoles
ammonium acetate	27 μmoles
3'5' AMP	0.5 μmoles
tRNA	100 γ
pyridoxine HCl	27 γ
triphosphopyridine nucleotide	27 γ
flavine adenine dinucleotide	27 γ
folinic acid	27 γ
p-aminobenzoic acid	11 γ
magnesium acetate	14.7 μmoles
calcium chloride	7.4 μmoles
ϕ80d*lac* DNA	50 γ
S-30	6500 γ protein

Methodology: A complete summary of all the procedures used from growth of cells to analysis of enzyme is given for the benefit of those who may wish to use cell-free synthesis studies in their work.

Growth of cells: The bacterial cells used in preparation of S-30s are grown at 28°C to mid-log phase in a New Brunswick microferm fermentor in the following medium: per liter distilled water; KH_2PO_4(anhydrous), 5.6g; K_2HPO_4(anhydrous) 28.9g; yeast extract, 10g; thiamine, 10–15mg; and 40 ml of 25% glucose added after autoclaving. Fermentors containing 10 liters of medium are inoculated with 1 liter of culture grown overnite on the same medium. About 4 hr after inoculation, cells are collected without otherwise interrupting the growth process in the fermentors. Cells from the fermentor are chilled to 2°C by passage thru a copper coil immersed in a water bath and collected in a Lourdes continuous flow centrifuge at a rate of 100 ml/min. The yield of cells is about 10gms of wet paste per liter of medium. The cells are removed from the rotor, flattened into pancakes about $\frac{1}{4}$ inch thick and allowed to freeze slowly at $-90°C$ in a Revco ultradeep-freeze. The cells are stored in this manner until used. Preparation of S-30 extract: The S-30 extract is prepared with minor modifications by the method of Nirenberg (1963). 50g of frozen cells are allowed to soften at 4°C for 30 min and washed by homogenization in a Waring blender with 500 ml of buffer I (0.01M tris-acetate, pH 8.2, 0.014M magnesiumacetate, 0.06M potassium chloride, and 0.006M 2-mercaptoethanol). The suspension is centrifuged for 30 min at 10,000 rpm in a large Serval rotor. The sediment of cells is rewashed by suspending in 200 ml of the same buffer and recentrifuged. The final sediment is resuspended in 65ml of buffer II (buffer I containing 0.001M dithiothreitol in place of 2-mercaptoethanol). The cell suspension is lysed in an Aminco pressure cell using pressures between 4000 to 8000 psi. Immediately after lysis, 1 μmole of dithiothreitol per ml is added to the lysate. No deoxyribonuclease is added to lysate. After two 30-min centrifugations at 30,000 $\times$ g, the supernatant is mixed with 8.0 ml of a solution containing:

6 mmoles tris-AC, pH 8.2, .06 mmoles dithiothreitol, .17 mmoles $Mg(Ac)_2$, .6 mmoles of the twenty amino acids, .048 mmoles ATP, 0.54 mmoles Na_3 PEP, 0.16mg PEP Kinase. The mixture is incubated in a light-protected vessel at 37°C for 80 minutes and dialyzed for 18 hours at 4°C against buffer III (buffer II containing 0.06M potassium acetate in place of the potassium chloride). The S-30 extract is rapidly frozen in 2-3ml portions and stored at −85°C. Before use, the S-30 is thawed at 4°C and used immediately.

DNA preparation: The DNA is obtained from a bacterial strain, *E. coli* HfrH, doubly lysogenic for $\phi80$ and $\phi80dlac$. The cells are grown in medium containing per liter of distilled water: bactotryptone (Difco), 10g; yeast extract, 5g; NaCl, 10g; 20% glucose, 5ml added after autoclaving and IM $CaCl_2$, 2.5ml added after autoclaving. Thirty liters of growth medium are inoculated with a 3-liter culture of the doubly lysogenic *E. coli* grown with aeration overnight at 33°C until a concentration of about 2×10^9 bacteria/ml is reached (about 3 hr). The temperature of the culture is then raised to 42°C for 7 min and then lowered to 37°C and aeration is continued about 3 hr, at which time lysis is complete. The lysate at 37° is pumped through a copper tube packed in ice water to reduce the temperature to 2°C. Subsequent steps in the isolation are carried out at 2°C. After passing through the cooling system, the liquid is transferred to a Lourdes continuous-flow system and centrifuged at 10,000 rpm in a CFR-2 rotor with a flow rate of 160ml/min. To the clear supernatant 8.4 Kg of $(NH_4)_2SO_4$ is added with stirring for 30 min. The solution is allowed to stand overnight. The precipitate is collected by centrifugation at 10,000 rpm for 10 mins. in a Lourdes VRA rotor and resuspended in 700ml of buffer (0.01 M potassium phosphate, pH 7.0; 0.01 M $MgSO_4$; 10γ/ml of bovine serum albumin) and dialyzed overnight against the same buffer. The dialyzate is centrifuged for 20 min in a Lourdes VRA rotor at 8500 rpm. The sediment is discarded. The supernatant is centrifuged for 2.7 hr at 16,500 rpm in a Lourdes 9RA rotor. The precipitate, containing the viruses, is resuspended in precisely* 130ml containing 0.01 M potassium phosphate, pH 7.0; 0.01 M $MgSO_4$, 10γ/ml of bovine serum albumin. To this solution, 98 gms of CsCl is added with stirring. The material is centrifuged for one hour at 20,000 x g. A viscous pellet at the top and some precipitate at the bottom is removed. The turbid virus-containing solution is centrifuged for an additional 23 hr at 27,000 rpm in a Spinco number 30 preparative rotor to give two virus bands. The lower one, containing the $\phi80dlac$ DNA, is removed. The pooled $\phi80dlac$ virus is dialyzed overnight against a solution 0.1 M in NaCl and 0.1 M in sodium phosphate buffer at pH 7.1 to yield a volume of 15 ml. The virus-containing solution is adjusted with the above buffer to obtain an OD at 260mμ of 13. 0.2ml of 25% sodium lauryl sulfate and an equal volume (15ml) of 88% redistilled phenol are added. The two-phase system is shaken for 2 min in a 125 ml erlenmeyer flask. Minimum agitation to assure mixing of the phases is used. After shaking, the phases are separated by centrifugation for 3 min at 20,000 x g. The top phase containing the DNA, is easily decanted because of its high viscosity. The phenol extraction is repeated twice (after each extraction the volume of the DNA solution is adjusted to the original 15 ml with the saline-phosphate buffer) and the final DNA-containing solution is dialyzed against 0.01 M versene, pH 8.0 for 16 hr followed by dialysis against 0.01 M tris-acetate, pH 8.0 for 4 hr. The final solution containing about 500γ DNA/ml is stored at 4°C over chloroform.

Incubation procedure: The amount of each component in the incubation mixture is given in μmoles or γs per ml. All components in Table 1, except the S-30, are mixed in the indicated order and warmed to 37°C for 3 min. The S-30 is added to the preheated mixture. Incubations are usually run for 70 min with shaking at 37°C. The shaking should be reasonably fast but bubbles or splashing should be avoided.

During the incubation, a viscous pellet is formed in the bottom of the tube or vessel. At

*See footnote on page 390.

the termination of the incubation, the precipitate is gently resuspended and aliquots for assay are removed.

Trouble-shooting: The DNA-directed cell-free system for β-galactosidase synthesis is more sensitive and more complex than most in vitro systems currently in use. Careful attention to the procedures described is essential if positive results are to be obtained. Decreases in activities of S-30s are noticeable after a few days. Any degradation of the DNA from enzyme or shear should be avoided. It has been found that the concentration of divalent ions and the ratio of divalent ions to PEP is a most sensitive factor in obtaining high incorporation and enzyme activity. If optimal results are not obtained, these factors should be investigated first.

step is blocked, and the activity in such controls is comparable to the spontaneous thermal rate of hydrolysis of the ONPG substrate. Activities can be precisely measured in 30 to 60 minutes, thus making the system ideally suited for quantitative studies of gene activity.

Recently we have been able to assay for the synthesis of thiogalactoside transacetylase, the operator distal enzyme of the *lac* operon. Activities obtained in the presence of DNA show only about 4-fold stimulation over controls in which the DNA is omitted. The low activity in large part is due to the poor sensitivity and selectivity of the enzyme assay. The amount of thiogalactoside transacetylase activity obtained is proportional to DNA concentration at values from 40 to 80 γDNA/ml.

Table 2

Enzymatic activities resulting from cell-free synthesis

Incubation System	β-galactosidase α-System	(units/ml) *lac*-deletion System
Complete System	6.0×10^{-3}	12×10^{-3}
no-DNA	$<.01 \times 10^{-3}$	$<.01 \times 10^{-3}$
$\phi80$ DNA instead of $\phi80dlac$ DNA	$<.01 \times 10^{-3}$	$<.01 \times 10^{-3}$
1 γ/ml Rifampicin	$<.01 \times 10^{-3}$	$<.01 \times 10^{-3}$
10^{-2}M Chloramphenicol	$<.01 \times 10^{-3}$	$<.01 \times 10^{-3}$

A unit of β-galactosidase is defined as the amount producing 1 μmole of O-nitrophenol per min at 28°C and pH 7.3.

Assays on complete incubation mixtures and controls were carried out at the end of the synthetic period by mixing 0.2 ml of incubation mixture with 1.5 ml of O-nitrophenyl-β-galactoside (ONPG) solution (0.55mg of ONPG per ml of buffer containing 0.1 M sodium phosphate, pH 7.3, and 0.14 M β-mercaptoethanol). The assay tubes were incubated for a length of time sufficient to develop significant yellow color. To terminate the assay, 1 drop of acetic acid was added to each tube to precipitate the protein. The tubes were quickly stirred, chilled on ice, and then centrifuged in the cold for 15 min at 2,000 x g. The supernatant liquid was transferred to a tube containing an equal volume of 1 M sodium carbonate. The optical density was determined at $420/420\mu$ by reading against a distilled water blank. The complete system has an OD_{420} at zero time of assay of about 0.035.

STUDIES WITH ISOPROPYL THIOGALACTOPYRANOSIDE (IPTG) AND CYCLIC 3'5' AMP

Small molecules of two classes exert a profound effect on the enzyme yield as a result of what appears to be a gene-regulating function. The first class includes inducers of the *lac* operon, of which IPTG is the strongest known. In systems, isogenic except for *lac* operon repressor, IPTG stimulates only that system containing repressor and shows no effect in a system devoid of repressor. At saturating levels of IPTG, the level of enzyme in the two systems is equal. A typical curve of the enzyme activity as a function of IPTG concentration for an S-30 containing repressor is shown in Fig. 1. The interaction of IPTG with the repressor is believed to result in the release of the latter from the operator. The amount of IPTG required to derepress the system depends upon the amount of repressor present. As predicted by the mass action law, more IPTG is required at higher levels of repressor.

The second class of small molecules exhibiting a regulating effect on enzyme yield are those associated with catabolite repression of which cyclic

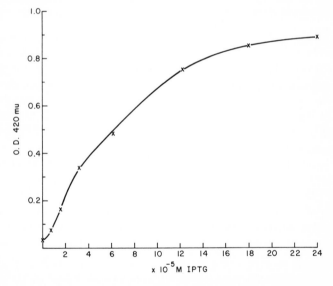

FIGURE 1. Enzyme activity as a function of IPTG concentration. The S-30 used was prepared from strain 19i^q. This strain contains the mutant repressor gene i^q and the M-15 modified β-galactosidase gene on both chromosome and episome (Zubay and Lederman, 1969). The inducer is usually added to the S-30 5 mins. before the S-30 is added to the incubation mixture, although addition as late as 5 sec before gives the same results. The ϕ80d*lac* DNA concentration was 47γ/ml incubation mixture. The O.D. 420 readings were all normalized to an assay time of 1 hr. Standard conditions for synthesis and assay were used.

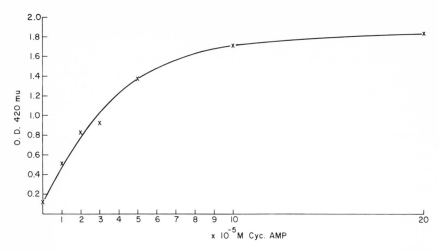

FIGURE 2. Enzyme activity as a function of cyclic 3'5' AMP concentration. The S-30 used was prepared from strain 514 which contains a deletion of the entire *lac* region including the repressor gene. The φ80d*lac* DNA concentration was 47γ/ml incubation mixture. Except for cyclic AMP variation standard conditions for synthesis and assay were used. The O.D. 420 readings were all normalized to an assay time of 2 hr.

3'5' AMP is a prime example. Cyclic AMP is usually added to the cell-free system as its omission results in greatly lessened enzyme activity (Chambers and Zubay, 1969; Zubay and Chambers, 1969). A typical curve showing the dependence of β-galactosidase activity on cyclic AMP concentration is presented in Fig. 2. Thiogalactoside transacetylase activity, the gene product of the third structural gene of the *lac* operon, is also strongly dependent upon the presence of cyclic AMP. This stimulatory effect of cyclic AMP is seen in the presence or absence of *lac* repressor.

The magnitude of the stimulatory effects obtained with IPTG or cyclic AMP when using an S-30 containing repressor are quite similar. This similarity can be demonstrated by omitting one of the reagents at the beginning of synthesis and adding it back at varying times. Such an experiment is illustrated in Fig. 3 where the enzyme yield is varied by adding either cyclic AMP or IPTG at different times after starting synthesis. The magnitude of the effect on enzyme yield is the same for the two reagents. This observation is consistent with the view that both IPTG and cyclic AMP act at points very near the initiation of RNA synthesis. These results have encouraged us to view the regulatory machinery for transcription from the *lac* operon as utilizing two molecular switches located in series. The first switch, involving the promoter locus (Ippen, et al., 1968), is turned on with the help of 3'5' AMP. The second switch, initially in the off position, is composed of a repressor-operator complex; this switch is

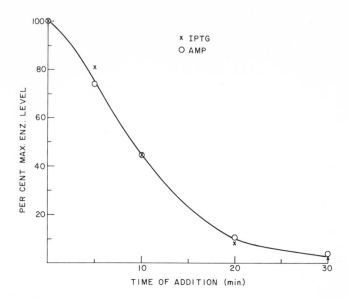

FIGURE 3. Enzyme activity as a function of the time of addition of IPTG or cyclic AMP. Two experiments are shown using the same S-30 prepared from strain Z19i^q (see Fig. 1). In one experiment $5 \times 10^{-4}M$ cyclic AMP was present throughout synthesis and $2.4 \times 10^{-4}M$ IPTG was added at 0, 10, 20 or 30 minutes after starting synthesis. In the other experiment, the use of cyclic AMP and IPTG was reversed. In all experiments the total time of synthesis was 70 minutes. Except for these variations, standard conditions for synthesis and assay were used.

activated by IPTG binding to the repressor and subsequent dissociation of the repressor-operator complex.

The proximity of the promoter and operator loci have led us to inquire into the possibility of interaction between these two molecular switches. In particular, we have wondered whether the function of the repressor-operator complex is to block initiation or propagation of RNA synthesis. If the repressor is bound at some distance from the initiation point for RNA synthesis, one wonders how the repressor-operator complex could stop initiation. On the other hand, a mechanism allowing initiation with subsequent arrest of propagation would seem inefficient. Attempts were made to demonstrate the existence of an initiation complex by allowing synthesis to begin under conditions where the vast majority of operator was complexed with repressor; this was accomplished by starting the synthesis in the presence of excess repressor with no added inducer. At varying times, rifampicin was added to block further initiation of RNA synthesis; IPTG finally was added. If the repressor-operator complex blocks propagation of RNA synthesis, one might expect some stimulation of β-galactosidase synthesis upon addition of IPTG. This stimulation would result from further transcription and translation of an "initiation complex" containing DNA, RNA polymerase and nascent RNA transcribed from the promoter to the point of the block. However, no stimulation was detected.

Observations concerning the β-galactosidase synthesized in the absence of cyclic AMP relate to the question of whether *lac* repressor normally prevents initiation or propagation of RNA synthesis. The amount of β-galactosidase activity obtained when cyclic AMP is omitted is about 5 per cent of the optimal level. This low level of activity does not result from stimulation of synthesis by endogenous cyclic AMP as shown by the fact that cyclic GMP, a potent inhibitor of cyclic AMP stimulated synthesis, has no inhibitory effect in the absence of added cyclic AMP. Other evidence suggests that in the absence of cyclic AMP a large part, if not all, of the β-galactosidase synthesis taking place results from initiations at points other than the promoter. Thus, in the presence of cyclic AMP, DNA with a defective promoter is only about 10% as effective as normal DNA in stimulation of β-galactosidase synthesis, but in the absence of cyclic AMP both DNAs are equally effective (Zubay, unpublished observations). Moreover, whereas 95% of the synthesis taking place in the presence of cyclic AMP is repressible, only about 50% is repressible in its absence. Abnormal initiations could occur on either side of the operator. In the absence of cyclic AMP, those abnormal starts that are repressible almost certainly originate at sites before the repressor-operator complex has been reached. If they are not in the promoter region, they are probably further away from the repressor-operator complex than the promoter and consequently less likely to be influenced by the presence of repressor during initiation. We have found derepression requires less IPTG under these abnormal conditions when cyclic AMP is absent. Typical results are illustrated in Fig. 4 in which the percentage of full gene expression is plotted as a function of IPTG concentration for the two sets of conditions. A possible explanation for the difference in IPTG required is that cyclic AMP-induced initiation at the usual promoter locus is blocked by the repressor-operator complex, but abnormal initiations farther from the operator are blocked at a later time during propagation. A relatively stable propagating complex could contribute substantial energy for the dissociation of the repressor-operator complex and consequently require less inducer to assist in the dissociation. Clearly more definitive results are necessary before this explanation could be accepted.

Studies were made to determine whether the action of IPTG and cyclic AMP is cooperative. For this purpose enzyme yields as a function of cyclic AMP were measured over a range of IPTG concentrations at a fixed level of repressor. The sensitivity to cyclic AMP was not appreciably affected by the level of IPTG and the maximum level of enzyme activity obtained

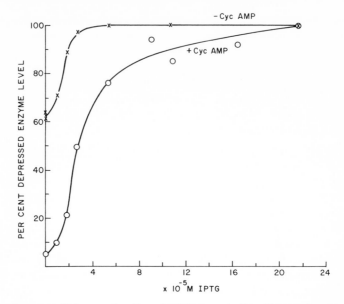

FIGURE 4. Enzyme activity as a function of IPTG concentration. The results of two experiments are shown using S-30 prepared from strain Z19i^q (see Fig. 1). In one of the experiments no cyclic AMP is added; in the other 5×10^{-4}M cyclic AMP is added at the start of synthesis. Enzyme activity is plotted in terms of the per cent of the enzyme level observed at saturating doses of IPTG. It should be remembered that the total enzyme activity observed in the presence of cyclic AMP is 10- to 20-fold greater. Except for these variations standard conditions for synthesis and assay were used.

was determined strictly by the amount of IPTG (see Fig. 5). Thus, no cooperative effect between the two triggering agents could be found.

QUANTITATIVE STUDIES ON
REPRESSOR-OPERATOR-INDUCER INTERACTION

Since the amount of enzyme activity formed in cell-free synthesis is directly proportional to DNA concentration under derepressed conditions (either no repressor present or repressor in the presence of a saturating level of inducer), it seems likely that under conditions of partial repression the amount of enzyme formed is proportional to the steady state concentration of operon which is repressor-free. Using this assumption, thermodynamic constants for the repressor-operator complex in the synthetic system have been calculated from the level of enzyme activity observed. Such studies give an estimate of the strength of the complex and tell us something about the mechanisms involved. Thus, we have concluded that one repressor molecule reacts with one operator molecule and that opti-

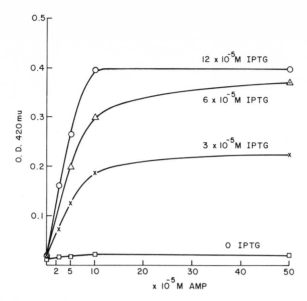

FIGURE 5. Enzyme activity as a function of cyclic 3'5' AMP concentration. The results of four experiments are shown carried out at varying levels of IPTG as indicated. The S-30 was prepared from strain Z19i^q (see Fig. 1). Except for the variation in cyclic AMP and IPTG concentrations, standard conditions for synthesis and assay were used. The O.D. 420 readings were all normalized to an assay time of one hour.

mum derepression is obtained by interaction of the "functional repressor" with two inducer molecules (Zubay and Lederman, 1969). It has also been suggested elsewhere that each tetrameric repressor molecule contains two operator binding sites and four inducer binding sites (Zubay and Lederman, 1969). Each operator binding site is sensitive to two of the inducer binding sites so that the tetrameric molecule can be visualized as two functionally independent subunits. Most arrangements for tetramers would lead to more than one operator binding site from symmetry considerations alone. The particular model described is consistent with most of the available data but requires further verification.

In the absence of inducer, the amount of "functional repressor" can be estimated by titration with DNA. At a point where the DNA has complexed all available repressor, addition of further DNA should result in full unrepressed expression. In Fig. 6, the per cent repression has been measured as a function of DNA concentration employing an S-30 prepared from a strain containing one gene copy of wild-type repressor. At very low levels of DNA, repression is 95 per cent complete. At the point where 50 per cent repression is observed, the total operon concentration is 13×10^{-10}M. If at this point nearly all the repressor is complexed to operator

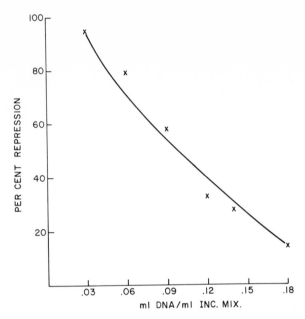

Figure 6. Per cent repression as a function of DNA concentration. Synthesis is carried out in the usual way using S-30 prepared from strain X-8554 obtained from J. Beckwith. This strain has one gene for wild-type repressor and a deletion of the entire β-galactosidase gene. At each DNA concentration studied, one tube was run with no inducer added; the other, with the saturating level of 2.4×10^{-4}M IPTG. Per cent repression is calculated from the ratio of these two values. The concentration of stock DNA solution is 420γ/ml.

and half the DNA is still unrepressed, the total repressor concentration in the system should equal half the DNA concentration or 6.5×10^{-10}M. Estimates which have been obtained similarly for the repressor concentration of strains containing the mutant i^q repressor gene on both chromosome and episome give values of 4 to 8 $\times 10^{-8}$M. Even taking into account the diploidy of the latter strains, the i^q repressor is synthesized in considerably greater amount than the wild-type repressor (Müller-Hill, Crapo, and Gilbert, 1968). The S-30 containing i^q repressor has too much repressor to be titrated directly so the S-30 was diluted with a 99-fold excess of an S-30 with no repressor and the mixture was used for the DNA titration.

When the operon concentration is fixed at a very low level, such that the total repressor concentration is always much greater than the total operator concentration, any lack of complete repression must be a measure of the dissociation of the repressor-operator complex. Provided the operon concentration can be sufficiently reduced, one should obtain an accurate measure of the formation constant of the repressor-operator complex under these conditions. Figure 7 shows such an experiment in

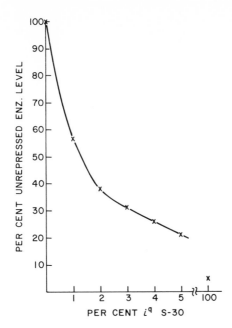

FIGURE 7. Per cent repression as a function of repressor concentration. Synthesis is carried out in the usual way with the following modifications: The repressor concentration is varied by using a mixture of two S-30's, the one containing repressor is derived from Z19i^q (see Fig. 1); the other derived from a strain isogenic with Z19i^q except for lacking a repressor gene. The abscissa is expressed in terms of per cent of i^qS-30 in total S-30 mixture and should be proportional to repressor concentration. The ordinate is expressed in terms of the per cent enzyme level attained when S-30 contains no repressor. The amount of DNA is fixed in all experiments at 3.1γ/ml incubation mixture. At 10 times this DNA concentration, the per cent repression is about the same as seen in Fig. 6 when S-30 contains 1 per cent i^qS-30. Thus, over the range of repressor concentration studied, the amount of repressor is always in large excess over the concentration of *lac* operon.

which the extent of repression is measured as a function of repressor concentration. Except for the zero point, the total repressor concentration is maintained at least 10-fold higher than the total operon so that $R_T \approx R$, where R_T represents the total repressor concentration and R represents the free repressor concentration. From the formation constant K_f^{RO} for the simplest reaction involving the reaction of one repressor molecule with one operon molecule we have

$$R + O \rightleftharpoons RO \qquad K_f^{RO} = \frac{(RO)}{(R)(O)}$$

where O represents concentration of free operon and RO represents concentration of repressor-complexed operon. Since $R_T \approx R$, a plot of

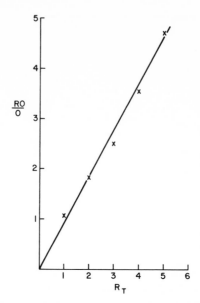

FIGURE 8. The ratio of repressor-bound operon to free operon as a function of total repressor concentration. This plot is calculated from the data presented in Fig. 7. R_T, the total repressor concentration, is plotted in arbitrary units, an estimate of its actual concentration is given in the text. Concentration of free operon is calculated from the enzyme activity at any particular point. Concentration of repressor-bound operon is calculated from the difference between the enzyme activity obtained in the absence of repressor to that obtained at any particular point on the curve in Fig. 7.

RO/O versus R_T should yield a straight line. That this is the case is seen in Fig. 8, where the data from Fig. 7 has been used. The slope of the curve in Fig. 8 should give the formation constant, K_f^{RO}. The numerical evaluation of this constant has been made using the estimated value for R_T (see above). The value obtained for K_f^{RO} is 1.6×10^9 moles^{-1} liters. The largest source of error in evaluating this constant is in determining an exact value for R_T. Comparison of the K_f^{RO} value we obtain with that where the binding of repressor to operator was measured directly (Gilbert and Müller-Hill; 1967; Riggs and Bourgeois, 1968) is difficult for several reasons: The i^q repressor binds substantially less than the wild-type repressor others have studied; the ionic strength in the synthetic system is much higher than in the system usually employed in the direct binding studies. Strength of binding is much lower at the higher ionic strength (Gilbert and Müller-Hill, 1967). When these factors are taken into account, the large differences between the values obtained for the binding constants is not surprising.

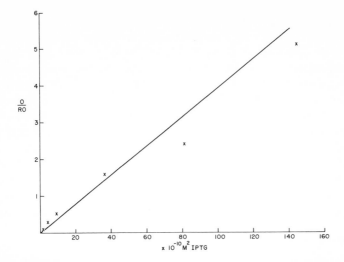

FIGURE 9. The ratio of free operon to repressor-bound operon, O/RO, as a function of (IPTG)^2. The method of calculating O and RO is similar to that used in Fig. 8; the value for O being proportional to the enzyme activity observed at any particular IPTG concentration and the value for RO being proportional to the difference between the enzyme activity observed at saturating IPTG to that observed at any particular IPTG concentration. The data used for calculation of this plot is from Fig. 1.

However, any useful comparison of values requires that the two measurements be done with the same repressor under comparable conditions.

The ratio O/RO may be calculated similarly from the derepression data shown in Fig. 1, where a large excess of repressor is present at all times and derepression is accomplished by addition of IPTG. A plot of O/RO versus the square of the IPTG concentration reveals a nearly linear relationship (Fig. 9) suggesting that the major equilibrium over the range of IPTG concentrations studied is represented by the equation

$$RO + 2I \rightleftharpoons RI_2 + O$$

where I represents IPTG, and RI_2 represents one operator binding site complexed with two IPTG molecules. Most operator-free repressor is probably in the form of RI_2 over the working range of inducer concentrations that lead to significant derepression (Zubay and Lederman, 1969).

It should be possible to independently determine the formation constant K_f^{RO} from this competitive equilibrium. This will require a careful determination of the strength of the repressor-inducer interaction constant under conditions of synthesis.

CONCLUSION

The cell-free system for β-galactosidase synthesis will probably provide the most precise and complete thermodynamic data for gene regulation. The data pertaining to formation constants of the repressor-operator complex presented herein represents a first step in this direction. This system has many other potentialities which we are just beginning to explore. Cyclic AMP, which appears to trigger RNA synthesis, has an unknown receptor. The cell-free system provides an assay that should enable detection of this receptor. The ability to detect synthesis of the third structural gene product, thiogalactoside transacetylase, should permit a study of polarity and related phenomena. Our immediate aims call for making further improvements in the efficiency of the cell-free synthesis and in applying this tool in areas where it can be used to best advantage.

ACKNOWLEDGMENTS

This work was supported by grants from the Damon Runyon Research Fund (DRG-989), the National Institutes of Health (GM 16648-01) and the American Cancer Society (Grant No. E-545).

We are deeply indebted to the following workers for strains used in this work: J. Beckwith, W. Gilbert, F. Jacob, C. Michels, J. Monod, B. Müller-Hill, A. Ullmann and D. Zipser. We are grateful to C. Michels for advice concerning the thiogalactoside transacetylase studies.

REFERENCES

CHAMBERS, D. A. and G. ZUBAY. 1969. The stimulatory effect of cyclic adenosine 3′,5′-monophosphate on DNA-directed synthesis of β-galactosidase in a cell-free system. Proc. Nat. Acad. Sci. *63:* 118.

DEVRIES, J. K. and G. ZUBAY. 1969. Characterization of a β-galactosidase formed between a complementary protein and a peptide synthesized de novo. J. Bacteriol. *97:* 1419.

GILBERT, W. and B. MÜLLER-HILL. 1967. The *lac* operator is DNA. Proc. Nat. Acad. Sci. *58:* 2415.

IPPEN, K., J. H. MILLER, J. SCAIFE and J. BECKWITH. 1968. New controlling element in the *lac* operon of E. coli. Nature *217:* 825.

MÜLLER-HILL, B., L. CRAPO, and W. GILBERT. 1968. Mutants that make more *lac* repressor. Proc. Nat. Acad. Sci. *59:* 1259.

NIRENBERG, M. W. 1963. Cell-free protein synthesis directed by messenger RNA. p. 17. *In:* S. P. Colowick and N. O. Kaplan [ed.] Methods In Enzymology. Vol. 6. Academic Press, New York.

*Recent experiments have shown that preparations of DNA are more reproducible when cells are initially resuspended in a buffer containing per liter of distilled water: 10ml of 1M Tris:HCl, pH7.6; 2.0 ml of 1M $MgSO_4$; 1.0ml of 1M $Cacl_2$; and 4 g of NaCl.

RIGGS, A. D. and S. BOURGEOIS. 1968. On the assay, isolation and characterization of the *lac* repressor. J. Mol. Biol. *34:* 361.

ZUBAY, G. and D. A. CHAMBERS. 1969. A DNA-directed cell-free system for β-galactosidase synthesis: characterization of the de novo synthesized enzyme and some aspects of the regulation of synthesis. Cold Spring Harbor Symp. Quant. Biol. *34:* 753.

ZUBAY, G. and M. LEDERMAN. 1969. DNA-directed peptide synthesis. VI. Regulating the expression of the *lac* operon in a cell-free system. Proc. Nat. Acad. Sci. *62:* 550.

Cyclic Adenosine Monophosphate Diesterase Activity and Catabolite Repression in *E. coli*

D. MONARD, J. JANEČEK*, and H. V. RICKENBERG

Division of Research
National Jewish Hospital and Research Center and
Department of Microbiology
University of Colorado School of Medicine
Denver, Colorado

Exogenous 3',5' cyclic adenosine monophosphate (cyclic AMP) overcomes the inhibition of the synthesis of β-galactosidase and of other enzymes subject to regulation by catabolite repression (Perlman and Pastan, 1968a,b; Ullmann and Monod, 1968). There is evidence that both catabolite repression and its reversal by cyclic AMP affect transcription (Perlman and Pastan, 1968b; Pastan and Perlman, 1968; Silverstone, Magasanik, Reznikoff, Miller, and Beckwith, 1969; Contesse, Crépin, and Gros, this volume). Little is known, however, about the mechanism by which an excess of catabolic over biosynthetic reactions leads to the inhibition of the transcription of genes that code for certain catabolic enzymes. Evidently an understanding of the mode of action of cyclic AMP will clarify the phenomenon of catabolite repression.

At least two mechanisms by which cyclic AMP overcomes catabolite repression may be envisaged. It may affect the interaction between RNA polymerase and the promoter (or an as yet unidentified regulatory gene adjacent to the promoter). Alternatively cyclic AMP may act as a "derepressor" by inactivating a hypothetical apo-repressor specific for catabolite repression. A third possibility that cyclic AMP in some manner lowers the rate of energy production and thus affects catabolite repression only

*Permanent address: Department of General Microbiology, Institute of Microbiology, Czechoslovak Academy of Sciences, Prague.

indirectly is rendered unlikely by the recent finding (Chambers and Zubay, 1969) that cyclic AMP enhances the synthesis of β-galactosidase in a cell-free system where presumably little energy metabolism occurs. We found that cyclic AMP at a concentration of 5×10^{-3}M slowed the rate of growth of strains AB 257 and K 12-3000 by 20 to 30 percent when glucose served as source of carbon. There is at present no experimental evidence that would permit one to differentiate between these and other conceivable mechanisms. In view of the demonstrated role of cyclic AMP as a cofactor in reactions catalyzed by mammalian protein kinases (Walsh, Perkins, and Krebs, 1968; Langan, 1968) and in view of the recent discovery of a protein kinase stimulated by cyclic AMP in *E. coli* (Kuo and Greengard, 1969), it is tempting to speculate that phosphorylation of a regulatory protein may also be involved in the function of cyclic AMP in overcoming catabolite repression.

Two predictions may be made, whatever the mechanism of action of cyclic AMP in *E. coli*: (1) An inverse relationship between the severity of catabolite repression and the cellular concentration of cyclic AMP is to be anticipated and (2) certain classes of mutants either resistant to, or hypersensitive to, catabolite repression would be expected to be abnormal with respect to their metabolism of cyclic AMP. We shall now present preliminary findings which are in accord with these predictions.

CELLULAR CONCENTRATION OF CYCLIC AMP

The findings presented in Table 1 show that when a wild-type, CR$^+$ culture was starved for carbon, the cellular concentration of cyclic AMP increased as the level of ATP fell. The inducibility of β-galactosidase was, as expected, enhanced. The increase in cyclic AMP during starvation has been observed earlier (Makman and Sutherland, 1965).

Table 2 describes experiments in which the cellular concentration of cyclic AMP was determined in cultures grown under conditions leading to low (glycerol as source of carbon), intermediate (glucose), and severe (mixture of glucose and gluconate) catabolite repression. Mutants AB 257^{pc-1} and LA-12G are resistant to catabolite repression when glucose serves as source of carbon, but are sensitive to the mixture of glucose and gluconate. Two facts emerge: (1) the cellular concentration of cyclic AMP in all strains is inversely related to the severity of catabolite repression; (2) in one mutant, but not the other, that is resistant to catabolite repression, the concentration of cyclic AMP is somewhat higher than in the wild-type strains. The differences in the concentration of cyclic AMP between cultures grown on glycerol and cultures grown on the mixture of glucose and gluconate are pronounced. Differences between cultures grown on glycerol and cultures grown on glucose and between CR$^+$ and

Table 1. Steady State Concentrations of Cyclic AMP, ATP, and β-Galactosidase-forming Capacity of AB 257 Growing on a Limiting Concentration of Glucose

Phase of bacterial growth	Cyclic AMP molar[a] $\times 10^{-5}$	ATP molar[a] $\times 10^{-3}$	β-galactosidase-forming capacity[b]
1. Log	2.4	2.7	3.8
2. Early stationary	2.4	2.2	5.1
3. Late stationary	10.8	1.3	50.0

[a] Molarity is based on the assumption of an accessible volume of 7.5×10^{-13} ml per bacterium.

[b] mμmoles of ONPG hydrolized/min/mμmole of ^{3}H-leucine incorporated; induction period = 15 min; inducer = 5×10^{-4} M thiomethyl-β-D-galactoside.

The cellular concentration of cyclic AMP was determined in the following manner. Bacteria were grown on a medium containing carrier-free ^{32}P and harvested by centrifugation at room temperature when a density of 4 to 5×10^8 bacteria/ml had been reached. The cyclic AMP was extracted by immediate resuspension of the bacterial pellet in 0.05 M HCl at 95°C and heating for 10 min. A known amount of ^{3}H cyclic AMP was added at the same time. The extract was treated with $BaSO_4$ ($ZnSO_4$ + $Ba(OH)_2$) to precipitate inorganic phosphate and the supernate submitted to ion-exchange chromatography (Dowex 2 and Dowex 50), followed by repeated treatments with $BaSO_4$. The ratio [3]H:[32]P remained constant during the later stages of the purification and thin-layer chromatography showed the radioactivity to be associated only with the spot corresponding to cyclic AMP. The recovery of cyclic AMP (calculated on the basis of recovered ^{3}H cyclic AMP) was between 40 and 50%. Details of the method will be published elsewhere. β-Galactosidase was assayed according to Müller-Hill, Rickenberg, and Wallenfels (1964). Dr. A. W. Hsie assayed ATP by the method of Forrest (1965).

Table 2. Steady State Concentration of Cyclic AMP in Growing Cultures

Strain	Source of carbon	Cyclic AMP molar $\times 10^{-5}$
AB 257 (CR[+])	Glycerol	2.6
AB 257 (CR[+])	Glucose	1.9
AB 257 (CR[+])	Glucose + gluconate	0.9
AB 257[pc-1] (CR[-])	Glycerol	5.6
AB 257[pc-1] (CR[-])	Glucose	2.7
AB 257[pc-1] (CR[-])	Glucose + gluconate	0.5
K 12-3000 (CR[+])	Glycerol	2.3
K 12-3000 (CR[+])	Glucose	1.8
K 12-3000 (CR[+])	Glucose + gluconate	0.3
LA-12G (CR[-])	Glycerol	1.0
LA-12G (CR[-])	Glucose	0.8
LA-12G (CR[-])	Glucose + gluconate	0.3

Cyclic AMP was determined as described in the legend to Table 1.

CR⁻ strains are barely significant. Conceivably either a certain threshold concentration of cyclic AMP suffices to overcome catabolite repression or the cellular concentration of cyclic AMP is subject to rapid oscillations which would not have been detected by the sampling procedures employed in our experiments. There is also the problem of the reliability of the techniques of sampling cultures for their content of cyclic AMP. We may conclude from the experiments described in Tables 1 and 2 that an inverse relationship obtains between the cellular concentration of cyclic AMP and the severity of catabolite repression.

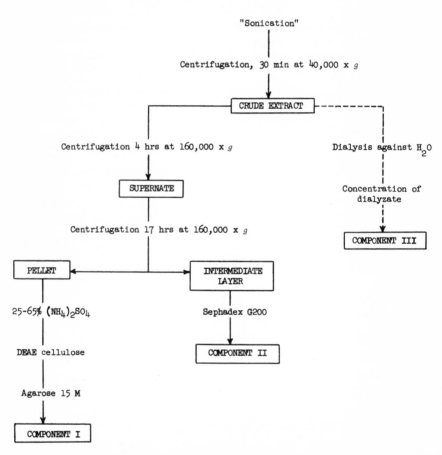

FIGURE 1. Purification of components of cyclic AMP phosphodiesterase. The purification was carried out at 0° to 4°C. The DEAE cellulose column was eluted with a 0–0.6 M NaCl gradient. It is estimated that Component I was purified 200–400-fold, Component II 50–100-fold.

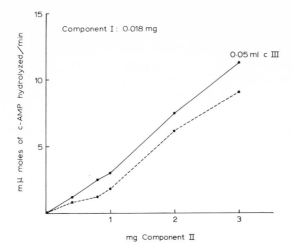

FIGURE 2. Interaction of components of cyclic AMP phosphodiesterase. Components I, II, and III were obtained as described in Fig. 1. Symbols for Figures 2 and 3:

————— no Component III   ——————— + Component III

The conditions of the assay have been published (Monard et al., 1969).

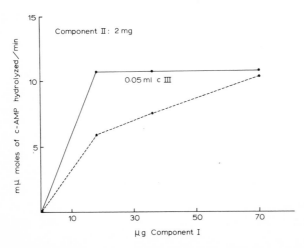

FIGURE 3. Interaction of components of cyclic AMP phosphodiesterase. Conditions and symbols as described in Fig. 2.

Table 3. Activation of Cyclic AMP Phosphodiesterase Activity of Dialyzed Crude Extract

	Addition to 4×10^{-4} M final*	Specific activity mμmoles/min/mg protein
Crude extract		25.5
Dialyzed crude extract		7.0
Dialyzed crude extract	+ Component III	15.9
Dialyzed crude extract	+ Glucose-6-P	12.1
Dialyzed crude extract	+ Fructose-6-P	11.6
Dialyzed crude extract	+ Ribose-5-P	11.1
Dialyzed crude extract	+ 6-Phosphogluconic acid	10.8
Dialyzed crude extract	+ Glucose-1-P	8.5
Dialyzed crude extract	+ Glucose-6-P + 6-Phosphogluconic acid	14.1
Dialyzed crude extract	+ Glucose-6-P + Ribose-5-P	14.0
Dialyzed crude extract	+ Glucose-6-P + Fructose-6-P	11.3
Dialyzed crude extract	+ Fructose-6-P + 6-Phosphogluconic acid	12.6
Dialyzed crude extract	+ Glucose-6-P + Fructose-6-P + 6-Phosphogluconic acid	10.1
Dialyzed crude extract	+ Glucose-6-P + Fructose-6-P + Ribose-5-P	12.6
Dialyzed crude extract	+ Fructose-1,6-diP	7.8
Dialyzed crude extract	+ Galactose-6-P	7.8
Dialyzed crude extract	+ 2-Deoxyglucose	8.6
Dialyzed crude extract	+ Fructose	7.9
Dialyzed crude extract	+ Glucose	7.8
Dialyzed crude extract	+ N-Acetylglucosamine	7.6
Dialyzed crude extract	+ 3-P-Glyceric acid	7.3
Dialyzed crude extract	+ 2-P-Glyceric acid	6.6
Dialyzed crude extract	+ Glyceraldehyde-3-P	7.8
Dialyzed crude extract	+ Glycerol	7.0

Preparation of the extracts and Component III as well as conditions of assay were the same as described (Monard et al., 1969).

* In the case of mixtures, each component added to final concentration of 4×10^{-4} M.

THE CYCLIC AMP PHOSPHODIESTERASE OF CR⁺ AND CR⁻ STRAINS

The fact that the cellular concentration of cyclic AMP was affected by conditions of growth indicates that these should also be reflected in the adenyl cyclase and the cyclic AMP phosphodiesterase activity of the cell. After initially abortive attempts to isolate adenyl cyclase from *E. coli* we turned our attention to the cyclic AMP phosphodiesterase and succeeded in partially purifying an enzyme complex which degrades cyclic AMP to 5′ AMP. At least two proteins and a dialyzable fraction are required for maximal cyclic AMP phosphodiesterase activity (Monard, Janeček, and Rickenberg, 1969). Figure 1 describes the method of purification employed. Figures 2 and 3 illustrate the interaction of the partially purified components. Preliminary observations indicate that the formation of Component I is not significantly affected by conditions of growth. The concentration of Component II appears to be higher in cells grown under conditions of severe catabolite repression than in cells grown under conditions of low catabolite repression. We have no information on the effect of conditions of growth on the cellular concentration of the dialyzable, and presumably heterogeneous, Component III.

We speculate that Component III may include several intermediates of energy metabolism which activate cyclic AMP phosphodiesterase activity. The results presented in Table 3 support this assumption. Several phosphorylated hexoses and pentoses stimulated the cyclic AMP phosphodiesterase activity of a crude extract from which Component III had been removed by dialysis. The possibility that the presence in optimal concentrations of several intermediates is required for maximal cyclic AMP phosphodiesterase activity should be considered.

An involvement of cyclic AMP phosphodiesterase in the mediation of catabolite repression in *E. coli* is also indicated by the finding that two CR⁻ mutants tested by us were abnormal with respect to their cyclic AMP phosphodiesterase activity (Monard et al., 1969). One may predict the occurrence of other mutants with defects in adenyl cyclase activity. One such mutant has in fact been described (Perlman and Pastan, 1969). Evidently an elucidation of the mode of action of cyclic AMP requires the isolation of yet another class of mutants unresponsive to either endogenous or exogenous cyclic AMP and hence presumably defective in the regulatory component affected by cyclic AMP. Efforts to isolate such mutants are currently under way in our laboratory.

ACKNOWLEDGMENTS

The work described here was supported by Grant No. AM 11046 from the National Institutes of Health and Grant No. GB-8292 from the National Science Foundation.

REFERENCES

CHAMBERS, D. A. and G. ZUBAY. 1969. The stimulatory effect of cyclic adenosine 3′,5′-monophosphate on DNA-directed synthesis of β-galactosidase in a cell-free system. Proc. Nat. Acad. Sci. *63:* 118.

FORREST, W. W. 1965. Adenosine triphosphate pool during the growth cycle in streptococcus faecalis. J. Bact. *90:* 1013.

KUO, J. F. and P. GREENGARD. 1969. An adenosine 3',5'-monophosphate-dependent protein kinase from *E. coli.* J. Biol. Chem. *244:* 3417.

LANGAN, T. A. 1968. Histone phosphorylation: stimulation by adenosine 3',5'-monophosphate. Science *162:* 579.

MAKMAN, R. S. and E. W. SUTHERLAND. 1965. Adenosine 3',5'-phosphate in *E. coli.* J. Biol. Chem. *240:* 1309.

MONARD, D., J. JANEČEK, and H. V. RICKENBERG. 1969. The enzymic degradation of 3',5' cyclic AMP in strains of *E. coli* sensitive and resistant to catabolite repression. Biochem. Biophys. Res. Commun. *35:* 584.

MÜLLER-HILL, B., H. V. RICKENBERG, and K. WALLENFELS. 1964. Specificity of the induction of the enzymes of the *lac* operon in *E. coli.* J. Mol. Biol. *10:* 303.

PASTAN, I. and R. L. PERLMAN. 1968. The role of the *lac* promotor locus in the regulation of β-galactosidase synthesis by cyclic 3',5'-adenosine monophosphate. Proc. Nat. Acad. Sci. *61:* 1336.

PERLMAN, R. and I. PASTAN. 1968a. Cyclic 3',5'-AMP: stimulation of β-galactosidase and tryptophanase induction in *E. coli.* Biochem. Biophys. Res. Commun. *30:* 656.

———, ———. 1968b. Regulation of β-galactosidase synthesis in *E. coli* by cyclic adenosine 3',5'-monophosphate. J. Biol. Chem. *243:* 5420.

———, ———. 1969. Pleiotropic deficiency of carbohydrate utilization in an adenyl cyclase deficient mutant of *E. coli.* Biochem. Biophys. Res. Commun. *37:* 151.

SILVERSTONE, A. E., B. MAGASANIK, W. S. REZNIKOFF, J. H. MILLER, and J. R. BECKWITH. 1969. Catabolite sensitive site of the *lac* operon. Nature *221:* 1012.

ULLMANN, A. and J. MONOD. 1968. Cyclic AMP as an antagonist of catabolite repression in *E. coli.* Fed. Europ. Biochem. Soc. Letters *2:* 57.

WALSH, D. A., J. P. PERKINS, and E. G. KREBS. 1968. An adenosine 3',5'-monophosphate-dependent protein kinase from rabbit skeletal muscle. J. Biol. Chem. *243:* 3763.

On the Mechanism of Catabolite Repression

G. CONTESSE, M. CRÉPIN, F. GROS, A. ULLMANN*, and J. MONOD*

Institut de Biologie Moléculaire, Faculté des Sciences
Paris and *Institut Pasteur, Paris

It has long been established that the presence of glucose or of an actively metabolizable carbon source inhibits the synthesis of certain bacterial enzymes, a situation usually referred to as catabolite repression. In spite of considerable work devoted to this phenomenon, little is known about its molecular mechanism.

Experiments by Nakada and Magasanik (1964), Loomis and Magasanik (1967), Tyler and Magasanik (1969) and by Jacquet and Kepes (1969) strongly support the idea that catabolite repression affects gene expression at the transcriptional rather than at the translational level. Moreover, studies by Pastan and Perlman (1968), Perlman et al. (1969), and Silverstone et al. (1969) indicate that certain mutations within the promoter site of the *lac* operon generate almost complete resistance to catabolite repression, which one would tend to interpret as showing that initiation of message synthesis is the sensitive step.

Involvement of 3′,5′ cyclic AMP in these phenomena was first suggested by work by Makman and Sutherland (1965) indicating that *E. coli* cells grown in the presence of glucose as a carbon source contain less of this nucleotide than cells maintained in milder repressing conditions. Quite significantly, it was shown by Ullmann and Monod (1968) and Perlman and Pastan (1968) that the presence of 3′,5′ cyclic AMP almost completely overcomes the transient or permanent glucose effect on β-galactosidase synthesis.

In this paper we wish to describe some experiments aimed at obtaining more information on the target and molecular mechanism of the catabolite effect.

Our results confirm that catabolite repression operates at the level of

401

initiation while also showing that some of its effects may become manifest only after transcription has actually been initiated.

RESULTS

It is known that the magnitude of catabolite repression depends not only on the nature of the carbohydrate itself, but also on the availability of a source of nitrogen. Thus it is an important requirement for the study of catabolite repression to set up standardized conditions under which the effect is either maximized or minimized.

The conditions of maximal derepression can be achieved using a slowly metabolized carbon source and a rapidly assimilated nitrogen source. Conversely, maximal repression can be obtained in the presence of a rapidly metabolizable source of carbon and a slowly utilizable source of nitrogen.

Table 1 summarizes observations on the differential rate of β-galactosidase synthesis under constant conditions of induction and in the presence of different carbon and nitrogen sources. As can be seen from

Table 1. Strain 3000 (wild-type) was induced with IPTG 5 $\times$ 10^{-4}M and the differential rate of β-galactosidase synthesis was followed for a period of two generation times. Cyclic AMP at 5 $\times$ 10^{-3}M was added to the cultures 5 minutes prior to the induction. The results are expressed in units of β-galactosidase/mg dry weight bacteria. (Abbreviations: IPTG = isopropyl-β-D-thiogalactoside; Gly-glu = glycyl-glutamate; His-glu = histidyl-glutamate).

Carbon source	Nitrogen source	Cy AMP	U/mg β-galactosidase
Succinate	(NH$_4$)$_2$SO$_4$	−	13,500
		+	13,400
Glycerol	(NH$_4$)$_2$SO$_4$	−	7,600
		+	9,500
Glucose	(NH$_4$)$_2$SO$_4$	−	4,400
		+	10,800
Glucose + fructose + ribose	(NH$_4$)$_2$SO$_4$	−	2,900
		+	10,600
Glucose	His-glu	−	60
		+	2,340
Glucose	Gly-glu	−	140
		+	4,500
Glucose	Glutamate	−	100
		+	4,300

Table 1, depending upon experimental conditions, one can achieve a spectrum of repression and derepression, varying by a factor of 200.

Moreover we isolated some mutants which show a very high sensitivity to catabolite repression. In one of these mutants (2AY36), when grown on glucose + $(NH_4)_2SO_4$ (generation time 80 min), the differential rate of β-galactosidase synthesis is of the order of 100 (as compared to a differential rate of 5000 obtained with the wild type), and is released in the presence of cyclic AMP to wild-type levels, that is to say 10,000.

Strain 2AY36 isolated in our laboratory has a very high sensitivity to catabolite repression; has not as yet been mapped but the mutation is not in the *lac* region. In glucose chemostat or by addition of cyclic AMP it can be derepressed to wild-type β-galactosidase (and acetylase) levels. The strain grows on glucose with a generation time of 80 min and does not grow on any other sugar. Therefore in all experiments where the carbon source was not glucose, the medium had to be supplemented with casaminoacids (see legends). This mutant was subsequently used in many experiments described in the following sections.

STUDIES ON THE GENETIC TARGET OF CATABOLITE REPRESSION

Experiments by Magasanik (1961) already suggested that, in the case of the lactose system, mutations altering the properties of the repressor or the operator do not modify the sensitivity of the operon to catabolite repression. We have reinvestigated this problem under conditions of severe catabolite repression (where the differential rate of β-galactosidase synthesis drops to 1% of the fully-induced level) and we found that all o^c and *i* mutants are as sensitive to catabolite repression as the wild type.

Sixteen different o^c mutants and five different i^- mutants were tested. They were tested under conditions where the magnitude of the catabolite repression was of the order of 99%. The magnitude of the repression varied between 98.4% and 99.6% for the different mutants (the wild type being 99.4%).

We also tested the sensitivity of strains bearing large deletions lacking the operator-promoter-regulator genes, and in which the *lac* region is fused to an unfortunately unknown segment of the genome. In such strains no synthesis of β-galactosidase can be detected while the ω peptide corresponding to the *z* distal segment is still produced, as are the thiogalactoside permease and transacetylase enzymes. Table 2 shows that the rates of ω-peptide and transacetylase synthesis are severely reduced under catabolite repression, this effect being released by cyclic AMP.

Results from these studies confirm that the *lac*-repressor-operator

Table 2. Strains B9 and O5 (large deletions) and M15 (small deletion) were grown on carbon and nitrogen sources as indicated. After six generations, extracts were prepared and ω and transacetylase assayed. The results are expressed in units/mg dry weight bacteria (abbreviations: NAGA = N-acetyl-D-glucosamine. For map positions of the deletions see Ullmann and Perrin, this vol.).

Strain	C source	N source	Cy AMP 5.10^{-3}M	U/mg ω	U/mg Ac
B9	Glycerol	$(NH_4)_2SO_4$	−	25	37
	Glucose	$(NH_4)_2SO_4$	−	4.5	6.9
	Glucose	$(NH_4)_2SO_4$	+	21	43
	Glucose	NAGA	−	0.67	2.6
O5	Glycerol	$(NH_4)_2SO_4$	−	9.5	23
	Glucose	$(NH_4)_2SO_4$	−	1.6	6.2
M15	Glycerol	$(NH_4)_2SO_4$	−	38	80
	Glucose	$(NH_4)_2SO_4$	−	7.1	29
	Glucose	Glutamate	−	1.6	1.7

interaction is not involved in the catabolic effect; moreover they lead one to think (Table 2) that either the integrity of the promoter site is not required for a strong catabolite repression effect to be exerted, or that the deletions we tested are fused to an operon which is sensitive to catabolite repression.

DECOORDINATION OF THE *lac* OPERON

In a series of experiments we compared the rate of synthesis of β-galactosidase and transacetylase under various conditions of catabolite repression, and we obtained the following results (Table 3): as long as repression remains relatively mild, the ratio of β-galactosidase to trans-acetylase synthesis is remarkably constant. However, when the repression is of the order of 95% or more, the ratio of β-galactosidase to transacety-lase increases over 10-fold. In other words, the repression appears to be much stronger in respect to transacetylase (the last enzyme of the operon) than to β-galactosidase, which is the first protein to be translated. It can also be seen from Table 3 that cyclic AMP restores completely the modified ratio.

These experiments suggest that either the transcription of the poly-cistronic messenger, or the translation of the protein has been interrupted, and consequently the last enzyme of the operon is formed at a much lower rate.

In order to obtain more information about the mechanism of the de-

Table 3. Wild-type strain was induced with IPTG in the absence ($-$) or presence ($+$) of Cy AMP 5×10^{-3}M. After a period of three generation times the differential rate of β-galactosidase (GZ) and thiogalactoside transacetylase (AC) were measured, and the ratio between the two are shown in the last column. β-galactosidase was measured by usual techniques, while transacetylase was assayed by a modification of the technique described by Leive and Kollin (1967). Under our assay conditions transacetylase activity can be linearly measured down to 0.002 U/mg.

Carbon source	Nitrogen source	Cy AMP	U/mg β-galactosidase	U/mg Transacetylase	Ratio GZ/AC
Succinate	$(NH_4)_2SO_4$	$-$	20,400	71	290
Glycerol	$(NH_4)_2SO_4$	$-$	10,000	33	300
Glucose	$(NH_4)_2SO_4$	$-$	5,000	17	290
Glucose	$(NH_4)_2SO_4$	$+$	12,000	38.5	310
Glucose	Glutamate	$-$	100	0.025	4,000
Glucose	Glutamate	$+$	4,300	13.8	310
Glucose	Gly-Glu	$-$	182	0.024	7,600
Glucose	Gly-Glu	$+$	2,800	6.4	440

coordination phenomenon, it seemed necessary to study the general features of the *lac* specific messenger RNA (mRNA) synthesis.

EFFECT OF CATABOLITE REPRESSION ON
lac mRNA TRANSCRIPTION

We have investigated in detail how "glucose repression" affects the rate at which the lactose operon from *E. coli* is transcribed. The DNA-RNA annealing technique was used and DNA from a ϕ_{80}d*lac* transducing phage ($\lambda C_{I~857}h_{80}$d*lac*) served as detector for *lac* specific mRNA (Contesse et al., 1966) after alkaline denaturation and irreversible binding to a nitrocellulose membrane filter (Gillespie and Spiegelman, 1965). In many of these studies we used *E. coli* 2YA36, a strain in which a strong inhibition of β-galactosidase synthesis by glucose can be achieved.

The pattern of *lac* mRNA synthesis during induction of a glycerol-grown culture was first studied as a control. Twenty second pulses of H^3 uracil were given every 10 sec from the induction onset, and radioactive RNA samples were separately hybridized to excess ϕ_{80}d*lac* DNA (Fig. 1). The distribution of points obtained by plotting each percent hybridization value vs. the time at which labeling is initiated is suggestive of a stepwise increase in rates of messenger transcription, a phenomenon analogous to what has already been described upon derepression of the tryptophan operon by Baker and Yanofsky (1968) and Imamoto (1968).

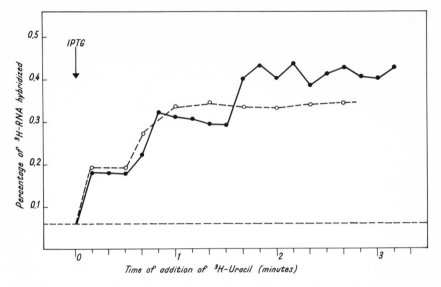

FIGURE 1. *Kinetics of lac mRNA synthesis (initial rates) during the early induction period.* *E. coli* MO was grown at 32°C on 63 medium supplemented with B_1, casaminoacids and glycerol. At an OD corresponding to 5×10^8 cells/ml, 5×10^{-4} M IPTG was added and every 10 sec, 5 ml samples were withdrawn, pulse-labeled for 20 sec with 20 µCi/ml H^3 uracil (20 Ci/mM). Labeling was stopped by pouring on 5 ml frozen medium containing 20% sucrose and 0.02 M sodium azide. RNA was then extracted by the conventional lysozyme-SDS technique after repeated freezing and thawing cycles, using cold phenol as deproteinizing agent. The hybridization percentage of each RNA preparation was determined either with 1 µg ϕ_{80}d*lac* DNA ——●—— or 1 µg ϕ_{80}EZ$_1$ DNA – – –○– – –.

The horizontal dotted line materializes the background (non-induced) level. It was determined by averaging the percent hybridization values calculated from two independent samples pulse-labeled 20 sec in the absence of IPTG. Results are expressed in percent hybridization versus the time at which labeling was initiated in the relevant sample. The percent hybridization values, using non transducing ϕ_{80} DNA as a detector were usually close to 0.01%.

When IPTG was added to a culture of 2AY36 which had been grown for many generations on a glucose-containing medium, the curve depicting the changes in the rate of *lac* mRNA synthesis (Fig. 2a) differed markedly from the one observed with a glycerol-grown culture. Instead of the transcription pattern characteristic of glycerol-grown cells, the curve displayed a "sawtooth" appearance, with important "bursts" of synthesis spaced approximately every 2 min. At each burst, the rate corresponding to the *maximal* level achieved in a glycerol-casaminoacid-grown culture was reached in about 20 sec. (This characteristic pattern is observed not only with the catabolite sensitive mutant, but also with the wild-type strain, as shown in Fig. 3). When cyclic AMP was added 1 min *before* IPTG a "glycerol-like" pattern of *lac* RNA synthesis was again observed (Fig. 2b).

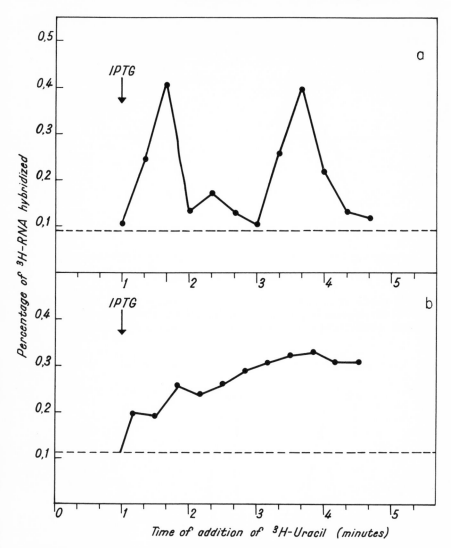

FIGURE 2. *Kinetics of* lac *mRNA synthesis during induction of glucose-grown 2AY36 cells.*
(a) A culture of 2AY36 pregrown on glucose was induced with 5×10^{-4} M IPTG, and the
rates of *lac* mRNA synthesis were measured as previously described for the MO strain
(Fig. 1). (b) 5×10^{-3} M 3′,5′ cyclic AMP was added 1 min before IPTG.

Cyclic AMP could also antagonize the catabolite repression effect on *lac*
operon transcription when added *after* the inducer (Fig. 4).

That the sawtooth pulse-labeling pattern is primarily a *lac* specific
phenomenon and is not related to some type of oscillating variations in
the nucleotide precursor pool is evidenced by the control in Fig. 5: both

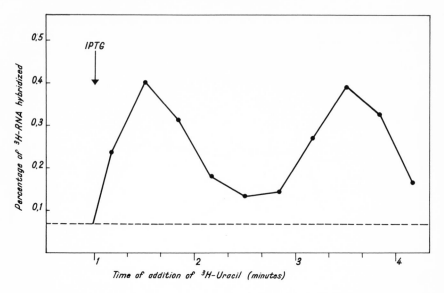

FIGURE 3. *Kinetics of lac mRNA synthesis during induction of glucose-grown MO cells.* A culture of MO pregrown on glucose was induced with 5×10^{-4} M IPTG, and the rates of *lac* mRNA synthesis were measured as previously described in Fig. 1 and 2.

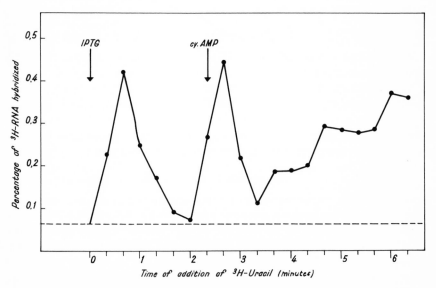

FIGURE 4. *Pattern of lac mRNA synthesis after suppression of catabolite repression by cyclic AMP.* A culture of 2AY36 grown on glucose is induced by IPTG and 130 sec later 5×10^{-3} M cyclic AMP is added.

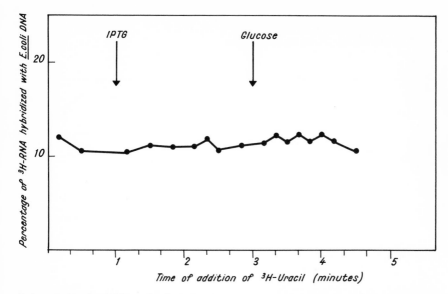

FIGURE 5. *Total mRNA synthesis in glycerol- and glucose-grown cultures of 2AY36.* 1% glucose was added to a 2 min IPTG induced culture of 2AY36 pregrown on glycerol. Rates of total (non-*lac*) mRNA synthesis were determined by measuring the percent hybridization values of 20 sec pulse-labeled RNA with 50 μg of *E. coli* Δ*lac* DNA. This DNA was derived from 2000 × 74 m, a strain bearing a complete deletion of the *lac* region.

the specific radioactivity of total RNA after each pulse, and the transcription rates, measured by hybridizing each sample to *total E. coli* DNA, remained constant during the experiment.

One way to interpret the "multi-bursts" pattern from glucose-grown cells was to assume that, during catabolite repression, many polymerase molecules (approximately three times the number corresponding to an elementary step) would initiate the synthesis of the operon-specific RNA, leading to a rapid and important increase in transcription rate, but that very few of these molecules would reach the operator distal end. This interpretation is clearly supported by the following experiment. Two cultures of 2AY36, grown either on mineral medium plus glycerol-casamino acid or on the same medium plus glucose, were induced for 30 min, a time sufficiently long to desynchronize *lac* operon transcription. At the end of this period, both cultures were pulse labeled with H^3 uracil for different lengths of time and each RNA sample was separately hybridized with ϕ_{80}d*lac* and ϕ_{80} EZ$_1$ DNA (phage ϕ_{80} EZ$_1$ carries only the *z* gene plus a very small portion of *y*). Results shown in Fig. 6 clearly indicate that, regardless of the pulse duration, the ϕ_{80}d*lac*/ϕ_{80}EZ$_1$ hybridization ratio which was close to 1.4 for the *glycerol*-grown cells never exceeded 0.9 in

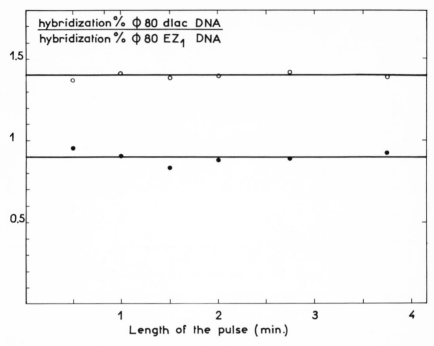

Figure 6. *Abortive transcription of the* lac *operon during catabolite repression.* Two parallel cultures of 2AY36 on 63 medium supplemented with casaminoacids and either with glucose or with glycerol, were induced with IPTG during 30 min. After this period each culture was labeled with H^3 uridine (10 μCi/ml) for different lengths of time. Samples were processed as usual for hybridization.

——o—— glycerol grown
——•—— glucose grown

the glucose induced culture. When cyclic AMP was added to the culture induced by IPTG in a glucose-containing medium the *hybridization ratio* was raised from 1 to 1.4 in approximately 1 min (Fig. 7). The best interpretation for these results is that under catabolite repression many RNA polymerases stop propagating at the end of the *z* gene or before, and that cyclic AMP can relieve this effect. The possibility that the *lac* operon could be transcribed in its entirety but that the RNA portion corresponding to the *y* and *ac* regions would be rapidly destroyed appears unlikely since, contrary to the situation described with strong polar mutants of *z* (Contesse et al., in prep.; Morse and Yanofsky 1969), the ϕ_{80}d*lac*/ϕ_{80}EZ$_1$ hybridization ratio is not greater after very short than after prolonged labeling periods. Sucrose gradient centrifugation analyses indicate that

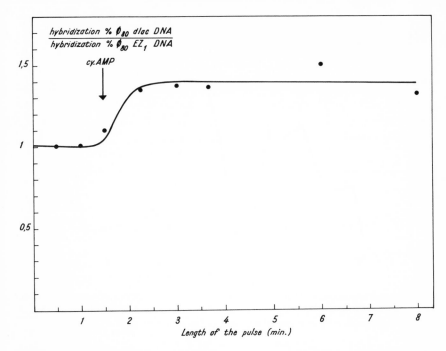

FIGURE 7. *Suppressive effect of cyclic AMP on "abortive transcription."* After an induction period of 30 min a glucose grown culture of 2AY36 received 10 μCi/ml H[3] uridine (20 μCi/mM) and this was followed 90 sec later, by 5×10^{-3} M cyclic AMP. Aliquots were then removed at various times and treated as for Fig. 6. The arrow shows the time when cyclic AMP was added.

$\phi_{80}dlac$ hybridizable RNA derived from glucose-grown induced cultures of 2AY36 contains very little material sedimenting faster than 10 S, whereas chains sedimenting at 30 S exist in very appreciable amounts within the material from glycerol-grown cultures (Contesse et al., data not shown).

The effect of "transient glucose repression" on the *lac* RNA forming capacity from a glycerol-grown IPTG induced culture was qualitatively similar to the one described for cells pregrown on glucose, albeit even more striking. Figure 8 for instance illustrates the incidence of glucose addition when the second round of *lac* RNA transcription consecutive to induction had been achieved. In less than 30 sec the rate of *lac* specific RNA synthesis declined to practically background level; the *lac* RNA forming capacity resumed and again followed a sinusoidal pattern with a 3 min periodicity. Moreover, it was shown that adding glucose to a glycerol-grown culture induced and treated immediately afterwards with rifampicin

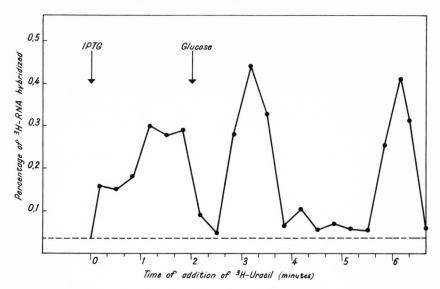

FIGURE 8. *Effect of glucose addition (transient repression) on* lac *mRNA synthesis.* 1% glucose was added to a 2 min IPTG induced culture of 2AY36, pregrown on glycerol. Rates of *lac* mRNA synthesis were determined as usual before and after glucose addition.

(Fig. 9) to block further reinitiation cycles did cause transcription of the *lac* operon to completely stop in about 20 sec. It therefore looks as if the transient glucose effect could, at least temporarily, inhibit the propagation of RNA growing points along repressible operons.

DISCUSSION

Many of the effects presently described point towards the fact that catabolite repression can interfere with gene expression at some other steps besides the initiation of transcription.

One such an effect is the sensitivity of *lac* promoter deletion mutants to (strong) catabolite repression as evidenced by the marked inhibition of ω peptide and transacetylase synthesis. The possibility nevertheless exists that, in these mutants, the remaining part of the *lac* operon is fused to a segment containing a "repression sensitive" promoter.

That the catabolic effect might deal with the process of RNA chain elongation is more directly supported by kinetic studies on *lac* mRNA synthesis.

Although "transient" or "permanent" glucose repression both seem to affect the initiation frequency of message synthesis as shown by the increase observed in the periodicity with which the *lac* operon is tran-

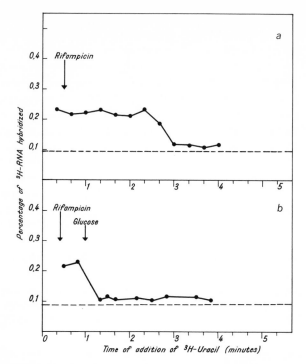

FIGURE 9. *Effect of transient repression on a single* lac *transcription round.* (a) 10^{-3} M EDTA treated cells (*E. coli* 2AY36) were induced 30 sec with 5×10^{-4} M IPTG. Rifampicin was added 30 sec after the induction onset and rates of *lac* mRNA synthesis were determined as described for Fig. 1. (b) Glucose added at 0.4% final concentration 1 min after the beginning of induction to the 2AY36 culture treated in the same way as in (a).

scribed, other features of the kinetics are interpretable on the basis of some arrest in the propagation of the RNA polymerase. This applies to the multi-bursts pattern of RNA synthesis when the *lac* operon is induced under catabolite repression. Each "burst" lasts no longer than 20 sec; a time insufficiently long for the polymerase to cover the entire operon length. Comparative annealing studies further establish that *lac* specific RNA from a strain induced for at least half a generation in the presence of glucose is lacking portions complementary to the *y* and *a* genes and possibly also to part of the *z* gene.

The cessation of RNA polymerase progression, as the enzyme moves away from the initiation point accounts well for the above described decoordination phenomenon. If a portion of polymerase molecules cannot reach the acetylase gene, it is clear that the ratio of acetylase/β-galactosidase will decrease. But if the interruption occurs before the distal end of the *z* gene, the abortive message thus formed will not be revealed as β-galactosidase. We have measured by in vitro complementation tests the N-terminal fragment of β-galactosidase (α-peptide), representing about $\frac{1}{5}$ of the total molecule, and corresponding to the operator proximal segment of the z gene. In a few preliminary experiments we measured the ratio of α-peptide vs. the total enzyme, synthesized by strain 2AY36 grown in the absence and presence of cyclic AMP. If in the presence of cyclic AMP this ratio equals 1, in its absence it is increased by a factor of 4 to 5. This means that under conditions of catabolite repression only 20% of the initiated polypeptide chains can go to completion.

Initiation of transcription may be considered to involve primarily the formation of a "competent" complex between DNA (specifically promoter DNA) and RNA polymerase. The data presented here together with the results of Beckwith and Magasanik (Silverstone et al., 1969) suggest that it is the formation of such a complex which is rendered less frequent or less efficient under conditions of catabolite repression. Abortive transcription might then be considered to result from the formation of defective initiation complexes. This interpretation does not necessarily imply that cyclic AMP plays a direct role in promoting the formation of the complex. The results recently obtained by Chambers and Zubay (1969) using an in vitro system appear to suggest however that the effect might be a direct one.

The most tempting speculation is to assume that cyclic AMP exerts directly a positive control over the initiation of transcription at the level of the promoter of glucose sensitive operons. The recent findings of the Harvard and MIT groups (Travers and Burgess, 1969; Losick and Sonenshein, 1969) concerning σ factor which specifies, and thereby controls, the initiation of transcription by RNA polymerase, make such a speculation at least permissible.

ACKNOWLEDGMENTS

We are grateful to A. Malhié and F. Tillier for skillful technical aid.

This work has been aided by grants from the Centre National de la Recherche Scientifique, the Commissariat à l'Energie Atomique, the Délégation Générale à la Recherche Scientifique et Technique, the National Institutes of Health, the Fondation pour la Recherche Médicale Française and the Ligue Française contre le Cancer.

REFERENCES

BAKER, R. and C. YANOFSKY. 1968. The periodicity of RNA polymerase initiations: a new regulatory feature of transcription. Proc. Nat. Acad. Sci. *60:* 313.

CHAMBERS, D. and G. ZUBAY. 1969. The stimulatory effect of cyclic adenosine 3'–5' monophosphate on DNA directed synthesis of β-galactosidase in cell free system. Proc. Nat. Acad. Sci. *63:* 118.
CONTESSE, G., S. NAONO, and F. GROS. 1966. Effet des mutations polaires sur la transcription de l'opéron lactose chez *Escherichia coli.* Compt. Rend. Acad. Sci., Paris. *263:* 1007.
GILLESPIE, D. and S. SPIEGELMAN. 1965. A quantitative assay for DNA-RNA hybrids with DNA immobilized on a membrane. J. Mol. Biol. *12:* 829.
IMAMOTO, F. 1968. On the initiation of transcription of the tryptophan operon in *Escherichia coli.* Proc. Nat. Acad. Sci. *60:* 305.
JACQUET, M. and A. KÉPÈS. 1969. The step sensitive to catabolite repression and its reversal by 3'–5' cyclic AMP during induced synthesis of β-galactosidase in *E. coli.* Biochem. Biophys. Res. Commun. *36:* 84.
LEIVE, L. and V. KOLLIN. 1967. Synthesis, utilization and degradation of lactose operon mRNA in *Escherichia coli.* J. Mol. Biol. *24:* 247.
LOOMIS, W. Jr. and B. MAGASANIK. 1967. The catabolite repression gene of the *lac* operon in *Escherichia coli.* J. Mol. Biol. *23:* 487.
LOSICK, R. and A. SONENSHEIN. 1969. Change in the template specificity of RNA polymerase during sporulation of *Bacillus subtilis.* Nature *224:* 35.
MAGASANIK, B. 1961. Catabolite repression. Cold Spring Harbor Symp. Quant. Biol. *26:* 193.
MAKMAN, R. and E. SUTHERLAND. 1965. Adenosine 3'–5' phosphate in *Escherichia coli.* J. Biol. Chem. *240:* 1309.
MORSE, D. and C. YANOFSKY. 1969. Polarity and the degradation of mRNA. Nature, *224:* 329.
NAKADA, D. and B. MAGASANIK. 1964. The roles of inducer and catabolite repressor in the synthesis of β-galactosidase by *Escherichia coli.* J. Mol. Biol. *8:* 105.
PASTAN, I. and R. PERLMAN, 1968. The role of the *lac* promoter locus in the regulation of β-galactosidase synthesis by cyclic 3'–5' adenosine monophosphate. Proc. Nat. Acad. Sci. *61:* 1336.
PERLMAN, R., B. DE CROMBRUGGHE, and I. PASTAN. 1969. Cyclic AMP regulate catabolite and transient repression in *Escherichia coli.* Nature *223:* 810.
PERLMAN, R. and I. PASTAN. 1968. Cyclic 3'–5'-AMP: stimulation of β-galactosidase and tryptophanase induction in *Escherichia coli.* Biochem. Biophys. Res. Commun. *30:* 656.
SILVERSTONE, A., B. MAGASANIK, W. REZNIKOFF, J. MILLER and J. BECKWITH. 1969. Catabolite sensitive site of the *lac* operon. Nature *221:* 1012.
TRAVERS, A. and R. BURGESS. 1969. Cyclic re-use of the RNA polymerase sigma factor. Nature *222:* 537.
TYLER, B. and B. MAGASANIK. 1969. Molecular basis of transient repression of β-galactosidase in *Escherichia coli.* J. Bacteriol. *97:* 550.
ULLMANN, A. and J. MONOD. 1968. Cyclic AMP as an antagonist of catabolite repression in *Escherichia coli.* F.E.B.S. Letters *2:* 57.

Mutants Missing a Factor Necessary for the Expression of Catabolite-Sensitive Operons in E. coli

DANIÈLE SCHWARTZ* and JONATHAN R. BECKWITH

Department of Bacteriology and Immunology
Harvard Medical School
Boston, Massachusetts

The *lac*† operon of *E. coli* is subject to at least two types of control. First, the well-known negative control in this system involves the action of a specific repressor protein which interacts with the *lac* operator to inhibit transcription of the *lac* operon (Jacob and Monod, 1961; Gilbert and Müller-Hill, 1967).

A second control mechanism consists of effects variously known as catabolite repression, transient repression or the glucose effect. In simple terms, it can be shown that the *lac* operon, and all other operons or genes which are inducible and determine the ability of *E. coli* to use various compounds as carbon and nitrogen sources are partially or nearly totally repressed in glucose minimal media. Until recently the mechanism of the glucose effect was obscure. However, within the last two years, evidence has accumulated both as to the nature of the effector (small molecule catabolite) and the site of action within the *lac* operon of the glucose effect. Following studies on 3′5′ cyclic AMP in *E. coli* by Makman and Sutherland (1965), it was shown by Perlman and Pastan (1968) and Ullmann and Monod (1968) that the glucose effect could be completely reversed by addition of 3′5′ cyclic AMP to growth media. Further, Silverstone and

---

* Present address—7 rue de l'épée de bois, Paris V^e, France.

† The following abbreviations are used: *lac, ara, mal, rha* for the genes determining the ability of *E. coli* to utilize lactose, arabinose, maltose, rhamnose; *pro, arg, met, pyr, trp* for the genes determining the ability of *E. coli* to synthesize their own proline, arginine, methionine, pyrimidines, tryptophan; AMP-adenylic acid; IPTG-isopropyl-β-thiogalactoside.

co-workers (Silverstone, Magasanik, Reznikoff, Miller, and Beckwith, 1969; Silverstone, Arditti, and Magasanik, 1970) and Perlman, deCrombrugghe, and Pastan (1969) have shown that mutants of the *lac* promoter site render the *lac* operon insensitive to glucose effects.

These findings have allowed the formulation of various mechanisms for the molecular basis of the glucose effect. Two general models exist. (1) Negative control—according to this model, there is a repressor molecule which interacts with the promoters of all operons subject to this effect. The role of cyclic AMP is to inactivate the repressor. (2) Positive control—according to this scheme, RNA polymerase alone is incapable of recognizing or initiating transcription at promoters of catabolite sensitive operons. What is necessary for recognition of such promoters is both a protein factor (Travers, 1969) which attaches to the core polymerase and cyclic AMP which may facilitate this attachment or may activate the polymerase-factor complex. (There are variations on this model: e.g., a single polymerase with different sites for different promoters, etc.). In both models, glucose effects are exerted through a reduction in the intracellular levels of cyclic AMP.

Each of these models allows the prediction of certain types of mutants. In this paper, we are interested in the type of mutation which results in the complete shut-off of all genes subject to the glucose effect (cat^s). According to the former model, such mutations might be super-repressor mutations analogous to the i^s mutation of the *lac* system. In the latter model, they could be mutations in the proposed factor gene or in one of the RNA polymerase subunit genes. In both models, mutations which no longer make cyclic-AMP would have the same properties.

In this paper, we describe the isolation and partial characterization of such mutations which result in a super catabolite repression.

RESULTS AND DISCUSSION

Our starting wild-type strain is 3000 (CA-8000), an Hfr Hayes prototroph. In order to detect cat^s mutants which are defective in the metabolism of more than one carbon source, we have used a technique described, according to our suggestion, by Perlman and Pastan (1969). After mutagenic treatment with nitrosoguanidine (Adelberg, Mandel, and Chen, 1965), approximately 500 bacteria are spread on tetrazolium agar (Ohlsson, Strigini, and Beckwith, 1968) containing either arabinose and maltose or lactose and galactose. Mutants incapable of metabolizing both of the two carbon sources in the media would give rise to red colonies on these plates. The arabinose and maltose operons are thought to be subject to independent specific positive control mechanisms (Englesberg, Sheppard,

Squires, and Meronk, 1969; Schwartz, 1967), while the lactose and galactose operons are both negatively controlled by specific repressors (Saedler, Gullion, Fiethen, and Starlinger, 1968). The two types of plates were used in case the inducible systems were separately controlled by glucose effects according to whether they were positive or negative control systems.

The frequency with which we have found red colonies on the arabinose-maltose plates was around 0.5%. Due to an apparent partial insensitivity of the galactose operon to the glucose effect in the strain used (CA-8000), very few mutants of the type sought were found on the lactose-galactose plates. Mutant colonies which appeared to be *ara⁻mal⁻* were purified and tested for growth on these and other carbon sources. Most of the *ara⁻mal⁻* mutants were also *lac⁻gly⁻rha⁻*. One mutant was *ara⁻mal⁻*, but could grow on all the other sugars.

We wished to rule out the possibility that the *cat^s* phenotype of these mutants was due to multiple mutations each occurring in a different operon, rather than a single mutation affecting all operons. Since we have isolated ϕ80 transducing phages carrying the *lac, ara* and *mal*A operons (Beckwith and Signer, 1966; Gottesman and Beckwith, 1969; Schwartz and Beckwith, unpubl. results), we could test this possibility for these operons. Lysates of these transducing phages were spotted onto lawns of the various mutants on minimal media containing appropriate sugar. We have found that all 10 mutants which are negative for the 5 sugars listed above are non-complementable for the metabolism of any of the individual sugars by these phages. In contrast, the one *ara⁻mal⁻* mutant mentioned above was transduced to *ara⁺* by ϕ80 *ara* and to *mal⁺* by ϕ80*mal*A (Table 1). This strain apparently carries two mutations, one in

TABLE 1

Sugar-negative mutant		
Transducing Phage	CA-7900 through CA-7909	The *ara⁻mal⁻lac⁺* mutant
ϕ80*lac⁺*	still *lac⁻*	—
ϕ80*ara⁺*	still *ara⁻*	*ara⁺*
ϕ80*mal*A⁺	still *mal⁻*	*mal⁺*
ϕ80*lac⁺*UV5	*lac⁺*	—

Effect of various transducing phages on sugar-negative phenotype of mutants. Cultures of the mutant strains were spread with thin paper strips on minimal plates containing the various carbon sources. (Five or six cultures could be spread on one plate.) A drop of an HFT lysate of the types indicated was applied to the strains. Complementation for the sugar-negative phenotype could be seen as heavy growth within two days.

the *ara* and one in the *mal*A operon. Thus, there are no mutants isolated so far which are negative only for the positive control systems.

In order to relate the phenotype of these mutations to the glucose effect, we have employed a promoter mutation of the *lac* operon, UV5, which is insensitive to this effect (Silverstone et al., 1970). If the phenotype of the *cat*[s] mutants is due to a super catabolite repression effect, the *lac*+ character should be restored by introduction of a φ80*lac* transducing phage carrying *lac*UV5. All 10 mutants were restored to *lac*+ phenotype by this transducing phage. This result makes it unlikely that the sugar-negative phenotype is due to a transport problem or to anything other than a catabolite repression effect.

The *lac* operon was used as a means to further characterize these mutants. The enzyme, β-galactosidase, was assayed in three of the mutant strains, CA-7900, CA-7901, and CA-7902. All three strains exhibited very low levels of the enzyme in the presence of 2×10^{-3} M IPTG. However, one of the three mutants, CA-7902, synthesized normal levels of β-galactosidase in the presence of cyclic AMP and IPTG. The other two were unaffected by cyclic AMP (Table 2).

The mutant, CA-7902, which responds to cyclic AMP may be an adenyl cyclase mutant similar to that described by Perlman and Pastan (1969). The other two mutants analyzed may contain mutations in the structural gene for the RNA polymerase factor or subunit proposed in the introduction or may be of the *i*[s] type.

It is difficult to conceive of genetic experiments which would precisely establish the nature of the gene product. The simplest approach to char-

TABLE 2. Levels of induced β-galactosidase as % of wild type

	No cyclic AMP	$+5 \times 10^{-3}$ M cyc AMP
CA-7900	3	3
CA-7901	2	2
CA-7902	3	100

The strains were inoculated into glucose-M63 (Pardee, Jacob, and Monod, 1959) minimal medium either after growth in broth or on a TYE (Gottesman and Beckwith, 1969) plate to a final concentration of 5×10^7 cells/ml. The strains were allowed to grow at 37°C in this medium for 3 hr at which point they were in exponential phase. The cultures were then divided into five parts and 2×10^{-3} M IPTG added to all but one. To three of the IPTG-containing cultures were added various concentrations of cyclic AMP (Schwarz) -10^{-3} M, 5×10^{-3} M, 10^{-2} M. Samples were taken every 10 min for one hr and assayed for β-galactosidase (Pardee et al., 1959). Rates of synthesis of β-galactosidase were determined from the slopes of the curves for specific activity vs. time. Care was taken to insure that the cultures did not contain a large proportion of revertants, since we have observed that there is selection in most media for reversion to wild type.

acterizing these mutations, and to using them for possible isolation of the proposed RNA polymerase factor, would appear to be the in vitro system developed by Zubay and co-workers (Chambers and Zubay, 1969). In order to use one of these mutants (CA-7900) in this system, it was necessary to construct a strain carrying the *cat*^{s} mutation and a complete deletion of the *lac* region. CA-7900 was crossed with an F$^-$ strain of genotype *argH*$^-$, *metB*$^-$, *pyrF*$^-$, *trp*$^-$, and *arg*$^+$*met*$^+$ recombinants selected. One recombinant (X-7900), which was *cat*^{s}*arg*$^+$*met*$^+$*trp*$^-$*pyrF*$^-$, was selected for further crosses. An Hfr, CA-7033, carrying the *lac-proA*, B deletion, X-111 (Cuzin and Jacob, 1964) was crossed with X-7900; *pyrF*$^+$*trp*$^-$ recombinants were selected and scored for the *pro*$^-$ character. A *pro*$^-$*trp*$^-$*cat*^{s} recombinant (X-7901), carrying the *lac-pro* deletion is used in a subsequent paper (Zubay, Schwartz and Beckwith, 1970) to detect a protein factor (CAP) necessary for the in vitro expression of the *lac* operon.

The results in that paper and in further experiments suggest that the product of this *cat* gene is a protein factor necessary for the transcription of *lac* and other catabolite-sensitive operons (Eron, Arditti, Tocchini-Valentini, Connaway, and Beckwith, in prep.).

ACKNOWLEDGMENTS

This research has been supported by grant GB8247 from the National Science Foundation and by Career Development Award GM9027 from the National Institutes of Health.

REFERENCES

ADELBERG, E. A., M. MANDEL, and G. C. C. CHEN. 1965. Optimal conditions for mutagenesis by N-methyl-N′-nitro-N-nitrosoguanidine in *Escherichia coli* K12. Biochem. Biophys. Res. Commun. *18:* 788.

BECKWITH, J. R. and E. R. SIGNER. 1966. Transposition of the *lac* region of *E. coli*. I. Inversion of the *lac* operon and transduction of *lac* by φ80. J. Mol. Biol. *19:* 254.

CHAMBERS, D. A. and G. ZUBAY. 1969. The stimulatory effect of cyclic adenosine 3′5′-monophosphate on DNA-directed synthesis of β-galactosidase in a cell-free system. Proc. Nat. Acad. Sci. *63:* 118.

CUZIN, F. and F. JACOB. 1964. Délétions chromosomiques et intégration d'un épisome sexuel F-*lac*$^+$ chez *Escherichia coli* K12. C. R. Acad. Sci. *258:* 1350.

ENGLESBERG, E., D. SHEPPARD, C. SQUIRES, and F. MERONK, Jr. 1969. An analysis of "revertants" of a deletion mutant in the C gene of the L-arabinose gene complex in *Escherichia coli* B/r: isolation of initiation constitutive mutants (I^c). J. Mol. Biol. *43:* 281.

GILBERT, W. and B. MÜLLER-HILL. 1967. The *lac* operator is DNA. Proc. Nat. Acad. Sci. *58:* 2415.

GOTTESMAN, S. and J. R. BECKWITH. 1969. Directed transposition of the arabinose operon: a technique for the isolation of specialized transducing phages for any *Escherichia coli* gene. J. Mol. Biol. *44:* 117.

JACOB, F. and J. MONOD. 1961. Genetic regulatory mechanisms in the synthesis of proteins. J. Mol. Biol. *3:* 318.

MAKMAN, R. S. and E. W. SUTHERLAND. 1965. Adenosine 3'5'-phosphate in *Escherichia coli.* J. Biol. Chem. *240:* 1309.

OHLSSON, B. M., P. F. STRIGINI, and J. R. BECKWITH. 1968. Allelic amber and ochre suppressors. J. Mol. Biol. *36:* 209.

PARDEE, A. B., F. JACOB, and J. MONOD. 1959. The genetic control and cytoplasmic expression of "inducibility" in the synthesis of β-galactosidase of *E. coli.* J. Mol. Biol. *1:* 165.

PERLMAN, R. L. and I. PASTAN. 1968. Regulation of β-galactosidase synthesis in *Escherichia coli* by cyclic adenosine 3'5'-monophosphate. J. Biol. Chem. *243:* 5420.

―――, ―――. 1969. Pleiotropic deficiency of carbohydrate utilization in an adenyl cyclase deficient mutant of *Escherichia coli.* Biochem. Biophys. Res. Commun. *37:* 151.

PERLMAN, R. L., B. DECROMBRUGGHE, and I. PASTAN. 1969. Cyclic AMP regulates catabolite and transient repression in *E. coli.* Nature *223:* 810.

SAEDLER, H., A. GULLION, L. FIETHEN, and P. STARLINGER. 1968. Negative control of the galactose operon in *E. coli.* Mol. Gen. Genetics *102:* 79.

SCHWARTZ, M. 1967. Expression phénotypique et localisation génétique de mutations affectant le métabolisme du maltose chez *Escherichia coli* K12. Ann. Inst. Pasteur *112:* 673.

SILVERSTONE, A. E., R. R. ARDITTI, and B. MAGASANIK. 1970. Altered catabolite sensitivity of *lac* promoter revertants. Proc. Nat. Acad. Sci. (in press).

SILVERSTONE, A. E., B. MAGASANIK, W. S. REZNIKOFF, J. H. MILLER, and J. R. BECKWITH. 1969. Catabolite sensitive site of the *lac* operon. Nature *221:* 1012.

TRAVERS, A. 1969. Bacteriophage sigma factor for RNA polymerase. Nature *223:* 1107.

ULLMANN, A. and J. MONOD. 1968. Cyclic AMP as an antagonist of catabolite repression in *Escherichia coli.* FEBS Letters *2:* 57.

ZUBAY, G., D. SCHWARTZ, and J. R. BECKWITH. 1970. The mechanism of activation of catabolite sensitive genes: a positive control system. Proc. Nat. Acad. Sci. (in press).

Glossary

i = gene for production of repressor for *lac* operon
p = promoter
o = operator
z = structural gene for β-galactosidase
y = structural gene for membrane protein of *lac* transport system
a = structural gene for thiogalactoside transacetylase
M protein = membrane protein; product of y gene; functions in the *lac* transport
    system
R = repressor protein; product of i gene
GZ = β-galactosidase; product of z gene
A–AC = thiogalactoside transacetylase; product of a gene
NEM = N-ethylmaleimide
XG = 5-bromo-4-chloro-3-indoyl-β-D-galactoside
lac = lactose (glucose-4-β-D-galactoside
mel = melibiose (6-O-α-D-galactosyl-D-glucose)
ONPG = orthonitrophenyl-β-D-galactoside; used in β-glactosidase assay
IPTG = isopropyl-β-D-thiogalactoside; effective gratuitous inducer
TMG = methyl-β-D-thiogalactoside; inducer; used in permease assay
ONPF = 2-nitrophenyl-β-D-fucoside; inhibitor of induction
TPEG = β-phenyl-ethyl-thio-galactoside
TDG = β-D-galactosyl-1-thio-β-D-galactoside
TPG = phenyl 1-thio-β-D-galactoside
gal = galactose
trp = tryptophan
his = histidine
F'*lac* = episome carrying *lac* operon
Sm = sensitivity for streptomycin
attλ = site of insertion of temperate phage λ
*att*80 = site of insertion of temperate phage ϕ80
*ton*B = locus determining sensitivity to bacteriophage T1
ϕ80*lac* = temperate phage ϕ80 transducing for *lac*
λ*lac* = temperate phage λ transducing for *lac*
ϕ80EZ$_1$ = ϕ80 transducing z gene plus a very small portion of y
ϕ80*dlac* = defective temperate phage ϕ80 transducing for *lac*
ϕ80*ara* = temperate phage ϕ80 transducing for arabinose
mol wt = molecular weight
ML = "Mutabile Lwoffi"
mRNA = messenger RNA
tris = hydroxymethylaminomethane
CR = catabolite repression
CRM = crossreacting material

AMEF = gene product of a z^- point mutant that can be activated by antibody

α = operator proximal region of z

ω = operator distal region of z

o^c = operator constitutive mutations

i^s = superrepressed mutant of *lac* operon; noninducible *lac*$^-$ phenotype is trans-dominant over wild type inducible one

i^Q = mutation in promoter of i gene allowing 10-fold increase in repressor protein production

i^{SQ} = mutation in promoter of i gene allowing 50-fold increase in repressor protein production

Index